PELICAN BOOKS

10 × ECONOMICS

Peter Donaldson was born in Manchester in 1934 but left
shortly afterwards for Kent, where he went to Gillingham
Grammar School and won an open scholarship to Balliol.
He read politics, philosophy and economics, and graduated
from Oxford in 1956. He then taught very briefly in a
secondary modern school and for two years in a college of
technology before taking up a university appointment at
Leeds. He was a lecturer in the department of economics at
Leicester University 1959–62, when he also did a good deal
of work for the Leicester and Nottingham University adult
education departments and for the Workers' Educational
Association.

At the end of 1962, he was one of the first British university
teachers to be seconded to key positions in underdeveloped
countries under the scheme for Commonwealth Educational
Cooperation. He was appointed, for two years, as Visiting
Reader in Economics at the Osmania University, Hyderabad,
and subsequently extended his stay in India to four years.

In 1967 he returned to England to teach at Ruskin
College, Oxford, where he is now Senior Tutor in Economics.
In recent years he has done a considerable amount of
broadcasting including two series for radio, *Managing the
Economy* and *Affluence and Inequality* – and two for B.B.C.
television, *Economics of the Real World* and *Peter Donaldson's
Illustrated Economics*. His publications include *Guide to the
British Economy*, *Worlds Apart*, *Economics of the Real World*
and *Peter Donaldson's Illustrated Economics*.

He is married and has three children.

Peter Donaldson

10 × ECONOMICS

*A Simple Guide to the Economics
of the Early Eighties*

Penguin Books

Penguin Books Ltd, Harmondsworth, Middlesex, England
Viking Penguin Inc., 40 West 23rd Street, New York, New York 10010, U.S.A.
Penguin Books Australia Ltd, Ringwood, Victoria, Australia
Penguin Books Canada Ltd, 2801 John Street, Markham, Ontario, Canada L3R 1B4
Penguin Books (N.Z.) Ltd, 182–190 Wairau Road, Auckland 10, New Zealand

First published 1982
Reprinted 1982, 1983 (twice), 1984

Made and printed in Great Britain by
Richard Clay (The Chaucer Press) Ltd, Bungay, Suffolk
Filmset in Monophoto Plantin by
Northumberland Press Ltd, Gateshead, Tyne and Wear

Contents

Preface   7

1. Whatever Happened to Full Employment?   9

2. Not Worth the Paper   27

3. The State Executioner   47

4. The Lost Bonanza   65

5. The Price of Pounds   80

6. The Death of Industry   96

7. One More Try   112

8. A Siege Economy?   131

9. Work without Workers   145

10. Which Way Out?   160

Index   177

Preface

10 × Economics is written for non-economists who feel that they ought to have some understanding of the economic issues which affect their everyday lives (and perhaps the way in which they vote), and as a supplement for introductory students of economics who find difficulty in relating what the textbooks say to what is actually happening. The aim is to explain relevant economic concepts and theories so that the reader is better able to assess recent economic policies and some of the broad alternatives which are currently being put forward.

Chapter 1 expounds the basic Keynesian principles (and their practical policy limitations) which provided the basis for government management of the economy during the twenty-five years or so after the war. Chapters 2 and 3 deal with the monetarist approach which subsequently came to dominate official economic thinking during the late seventies and early eighties – with some of the implications of such policies examined during the next three chapters. Chapters 7 and 8 look at alternative devaluationist/incomes policy and import control strategies, with Chapter 9 stressing some of the problems of rapid technological change which are likely to beset policy-making during coming decades. And Chapter 10 tries to set current controversies within a framework of broader political and economic choices and to suggest the only limited extent to which economics can be expected to provide clear-cut answers.

10 × Economics is also the title of the television series which I wrote and presented for Yorkshire Television and which was first broadcast on I.T.V. for schools in 1982. However, although the book is closely linked chapter-by-chapter to the series and provides fuller discussion of the topics dealt with in the programmes, it is directed at a wider audience.

I have tried to offer a balanced presentation of conflicting views which leaves the reader free to see more clearly where he or she stands. But that is not to claim a spurious objectivity in

7

Preface

dealing with subjects that necessarily involve differences of political values as well as technical disputes. My own scepticism about the theoretical basis for recent policies and my dismay at the human and economic consequences of implementing them will be evident.

I am indebted, as often in the past, to Peter Wright of Penguins for his initial support and to Chris Jelley (now Head of Education at Y.T.V.) for his many comments and suggestions about both the content and the presentation. I am also grateful to Mike Burns for assembling some of the material and to Sue Hearne for organizing the typing. And to Sheila, Sally, Adam and Amanda – who this time were perhaps relieved to see me back in the old routine.

[1] Whatever Happened to Full Employment?

A bad year for the people of Britain. Lengthening dole queues as unemployment passes three million with forecasts of worse still to come. The jobless march on London in protest and organize demonstrations in the areas hardest hit – the Northeast, South Wales, Merseyside ... The ranks of the unemployed increasingly consist not only of those who have been thrown out of work but also of school leavers who have never had a job. The government expresses concern but warns sternly that 'unemployment will not begin to fall until wages can be held at a sensible level. What is happening is that workers are simply pricing themselves out of jobs.'

A bad year for British industry. Investment in new factories and equipment on which the future of the economy depends has virtually dried up. Profits are being squeezed and more and more firms are being forced into bankruptcy. The captains of industry warn that if things go on as they are there will be a permanent crippling if not destruction of the country's manufacturing base. At home they face increasing import penetration from foreign competitors. Abroad, they blame their inability to compete on an over-valued pound. The government is sympathetic but insists that cuts in public spending and the establishment of 'sound finance' are essential prerequisites for getting the economy moving once again.

A bad year for the world. It is not only Britain which is suffering. There is a world recession in which the other leading industrial nations find themselves beset by similar economic problems which they try to cure by similar restrictionist policies. There is an imminent possibility that they will resort to protecting their own industries by import controls of one kind or another. But if they all adopt such policies the amount of world trade will be reduced and the situation will be made even worse. As usual when the world economy is depressed it is the less developed countries, the poorest of the poor, which suffer the most.

A bad year all round. But which year? Was it the year in

which a National Government was formed under the premier-ship of Ramsay MacDonald? Or was it Mrs Thatcher in office? Was it 1931 or 1981?

One of the themes of this book is the frightening extent to which the economic events of the early eighties seem to be a re-run of the economic history of the early thirties. But there is also half a century of differences between the two periods. In 1931 prices were actually falling (they did not begin to go up until 1934). In 1981, prices were rising sharply and we had already experienced several years of inflation well in excess of 10% (including 24% in 1975 and 18½% in 1980). In the thirties, the main impetus of technological change seemed to have exhausted itself; in contrast, recent years have seen dramatic technological developments, and the so-called 'new technology' is bound to have profound economic and social implications for the fairly near future; moreover, the British economy today is bolstered by the windfall discovery of North Sea oil and gas. On the other hand, Britain in 1931 was still a major imperial power; by 1981 the Empire had gone and Britain was a member of the European Economic Community.

Not least of the differences between the thirties and the eighties is that the study of economics is fifty years older. For a subject so young as it is, these years have seen quite remark-able transformations in its development. What we have witnessed in these years is no less than revolution and counter-revolution in the way in which economic problems have been approached, a turmoil of ideas which must be understood if an answer is to be found to the question – whatever happened to full employment?

The Rise and Fall of Full Employment

It may not have seemed so at the time, but having a job during the first couple of decades after the Second World War repre-sented a security of livelihood never experienced before in the history of industrial Britain – or, for that matter, since.

Jobs were easy to come by. In this unique period, no less than ninety-eight or even ninety-nine out of every hundred people who wanted work were in work. And a sizeable propor-tion of the remaining few hundred thousand only appeared as

Fig. 1. *% of U.K. workforce unemployed 1931–81*

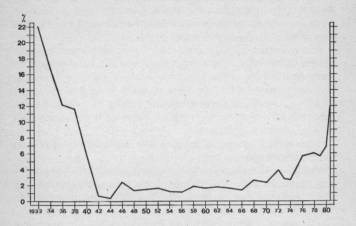

(Source: Abstract of Labour Statistics and Ministry of Labour)

an unemployment statistic because they were temporarily between jobs – 'frictional' unemployment.

Those just leaving school or college generally found work
rapidly. Even losing a job because a particular firm or industry
hit hard times was not the end of the world, because job
vacancies at the labour exchanges usually, and sometimes
greatly, exceeded the number looking for work.

Admittedly, many of these vacancies were concentrated in
the most prosperous parts of the country, stretching from the
South-east through London to the industrial Midlands. In
other areas, unemployment exceeded the national average – for
example 2.4% in Wales compared with the 1954 U.K. average
of 1.4%, or 3.7% in Scotland when the national average was
1.8% in 1964. But, it was argued, the right to work did not
mean that everyone was guaranteed a job in a particular local-
ity; a small proportion of workers might have to move to find
jobs – and retraining and mobility allowances were available to
make it easier for them.

And, of course, 'full employment' did not mean that everyone was doing just what they wanted to do, and being well

paid for it. A job might well have been boring, dehumanized and lowly paid. But at least during this period working people were largely saved from the dreadful indignity of wanting to work to support themselves and their families and finding that no one wanted to employ them.

Just how exceptional these decades were can be seen by comparing them with what went before and what has happened since. During the interwar years as a whole, unemployment in Britain *averaged* 14%. In 1931 it stood at 21.3%, rising to 22.1% by 1932 and only gradually falling to 11.6% by the outbreak of war in 1939 (and then principally because of increased arms expenditure).

The unemployment of today is now beginning to approach these dimensions:

(i) By mid-1981, the number officially registered as unemployed was 2.6 million. This was the same as the number out of work in 1932 although, because the labour force is now larger, it was a smaller percentage – nearly 11%.[1] But it can be argued that these figures underestimate actual unemployment, chiefly on account of the number of married women who want work but do not bother to register as unemployed because of the unlikelihood of their obtaining work and because they are not entitled to any social security benefits which require registration.

(ii) Unemployment is again becoming a long-term condition rather than a temporary setback for those who lose their jobs. The average period experienced by those out of work has sharply risen and so has the number of 'hard-core' unemployed, those who have been out of work for more than a year.

(iii) As always, mounting unemployment hits certain regions and groups within the workforce disproportionately hard. The South-east has suffered least, with 7% unemployment in mid-1981 and a higher proportion of job vacancies than elsewhere. Northern Ireland, on the other hand, had 17% out of work at that time, Wales and the North 14%. Within these were even wider extremes of unemployment ranging, for example, from

1. By the latter part of the year this had risen to nearly 3 million, some 12.5%.

4.2% in St Albans to 34.5% in Strathbane. It is the youngest and the oldest who have been the principal victims. School leavers comprise the age-group with the highest rate of unemployment (over 30%) and also that which has most rapidly risen over the years. And racial minorities, too, have experienced rises in unemployment far in excess of the national average.

Fifty years on, we seem to be back where we started. So how did we manage to achieve full employment in the forties, the fifties and the sixties? And why, having learned that lesson, have we subsequently allowed the spectre of mass unemployment to reappear?

The Rise and Fall of J. M. Keynes

Government today, as in the thirties, places the blame for unemployment on excessive wages. The market for labour, it is said, is just like the market for anything else. Thus if a greengrocer is failing to clear his stock of tomatoes, it must be because he is charging too much; to get rid of them, he must lower his price. Likewise, unemployment means that the number of workers offering themselves for hire is greater than that which enterprises are willing to employ at the going rate. If workers would only see that they are pricing themselves out of jobs and be prepared to accept lower wages, then the unemployment problem would be solved. Trade unions, in resisting wage cuts, simply make the situation worse.

On this view, governments are not responsible for unemployment. *Their* role is essentially one of good housekeeping. They should observe the canons of sound finance, make sure that their spending is paid for by taxation, and then leave business to mind its own business as it knows best.

It was notions like these lying at the heart of the great body of orthodox 'classical' economic theory which were challenged by John Maynard Keynes with the publication in 1936 of his *General Theory of Employment, Interest and Money*. His ideas represented such an overturn of traditional thinking, and the policy implications of the ideas were so radically different from what had so far been practised, that their acceptance and development became known as the 'Keynesian revolution'. In retrospect, the essence of the Keynesian approach seems absurdly simple, obvious and easy to understand.

Unemployment arises when firms lay off their workers (or fail to employ new workers to replace those who have retired or left of their own accord). Now why should they do so? It must be, Keynes argued, because they have failed to sell the output which those workers had been producing. Their customers have not been spending enough to make it worthwhile for them to maintain their previous output, and therefore employment levels.

This might be due to a change in the *pattern* of consumer spending – with some firms failing to sell their output because their products have become less popular. For example, a company making record players may find that its sales are declining and therefore decide to lay off some of its workers. But other firms, producing video recorders, may be enjoying increasing sales and be anxious to employ more workers than previously. In this case, there has simply been a switch in consumer spending, with unemployment of more than a temporary nature only occurring to the extent that labour shed by declining enterprises has difficulty in moving to those that are expanding.

What is much more serious is when *most* firms simultaneously find that they are unable to sell all their output because of a shortfall in *total* spending. In this case, workers who are laid off will not be able to find jobs elsewhere. This can happen because decisions about how much to spend are taken by various groups in the economy quite independently and in ignorance of decisions about how much to produce.

To see this, suppose that to begin with the economy is running at full employment. With all resources fully used, the value of the output produced is represented in Fig. 2(a).

Whether this output will all be bought depends upon decisions about spending which are made by four main groups. First, *consumers* choose to spend a certain proportion of their incomes – and to save the rest. Quite what that proportion is depends on a host of factors: they may be saving, for example, for a summer holiday, to put down a deposit on a house, or for their old age. Second, firms are also major spenders – on new factories, machines, stocks of raw materials and other capital requirements. (In economic terminology these are collectively

Fig. 2.

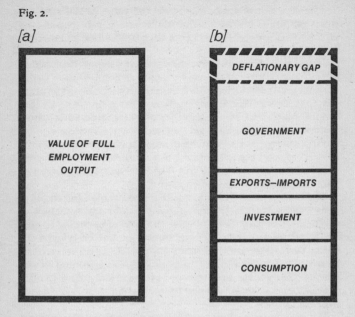

[a]

VALUE OF FULL
EMPLOYMENT
OUTPUT

[b]

DEFLATIONARY GAP

GOVERNMENT

EXPORTS—IMPORTS

INVESTMENT

CONSUMPTION

known as 'investment'.) Third, *foreigners* buy that part of our output which is exported; and similarly part of our own spending may be on imports from abroad. And finally, *government* is a big spender in any modern economy – on items like defence, social services and the nationalized industries.

Now suppose that for the coming year the spending plans of these various groups add up in the way shown in Fig. 2(b).

It is clear that total spending, 'aggregate demand' as it is frequently called, is not sufficient to buy all the output which is produced with full employment. The value of full employment output is, say, £150,000 million, and total spending is only £140,000 million. Producers will find that they have unsold stocks of goods on their hands and take action to bring output into line with what is being bought. Because spending did not add up to the value of full employment output, workers are laid off and the amount produced is reduced to a level that enterprises think they can sell.

The shortfall of spending below the value of full employment output is known as the 'deflationary gap' because its effect is to cause employers to cut back production and thereby create unemployment.

It was this 'demand-deficiency' which Keynes identified as the principal cause of pre-war unemployment. Workers were without jobs. Factories and machines lay idle or underused. All that was missing was sufficient spending to buy the output which they could together produce. And such a situation was the likely outcome, stressed Keynes, of an unregulated free enterprise economy because in such an economy plans to produce and plans to spend were formulated by different people from different motives and were extraordinarily unlikely to amount to the same total.

The answer, said Keynes, was that if we wanted full employment, then governments would have to intervene somehow to fill the deflationary gap – to raise the level of spending so that the whole of full employment output would be bought. In doing this, there are two main approaches open to governments. First, they can try to stimulate the spending of the private (non-government) sector of the economy. And second, they can choose to fill the gap by increasing their own spending.

If it aims at increasing private consumption and investment (leaving aside for the time being export demand which is less directly controllable) then a government can use either monetary policy or fiscal policy or some combination of the two.

Monetary policy in the Keynesian sense (and we shall see in Chapter 2 that it can be operated in a quite different way) means trying to alter spending through changes in the rate of interest. In its capacity as a major borrower itself and in regulating the banking system via the Bank of England, government can exercise considerable influence on the level of interest rates.

Thus lower interest rates may induce more consumption spending as saving is made less attractive and borrowing to buy consumer goods becomes cheaper. However, the evidence available suggests that not too much can be hoped for along these lines; neither saving nor credit purchases seem particularly sensitive to changes in interest rates.

Cheaper money might also be expected to stimulate private

investment spending. Firms contemplating new investment have to weigh up the returns which they hope to obtain from the investment against the cost of borrowing funds to finance it. A reduction in interest rates may therefore render some projects feasible which previously had been rejected as unprofitable. But once again, the evidence fails to support the view that investment decisions are very responsive to alterations in the level of interest rates – unless they are very large ones.

Therefore, greater emphasis was laid by Keynes on *fiscal* policy – the manipulation by government of its taxation and expenditure – in attempting to fill a deflationary gap by stimulating private sector demand. It is much more probable that consumption will be increased by cuts in taxation – either direct taxes like personal income tax or indirect taxes like V.A.T. – than by changes in interest rates. Similarly a boost to investment spending by firms can be expected to follow from reduction in taxes on business or from allowing firms to offset their investment expenditure against taxes.

As well as influencing private sector demand, a government can also try to fill a deflationary gap directly through increasing its own spending. Quite apart from fiscal hand-outs to individuals and families (like higher pensions and other social security benefits) and to firms (for example, through grants for new investment projects), government can itself undertake 'public works' programmes, spending on new roads, hospitals, council houses and so on. To the extent that such spending is in excess of its tax revenue, it thereby adds to aggregate demand in the economy. This implies that the government must borrow from either the general public or the banks the extra amount it needs to pay for such programmes. Such 'deficit financing' was anathema to traditional economists and politicians but, argued Keynes, made all the sense in the world when it came to dealing with mass unemployment.[2]

To sum up. Keynes identified the main cause of pre-war unemployment as a failure of spending in the economy to reach the level needed to buy the output which could be produced

2. And it might well prove to be self-financing in the end, as the tax revenue of government rose as a result of the higher employment and therefore incomes caused by the initial deficit.

with full employment. And, he said, the means were available to rectify the situation. Full employment was unlikely to come about of its own accord. If unemployment was to be conquered, then governments would have to accept responsibility for achieving that objective and they would have to intervene in the working of the economy to a much greater extent than in the past. They would have to be involved in a continuous process of 'demand management' – trying to establish and maintain spending at an appropriate level.

Tax cuts, deficit financing, public works, regular intervention by government – all these were very hard to swallow for economists and politicians wedded to the idea of a self-regulating economy. It is not surprising that Keynes's ideas were not immediately acclaimed and put into effect. In fact, unemployment in the late thirties and early forties was only reduced by increasing government spending on rearmament and then war – an unconscious if wasteful application of the Keynesian approach.

But in a famous White Paper of 1944 the British Government *did* explicitly accept responsibility for achieving 'a high and stable level of employment'. And the first decades after the war saw the systematic adoption of Keynesian policies in Britain and many of the other major industrial nations – with governments manipulating taxes and their own spending in an attempt to match aggregate demand to full employment output.

Judged by the results charted in Fig. 1, they were remarkably successful, although just how far the full employment of these years could be ascribed to the Keynesian revolution is debatable. It can be argued that the conditions of this period – the need for massive reconstruction expenditure, the setting-up of the Welfare State, continued high spending on arms, new technology and rapidly growing world trade – would have led to much higher employment levels had Keynes never written a word. But it seems unlikely that the consistent achievement of full employment during this period would have occurred without the management of the economy which governments undertook through monetary and fiscal policies along Keynesian lines.

So what went wrong? Why, from the second half of the sixties, was there mounting criticism of Keynesianism in practice? Why, from that time on, did unemployment begin to rise to reach its present alarming proportions? There are four major reasons: the technical crudeness of the Keynesian techniques; the emergence of other sorts of unemployment not so susceptible to demand management; the conflict of policy objectives; and the questioning of Keynesian theory to the point where it was ousted by those with a new belief in 'monetarism'.

(i) LEVERS AND LEVELS

To the extent that jobs depend on spending, Keynesianism requires that aggregate demand in the economy is set at the appropriate level. This is done by operating the levers of monetary and fiscal policy so that the total spending rises or falls by the desired amount.

In practice, considerable difficulties arise, particularly when the aim is the maintenance of very low unemployment, as it was for much of the post-war period. The complications of 'fine tuning' the economy in this way can be illustrated by considering the problems confronting a Chancellor of the Exchequer in preparing a Budget on Keynesian principles.

Referring back to Fig. 2, the first thing he has to decide is what the value of full employment output (at present prices) will be for the coming year. This is not an easy task in itself. If there is less than full employment to begin with, he first has to estimate what extra output will be produced by bringing unemployed workers back into jobs. On top of that, he has to add an amount which takes into account the likely growth of productivity – the extent to which output will rise over the years as a result of resources being used more efficiently than before.

Having done that, he now reaches the most difficult stage, that of estimating the probable level of demand in each of the four categories listed in Fig. 2. How much is likely to be spent during the next twelve months on consumption? How much are firms going to invest? What will be happening to exports and imports? How much government spending will there be if he leaves policies unchanged?

He is having to peer into the future, and the only guide he has available is a mass of data coming in about what has been happening in the recent past. He is not even sure about just where the economy is now, let alone how it will move over the coming year. And yet it is on that highly unreliable basis that he has to formulate his Budget judgement about whether there is a deflationary gap and, if so, how much it is.

Suppose that, as in Fig. 2, he estimates that spending will fall short of the amount needed to buy full employment output by £10,000 million. It is time for him to pull the monetary and fiscal levers. In predicting their effects, he can be reasonably confident about the direction in which they will work – that easier credit, tax cuts and more government spending, for example, will stimulate demand. But what he does not know with any degree of certainty is *by how much* spending is likely to be increased – or exactly *when* that spending will take place. Firms may well be induced to build new factories and install more equipment as a result of grants from the government. But will investment rise by £1,000 million or £2,000 million? Will firms undertake it this year or next year?

And if the timing and extent of the response of private investment to his measures is difficult to predict, the future level of imports and exports is even more so. Here, world factors completely outside his control can make nonsense of his calculations – like political disruption in an oil-producing area, a minor war in a remote part of the world, poor food harvests, or the economic policies of other leading industrial nations.

Not surprisingly, therefore, when Keynesian policies were being practised, the Chancellor's sums turned out to be wrong time after time. The crudeness of the techniques of control and the existence of categories of spending which were inherently difficult to predict meant that the total of spending frequently proved to be either smaller or greater than was intended. If it was too little, there was a bigger shortfall from full employment than had been planned. Too much spending, on the other hand, was likely to cause inflation, as we shall see in a moment.

(ii) NON-KEYNESIAN UNEMPLOYMENT

Even in the heyday of Keynesianism, when overall employment was at a very high level, many parts of the country continued to suffer from persistent unemployment sufficiently great to warrant concern. And this regional unemployment was not easily capable of being solved by demand management policies. If the government pumped more demand into the economy, people in for example the North-east or Wales might find themselves with more money in their pockets. But when they went out to spend it, it might be products made in the South-east or some other relatively prosperous region that they bought. Industry and employment in the regions with already higher numbers out of work might benefit hardly at all.

That is because regional unemployment is not primarily due to demand deficiency, or an inadequate level of national spending. Instead it arises from a shortage of factories and machines for workers to work with – a 'supply-deficiency' resulting from the failure of certain areas to attract sufficient firms to set up business there. It is therefore a different sort of unemployment from that which Keynes set out to deal with, and it calls for quite different policy measures aimed at improving the capacity of the regions to produce what is demanded rather than at increasing demand itself. Similarly, as will be explained in Chapter 9, unemployment caused by the introduction of new technology may also not be amenable to solution by Keynesian methods.

(iii) CONFLICTS OF OBJECTIVES

So far we have just been looking at problems which arise in applying Keynesian demand-management policies on the assumption that the government's sole commitment is to the achievement of full employment. In fact, even when full employment was their top priority, post-war governments aimed at a number of other objectives: stable prices, a sound balance of payments, and sustained 'economic growth' – increasing living standards by making the economy capable of producing more and more year by year.

The simultaneous achievement of these various objectives simply by manipulating the level and types of spending in the economy proved very difficult. Indeed it became increasingly doubted whether the aims were compatible within that policy framework. Different objectives often seemed to require that the levers of control were pulled in opposite directions.

For example, higher interest rates might be called for to help the balance of payments, in inducing foreigners to lend to us on a greater scale. But the higher cost of borrowing might deter firms from investing, with adverse effects on employment and economic growth. Or, pumping in more spending to eliminate unemployment might set up inflationary pressures within the economy at below the full employment level of output – or lead to imports being sucked in with consequent balance of payments weakness.

It was the potential conflict between full employment and price stability which came to cause most concern. By the end of the sixties, inflation had risen from its customary 2–3% per annum to nearly double that level, with much worse to come in the seventies. Many economists argued that the inevitable result of trying to run the economy at a very high employment level was a dual threat to price stability.

The first danger, illustrated in Fig. 3, is that spending can overshoot the full employment target level to create an 'inflationary' rather than a deflationary gap. Higher spending by consumers, firms, foreigners and government on the same

Fig 3 *Demand-pull inflation*

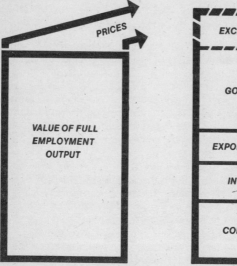

volume of output can lead to shortages, which enables sellers to put up their prices. Firms trying to meet the higher demand for their products will also be bidding against each other to get hold of scarce raw materials and labour. The upshot is the emergence of *demand-pull* inflation, with prices being dragged up by excessive spending.

A second possibility, shown in Fig. 4, is that prices rise in a process of *cost-push* inflation. Producers set their prices to cover their various production costs - labour, government taxes, materials and capital – and yield them a satisfactory rate of profit. Therefore if any of these items becomes more expensive, or if they aim at increasing their profit margins, they will try to put up prices accordingly. Thus, for example, if wages rise at a faster rate than the growth of output per worker, firms will attempt to preserve their profits by passing on the increased labour costs to consumers in the form of higher prices. And that will not be the end of the story. The consequent rise in the cost of living will lead to demands from other

Fig. 4. *Cost-push inflation*

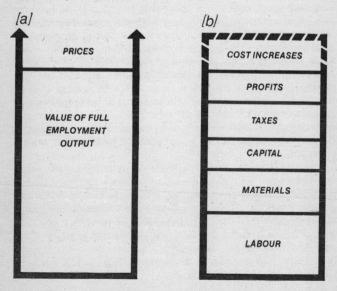

23

trade unions for wage increases to restore their members' standard of living. The economy becomes caught in a 'wage-price spiral' of wages pushing up prices and price rises causing new wage demands.

However, although inflation is generally accompanied by a wage-price spiral, it may not be wage increases which are the root cause of inflation. Wage demands could instead simply be a response by trade unions to price increases caused by a rise in any of the other production costs, e.g. imported raw materials (like the four-fold increase in the price of oil in 1973–4), higher interest rates or taxes.

Cost-push inflation can occur below full employment levels of output, but is most likely when demand is high and the economy is running close to capacity. In these circumstances, resources are in short supply, union bargaining power is at its greatest, and employers feel able to pass on increased costs in higher prices without fear that the demand for their products will be much affected.

By the late sixties and early seventies the view increasingly gained acceptance that price stability could therefore only be achieved at the expense of somewhat modifying the full employment objective, which had hitherto been regarded as sacrosanct. Running the economy below the full employment level seemed to offer the opportunity of killing two inflationary birds with one stone. It would strike directly at the cause of demand-pull inflation, eliminating any excess spending. And it would also make producers more chary of passing on cost increases through higher prices, and stiffen their resistance to exorbitant wage claims which were felt to be a major source of cost-inflationary pressure. (Historical evidence suggested that in the past the rate of wage increases had fallen as unemployment rose.)

There was, it was argued, a 'trade-off' between employment and prices. If therefore we wanted to check inflation, then a higher level of unemployment would have to be accepted as the price to be paid. About $2\frac{1}{2}$–4% was the contemporary guess about the unemployment which would be needed, a level regarded by critics as a quite unacceptable retreat from previous standards. But when, during the early seventies, unemployment did rise to these levels, inflation was not curbed. Instead, prices rose even more rapidly.

(iv) A NEW VIEW OF INFLATION

The explosion of prices since 1973 despite substantially higher unemployment led to a counter-revolution in economic thinking about the causes of inflation. The view gathered strength that neither the demand-pull nor cost-push theories offered satisfactory explanations of the inflationary process. Instead, both excessive spending and the ability of producers to pass on cost increases were ascribed to a common underlying cause – the existence of *too much money* in the economy. Gradually to begin with and then quite dramatically, governments became converted to the view that strict control of the money supply was the main weapon by which they should regulate the economy. It is this view which has usurped Keynesianism and led to new policies and priorities.

And yet the period from 1945 to the early seventies had been in many ways a remarkable economic success story. Never before had full employment (of a very much larger working population than previously because of the number of women entering the labour market) been sustained for so long. In addition, material living standards were enormously increased as a result of improvements in efficiency which allowed more and more goods and services to be produced year by year; economic growth occurred at an historically unprecedented rate. On the debit side of the account, balance of payments crises forced the economy into a regular cycle of 'stop–go'; Britain's growth record was compared unfavourably with that of many other leading industrial nations; prices rose persistently, albeit at a rate which we would now consider pleasingly low. There was widespread awareness of the limitations of Keynesian demand management techniques both in 'fine-tuning' the economy and in dealing with structural problems which loomed increasingly large.

But these problems hardly explain the speed and comprehensiveness with which Keynesianism has subsequently been abandoned. Full employment has given way to large-scale unemployment not as a result of world forces outside our control but because governments have deliberately allowed it to happen for two connected reasons. First, a change in policy priorities, which has replaced as the government's prime economic responsibility the provision of jobs for all who want them by the need to squeeze inflation out of the system at any cost. And second, a growing and ultimately exclusive acceptance of an economic theory which suggests that government's key economic function is to ensure a tight control of the money supply and that other forms of intervention are simply 'tinkering' with the economic system which is otherwise best left to its own devices. Chapter 2 sets out the main elements of this 'monetarist' approach, with some of its implications the subject of later chapters.

[2] Not Worth the Paper

Most people spend a lot of their time worrying about money. Their problem is simply that they don't have enough of it, particularly when they are faced in the shops and showrooms with often very sharply rising prices. Governments also spend a lot of their time worrying about money. But their concern is a very different one. Increasingly in recent years they have become imbued with the idea that there is too much of it floating around the economy – and that this is *why* prices rise year after year.

The common element between the two seems to be anxiety about inflation. As individuals we regularly complain about how expensive everything is – that we are getting less and less for our money all the time. And governments have elevated 'squeezing inflation out of the economy' to their number one policy priority.

However, before examining how they have tried to do this, it is worth asking just how serious a problem inflation really is, how far alarm at rising prices is in fact justified.

Why Worry about Inflation?

In 1980 prices rose on average by about 18%. In the same period average earnings in the economy increased by some 21%. A large jump in the *cost* of living, but the rise in earnings was sufficiently great to more than offset this so that we were able to buy more goods and services even though they had become pricier. So long as the *standard* of living is increasing in this way, why bother about inflation? (And even if prices rose faster than earnings, shouldn't we perhaps be more concerned about the slow growth of incomes than about why prices are going up?)

One valid reason for worrying about inflation is that the figures just used are averages which conceal what is happening to the distribution of income and wealth as a result of rising prices. There are many whose incomes are now rising more slowly than prices and who, in real terms, are therefore becoming poorer. One major group has in recent years been relatively well protected against inflation. State retirement pensions and the occupational pensions of many working in the public sector are currently 'indexed' to rise in line with the cost of living. But others are on fixed incomes or lack the bargaining power to maintain their position in the income league. Borrowers have traditionally benefited from inflation at the expense of savers. All in all, inflation has unfortunately random effects in dictating who is better off and who is worse off.

The main measure of inflation, the Retail Price Index, is itself an average figure indicating the change in the cost of a typical 'basket' of goods and services; the degree to which particular individuals and families are affected by a rise in the R.P.I. depends on how far they happen to buy the items which go into that basket. For example, low income groups tend to spend a greater than average proportion of their incomes on necessities like food, clothes, heating and housing; if, as often happens, these rise in price more than other things, they suffer more than higher income groups.

Then again, borrowers are generally the beneficiaries of inflation at the expense of savers. The most obvious example of this is that those buying their houses with mortgages find that their repayments fall as a proportion of their rising incomes – while building society savers, on the other hand, earn rates of interest which are frequently below the rate of inflation so that the purchasing power of their savings is whittled away.

Inflation can therefore have unfair consequences for the distribution of income and wealth. But two points need to be borne in mind. First, these may be small when compared with the basic inequalities which are the result of other causes. And second, *if* they are a matter for concern then policies can be devised to protect potential losers from the effects of rising prices.

A further problem arising from inflation is that the prices of British goods get out of line with those of our international competitors. If our inflation rate is higher than theirs, then our exports become more difficult to sell and our imports from them become more attractive to domestic consumers. However, the extent to which this occurs partly depends on exchange rate policy – to be discussed in Chapter 5.

But on one point there is general agreement. Inflation at a rising rate – with the expectation that prices will go up still faster in the future – is a very dangerous state of affairs. It is unstable, self-fuelling and the road to hyper-inflationary price increases where people's confidence in money is ultimately destroyed.

So there are certainly grounds for concern about inflation and its consequences. And it would be nice to have a perfect economic world in which the prices were more or less stable. But this is quite different from the proposition that inflation is an evil which must be eliminated *at all costs*. So long as price rises are held in control it is possible to live with inflation and learn to compensate for its undesirable side-effects. The cost of achieving price stability may, as we shall see, be very high indeed. There may therefore be some level of inflation at which we would rather suffer its consequences than pay the price of getting rid of it.

Money and Prices

At the end of the last chapter two theories about what causes inflation were briefly outlined. There was the view that rising prices are brought about by spending plans in the economy (by individuals, firms, foreigners and the government) totalling more than the present value of full employment output – demand-pull inflation. Or prices might rise because of an upward pressure exerted by higher wages, profit margins, taxes or raw material costs – cost-push inflation.

Our concern now is to look at a third explanation of inflation. This suggests that prices rise, not because powerful trade unions obtain excessive wage increases, or because oil-producing countries suddenly charge us four times as much, or because Keynesian expansion of demand has overshot the mark – but because the quantity of money in the economy has been allowed to grow at too fast a rate.

Money, so it is claimed, behaves just like other commodities. A glut of tomatoes pushes their price down; a shortage of tomatoes leads to their price rocketing up. Similarly, if there is

too much money in the economy its value is bound to fall.
It buys a smaller quantity of goods and services. In other
words, their price has risen.

It is this belief in the paramount significance of money
which has come to dominate recent government economic
policies. The starting point in understanding these policies
and their implications is to see just what is meant by money – a
matter which is not quite as obvious as it seems.

THE NATURE OF MONEY

A common source of confusion among non-economists arises
from the fact that in everyday language we use the terms
'money', 'wealth' and 'income' as though they were inter-
changeable whereas strictly they are quite different things.
The distinction between them is quite essential in discussing
what role money plays in the economy.

Thus when we speak of a wealthy individual as having a lot
of money we do not generally mean it literally. What we are
really referring to is that the person has substantial *assets* –
like a large house, an expensive car or two, a business perhaps,
and stocks and shares. Certainly among those assets will be
some money, pounds in his pocket and a bank account to enable him to settle his immediate bills. But the likelihood is that
he will hold as little money as possible because holding money
does not earn him any interest or profit.

Similarly, money is frequently equated with income. But
once again, this is not in fact correct. Income is a *flow* – so
much per week or month or year depending on whether it is
wages or salaries or the return from a business investment.
Usually, of course, it is paid in money although it can take
other forms, e.g. fringe benefits like a company car or free
coal, or goods received through barter. But the total amount of
money in the economy is a *stock*, a certain quantity which turns
over more or less rapidly during any given period of time during the course of which it may be used in the payment of
many incomes. Thus car workers, newsagents and grocers all
have incomes; but when the car worker pays his paper bill, and
the newsagent buys groceries, the same pound notes may
appear in each of their incomes at different times.

So although money is one of the many ways in which wealth

can be held and is also the form in which most incomes are paid, money is not the same thing as wealth or income. The 'quantity of money', the 'stock of money' and the 'money supply' *are* all ways of describing the same total. But a nation's wealth or national income are altogether different quantities. The confusion between them probably stems from the fact that for an individual, money, wealth and income are often very closely connected. If, for example, the government decides to send you regularly one hundred pound notes a week, then you have £100 more money, £100 more income, and, if you save it, £100 more wealth. You can either buy an extra £100 worth of goods now or hold a claim on them at some time in the future. But for the economy as a whole, increasing the quantity of pound notes does not automatically make the nation better off; there are more intrinsically worthless bits of bluish-green paper in circulation but not necessarily more things available on which to spend them.

WHAT IS MONEY?

Money can be defined as anything which is generally acceptable in payment of debts. Usually, this acceptability is based on the 'liquidity' of whatever is serving as money, the fact that it gives immediate purchasing power over goods and services. On this definition, notes and coin are clearly money, but beyond these, deciding what should be included in the 'money supply' becomes less straightforward. To begin with, what about cheques? Cheques are certainly widely used in settling debts, but they are not always acceptable as a means of payment. That is because the acceptability of a cheque depends on the recipient's assessment of the credit-worthiness of whoever is writing the cheque, on whether he thinks there is money in the bank to cover it. So a current account at a bank *is* money; cheques are simply the means of transferring money from one account to another.

To those uninitiated into the mysteries of banking it might seem like double-counting to include both cash (notes and coins) *and* bank deposits as part of the money supply. Since we are free to exchange our bank deposits for cash at any time, it might be presumed that the banks hold quantities of cash equivalent to their total deposits. In fact, banks themselves create 'credit' money far in excess of their cash reserves. Their ability to do so stems from their knowledge, based on long experience, that daily withdrawals of cash are largely balanced by fresh deposits of cash. Therefore only a very small proportion of total deposits needs to be kept as banknotes in their tills to meet any excess of withdrawals over new deposits.

In this knowledge, the banks are able to lend vastly greater sums than they have in the form of cash. And when they do so, e.g. by granting somebody an overdraft, they create an additional deposit which is just as much 'money' to that individual as if he had been handed the same amount in banknotes. In practice, something like 95% of bank deposits are 'unbacked' by cash. *If* we all went along to the banks and withdrew our deposits at the same time, the banks simply would not have the cash to meet our demands. But we don't and we shan't – so long as we remain confident that the banks keep *sufficient* cash to meet our requirements. That, as we have seen, is a relatively small amount, in addition to which banks always keep a second line of 'reserve assets' which could be quickly converted into cash if need be.

Thus bank deposits are as indisputably money as cash is, and quantitatively a great deal more important. Or, at least, *current* bank deposits – those which can be immediately changed into cash and on which cheques are drawn – are certainly money. But what about deposit accounts (sometimes called 'time' deposits as opposed to 'sight' deposits)? Deposit accounts are those on which interest is paid and which generally require a period of notice before they can be withdrawn. They are therefore not as liquid as cash or current accounts. But they are very nearly so, usable to make payments in a week's time. But if on that ground they, too, are included in the money supply, why should building society deposits not be added in as well? Or, for that matter, an insurance policy about to mature during the coming week?

We are entering a grey area in which there is no clear rule about what should be counted as money and what should not. In an economy like ours, wealth can be held in a great variety of forms ranging from perfectly liquid cash to highly illiquid assets like the ownership of a specialized piece of machinery ('illiquid' because in order to buy other goods or services, the owner must first find a buyer for it at a satisfactory price, i.e. convert it into a form of acceptable payment). There is, in other words, a wide spectrum of liquidity rather than a clear distinction between 'money' and 'non-money'. And these problems of defining quite what constitutes the money supply become more than academically pedantic when a government has as the lynch-pin of its economic policy the control of the quantity of money.

The Quantity Theory of Money

The basic tenet of monetarism is that inflation is caused by too much money. This is not a modern breakthrough in economic thinking but a resurrection of a belief dating back into the nineteenth century and deeply embodied in the so-called 'classical' economic theory of the pre-Keynesian era.

The doctrine is enshrined in the well-known Fisher equation $MV = PT$. On the left hand side of the equation, M stands for the quantity of money in the economy, in whatever way it is decided that should be defined. V is the velocity of circulation of money, how often the stock of money is turned over in any given time period. For example, if the money supply consisted only of banknotes, the velocity of circulation would be the number of times, on average, that a note changes hands during the course of a year. On the other side of the equation, P denotes the general price level, and T the number or volume of transactions which take place at this average price.

There can be no argument about whether or not $MV = PT$. It is a proposition which is indisputably true. A little thought shows that if the quantity of money in an economy is multiplied by the number of times it circulates, the total which will result is the value of national expenditure, the aggregate amount of spending in the economy during the course of the year. And if the average price of all goods and services is multiplied by the volume of transactions which take place at that price ($P \times T$), then exactly the same total results – national expenditure. The left hand side and the right hand side of the equation are alternative ways of looking at precisely the same amount broken down into different categories.

$MV = PT$ is thus an identity or tautology rather than an

equation. That is to say, it is true by definition. It is true in all circumstances and at all times – in socialist as well as capitalist economies, during the nineteenth century as well as the twentieth century, true ten minutes ago and ten years from now.

But the Quantity *Theory* of Money is more than this. The Quantity Theory of Money suggests that two of the four elements in the identity are vitally related to each other. It postulates that M *causes* P, that it is variations in the supply of money which bring about changes in the level of prices. If, for example, the money supply rises by 20%, then the result will be a 20% increase in the level of prices; if the rise in the money supply is held back to 10%, inflation will in turn fall to 10%. This claim that there is a causal relationship between M and P is of a quite different order from the original statement that $MV = PT$. Unlike the overall identity, the proposition that M causes P is either true or false, or possibly true in certain circumstances and at certain times, and false in others.

Closer inspection of $MV = PT$ and putting some simple illustrative figures to the four symbols provides a good starting point for seeing the conditions which would be necessary for M to be the cause of P. Suppose that the money supply amounts to 2000 and is used on average three times so that $V = 3$. And also suppose that the price level to begin with is 10 and the number of transactions taking place is 600. We then have M $(2000) \times V(3) = P(10) \times T(600)$. MV (6000), of course, $= PT$ (6000).

Now according to the Quantity Theory, if M is doubled to 4000, the outcome will be an increase in the general price level, P, to 20. It is not difficult to see that whether this will actually happen depends on how the other two variables, V and T, meanwhile behave.

If, for example, at the same time V falls to $1\frac{1}{2}$ while T remains constant, then what would happen to P?

$$M (4000) \times V (1\tfrac{1}{2}) = P (10) \times T (600)$$

In this case the rise in the money supply has been offset by a fall in its velocity of circulation so that P has remained unchanged. The Quantity Theory has not worked.

Or take another case where, when the money supply is doubled, the volume of transactions also, for some reason, doubles:

$$M(4000) \times V(3) = P(10) \times T(1200)$$

Once again, the general price level remains unchanged, with the impact of the larger money supply falling on the volume of transactions rather than the price level. Once again, the Quantity Theory has not worked.

For increases and decreases in the money supply to lead to corresponding changes in the price level, a minimum condition therefore seems to be that the velocity of circulation of money and the volume of transactions in the economy meanwhile remain constant.

The classical economists who first put forward the Quantity Theory of Money were of the view that these conditions *would* hold. And after the decades in which the basis of the theory appeared to have been destroyed by Keynesian analysis (which suggested that the quantity of money affected interest rates rather than the price level), the recent resurgence of monetarism has rested on a similar view. The chief advocate of monetarism, Professor Milton Friedman, and his many followers claim that over long historical periods, variations in the velocity of circulation and in the volume of transactions have not been sufficient to offset the close connection that they observe as existing between changes in the money supply and the rate of inflation. This impact of money on prices is, they suggest, likely to be time-lagged, with tighter control over the quantity of money reducing the rate of price increases about eighteen months later.

The idea that inflation is caused by too much money does not in itself carry any political implication. It is simply a theory about a technical relationship between the two, and one which may be right or wrong. In practice, however, it has become associated with a 'right-wing' philosophy because of conclusions drawn from it by many economists and politicians about what the State should and should not attempt to do in the economy, and because of their belief about just what causes the money supply to be excessive.

Thus in Britain in recent years, it has been held that control over the money supply is *the* regulator of the economy, the key variable in the economy on which governments can and should operate. This is a view which not only gives pride of place to the conquest of inflation as a government economic objective but also asserts that only in this way will other objectives be achieved. Close control of the money supply will bring down inflation and only then will the balance of payments be put right and economic growth be resumed. (And as for employment, that will settle at a 'natural' rate compatible with price stability.) It is a view which rejects other types of government economic intervention – Keynesian techniques, prices and incomes policies, industrial restructuring and economic planning – as dangerous meddling.

Secondly, in looking for the cause of excessive monetary growth, the blame has generally been put squarely at the door of government itself. Governments, it is argued, have promised and undertaken spending programmes far in excess of what they could finance from taxation. The amount of taxation they would have needed to pay for their spending would either have been politically unacceptable or have had adverse consequences for the economy through disincentive effects.

But governments are a law unto themselves. Whereas you or I ultimately have to cut our coats according to our cloth and bring our spending into line with our incomes, governments have an option which is not open to the rest of us. They can resort to the printing presses and create new money to fill any gap between their spending plans and revenue from other sources.

This, say the monetarists, is just what has been happening under the guise of Keynesianism. It is this, they claim, which lies at the heart of the inflationary problem. Only with the establishment of 'sound' money and prices being brought under control will the economy be restored to health.

Monetarism in Practice

There are a number of links in the monetarist chain of argument. It is asserted:

    (i)   that the 'money supply' is an identifiable quantity for which growth targets can therefore be set;

   (ii) that it is possible for this money supply to be regulated by governments;

  (iii) that the effect of controlling the money supply will not be offset by changes in the velocity with which money circulates; and

(iv) that limiting the growth of the quantity of money in the economy will be transmitted into lower inflation.

Doubts that monetarism works arise at each of these stages.

WHICH MONEY SUPPLY?

A government intent on regulating the economy through control of the money supply has to decide, first of all, just what it is that it is trying to control. But as we have already seen, defining money is far from straightforward. Instead of there being a sharp distinction between 'money' and 'non-money', there exists a very wide range of ways in which wealth can be held of varying degrees of liquidity. Quite where to draw the dividing line which distinguishes the quantity to be controlled is therefore a matter for judgement and debate.

The Bank of England offers a large number of alternative definitions (and in other countries many other variants are used). 'Retail M1' is the narrowest, comprising notes, coin and private sector current account deposits. M5 is a much wider concept, including for example building society deposits. Of those in between, it is Sterling M3 (£M3) to which since 1976 governments have devoted most attention.

£M3 consists mainly of notes and coin, current accounts in this country of both private and public sectors, and time deposits (those earning interest and requiring notice of withdrawal). Among the arguments for using this particular definition are that it gives a fair indication of what is happening on the broader financial front, it is relatively easy to identify and understand, and it includes the elements over which government is most likely to have control. However, in practice regulation of £M3 has posed considerable difficulties; and it is far from certain that achievement of elusive £M3 targets would in fact mean that the government's monetarist policies were working successfully.

CONTROLLING THE MONEY SUPPLY

It is since 1976 that explicit targets have been set for monetary growth, and only since 1979 that there was total conversion to exclusive reliance on control of the money supply as *the* regulator of the economy. But since the fifties, governments were frequently concerned with influencing the level of bank deposits as an instrument of Keynesian demand management. Their attempts to do so were thwarted or bypassed time after time by the commercial banks – mainly the Big Four (Midland, Barclays, Lloyds and NatWest) – which are in business to make profits and will therefore take every opportunity to increase their lending to earn as much interest as possible. The history of post-war monetary policy has thus been littered with episodes in which governments have devised a new method of control over bank deposits, and banks have been quick to discover loopholes and ways to evade it.

As we have seen, banks create deposits whenever they make loans. The same thing happens if they buy, for example, a government bond from Mr X whose deposit is increased when he pays in the cheque which he receives from them. Deposits are liabilities of the banks, IOUs against them on which the holders are entitled to draw, and they are all necessarily matched by the acquisition of assets by the banks as a result of which the deposits came into existence. At the simplest level this can be seen when a shopkeeper puts his day's cash takings into his bank. The additional cash is an asset which the bank now holds; its liabilities have increased by the larger deposit which the shopkeeper now has. Fig. 5 shows an outline balance sheet of a commercial bank.

Fig. 5.

ASSETS	equal	LIABILITIES
Cash		
in tills		
at Bank of England		Bank deposits
Money at call and short notice		current account
Bills		time deposits
Investments		
Advances		

On the asset side, the bank holds its cash reserve partly in the form of notes and coin in its tills, and partly in an account at the Bank of England. All the commercial banks hold such 'bankers' deposits' at the Bank of England, which serves as the banks' bank. 'Money at call' consists of very short-term loans to other financial institutions; together with 'bills' (mostly government borrowing due to be repaid in the next few weeks) these make up the bank's 'liquid assets', i.e. they are translatable into cash very quickly and easily. 'Investments' in banking jargon are holdings of government gilt-edged securities. 'Advances' are loans and overdrafts, which form the most lucrative part of the bank's business.

In distributing their assets banks have to balance conflicting responsibilities. From the point of view of their shareholders, the more high-yielding investments and advances that they have the better. But to protect their customers, the banks have to ensure that all possible withdrawals can be met; they must always have a very safe margin of liquidity.

The ability of the banks to expand their lending and holding of other profitable assets (and, of course, increase the money supply through the consequent rise in bank deposits) is therefore limited by their ability to acquire cash and other liquid assets to keep in reserve. Since the Bank of England determines the amount of notes and coin in circulation and is the prime source of other liquid assets (and since also, under the Bank of England Nationalization Act of 1946, it has the power to issue directives to the commercial banks), control of the level of bank deposits might seem to be fairly straightforward. Unfortunately this is not so.

(i) Early post-war attempts at control focused on the banks' cash reserves. 'Open-market operations' involving the sale of government bonds entailed customers drawing cheques in favour of the government which would ultimately lead to a reduction in bankers' deposits at the Bank of England. It was hoped that this depletion of their cash reserves would force the banks to cut down their level of lending. But because the tradition had developed that the Bank of England should act as 'a lender in the last resort' and always be prepared to assist the banking system when it was under pressure, the commercial banks were able to exploit this facility and replenish their cash reserves simply by selling back to the Bank of England some of their holdings of bills.

(ii) Later, emphasis was placed on getting the banks to

observe minimum 'liquidity ratios' (keeping a certain proportion of liquid assets rather than investments and advances) and then seeking to limit the amount of such assets available by reducing the quantity of short-term government bills available. But once again, this did not deter the banks from further lending as they were prepared to sell off part of their holding of government bonds in order to obtain extra cash.

(iii) The authorities also tried to limit the basis of bank lending by getting them to make 'special deposits' with the Bank of England which were not to be regarded as part of their reserves. But the banks were still able to obtain the cash they needed by attracting a larger volume of 'time deposits' through higher interest inducements.

(iv) More recently, under the system known as the 'corset', controlling the liquidity of the banks was attempted by specifying maximum limits to the growth of such interest-bearing deposits.

These, together with more direct requests to the banks to restrain the quantity or type of lending they engaged in, have been just some of the ways in which the authorities have tried to exercise monetary control during the post-war years. The relative failure of these various methods provided an inauspicious background to the hopes of the Conservative government elected in 1979, committed to full-blooded monetarism as the basis of its economic policy.

Monetarism implies that ultimately the money supply should not be allowed to expand faster than the volume of output in the economy. Strictly applied, this would in recent years mean no increase at all. However, the government adopted a gradualist position, aiming at moving *towards* such a position in stages. Thus the initial target growth which it set for £M3 during 1979–80 was within the range 7–11%.

In the light of past experience, attempts to control the money supply directly were eschewed in favour of the indirect approach of regulating the *demand* for money; banks can only create more money to the extent that customers are prepared to hold their wealth in that form. The demand for money can come from private individuals and companies, and from the public sector including the government itself. 1979–80 therefore saw a two-pronged attack, with the government trying to reduce the public sector's demand for money through expenditure cuts (which are the subject of Chapter 3) and the private sector's demand for money through interest rates.

The government is able to influence interest rates throughout the economy by its ability to set the Minimum Lending Rate (M.L.R.)[1] at which the Bank of England is prepared to assist the banking system. Variations in M.L.R. tend to be followed by other interest rates as the financial institutions compete with each other for funds. Thus in June 1979 M.L.R. was raised to 14%, and in November 1979 to 17%, historically unprecedently high levels. But neither this nor the public spending cuts which accompanied high interest rates succeeded in bringing £M3 within the target range. Its actual expansion during this year was over 20%. Fig. 6 shows that just when greater reliance than ever before had been placed on control of £M3 as an instrument of policy, the target set was overshot by an even greater margin than in previous years.

The reasons for this disastrous failure to meet the £M3 target are not difficult to find. Private industry has recourse to bank borrowing not only in order to finance its expansion; it is also forced to borrow more when times are bad. The

Fig. 6. *Targets for growth of £M3.*[2]

PERIOD OF TARGET	£M3 TARGET (annual growth rate)	£M3 OUT-TURN (annual growth rate)
12 months to April 1977	9–13%	7.7%
12 months to April 1978	9–13%	16.0%
12 months to April 1979	8–12%	10.9%
12 months to October 1979	8–12%	13.3%
10 months to April 1980	7–11%	10.3%
16 months to October 1980	7–11%	17.8%
14 months to April 1981	7–11%	22.2%

1. The practice continues but the formal title was abolished in August 1981.
2. Third Report, Treasury and Civil Service Committee, H. of C. Session 1980–81, Vol. I, *Monetary Policy*, H.M.S.O., p. xiv.

effect of the government's monetarist strategy was, as we shall see, to engineer a severe recession, and in these circumstances private sector demand for money increased *despite* higher interest rates – money needed to finance unwanted stocks of finished goods which were piling up, holdings of unused raw materials, to pay wage bills and keep firms just about in business. A secondary demand built up subsequently as still further borrowing was necessary in order to meet the higher interest payments which became due (so that the small reductions in M.L.R. which the government permitted – to 16% in July 1980 and 14% in November 1980 – had, paradoxically, the same intention as the initially higher rates).

On top of this came the once-and-for-all increase in £M3 brought about by the removal of the 'corset' in June 1980 because of doubts about its effectiveness. This suspicion proved to be even more well-founded than the authorities had feared, with an astonishing upsurge in £M3 by £3,500 million making nonsense of the government's target for the money supply. What happened was that companies simply reverted to their more convenient traditional bank sources after previously being frustrated by the control in their attempts to borrow from the banks in the normal way. In the meantime they had turned, with the connivance of the banks, to roundabout methods of finance which did not show up in the £M3 figures, examples of which will be outlined in the next section.

High interest rates paid as well as charged by the banks also resulted in the banks' attracting additional time deposits. And since the other arm of government policy, the reduction in public spending, was failing to have the desired effect on the demand for money (for reasons to be explained in Chapter 3), the overall strategy was in some disarray.

Monetarism in practice thus fell at the very first hurdle. What was to be the key regulator of the economy proved to be an embarrassingly awkward quantity to control. There was growing uncertainty about both how the money supply should be brought within the target range and whether, after all, £M3 was the appropriate quantity to which attention should be exclusively directed.

VELOCITY OF CIRCULATION

When a monetary squeeze is placed on a particular type of
finance like bank lending, or within the total bank lending is
restricted to certain categories of customers, the effect may be
simply to drive frustrated borrowers elsewhere rather than to
curtail the overall level of credit in the economy. In a sophisticated financial system such as ours, there is no shortage of
such alternatives, and indeed controls over one part of the
system can lead to the creation or proliferation of 'secondary'
or 'parallel' banking institutions outside the ambit of regulation. At a personal level this can be seen in offers by credit
card and finance companies to increase borrowing limits and
finance personal loans when getting an overdraft from a bank
is proving difficult. For firms, the borrowing options are even
wider.

Thus banks may divert potential borrowers to their overseas subsidiaries as a source of finance, or switch them from
traditional overdrafts to shorter-term bills; these were among
the ways that the 'corset' control was effectively evaded, together with simple 'disintermediation'. This ugly piece of
jargon refers to the process by which a bank facilitates the
bringing together of lenders and borrowers without itself acting as an intermediary in a way which will show up in the
normal banking statistics. For example, a customer may approach a bank intending to put on time deposit a quarter of
a million pounds. If subject to a corset limit on the growth of
its interest-bearing liabilities, the bank may indicate to the
customer that it is in no position itself to re-lend the deposit.
Instead it may put the customer in touch with a would-be
borrower and charge a commission for the service. £M3 will
not have altered in the process, but increased lending has
nonetheless occurred. Similarly, longer 'trade credit' from
firms in surplus re-lending to those in deficit can act as a substitute for the deposit with the banks.

In other words, in a complex financial system there is considerable scope for changes in the velocity of circulation.
Even if the authorities were able to achieve what has eluded
them so far, tight control over the money supply defined as
£M3, its effect could be offset by increased economy in the
use of that particular type of finance. A given money stock so

43

defined can be associated with larger or smaller amounts of spending.

If it is observed that 'over the medium term, its velocity of circulation has been broadly stable',[3] this is hardly surprising, since the money supply has been rising at a rate which has obviated the need for a rise in velocity. But when in the past governments have succeeded in making money relatively tight, considerable changes in velocity have taken place.[4]

PRICES AND OUTPUT

Even if the money supply could be unequivocally defined, even if it were possible for the government to control it rigorously, and even if such control were not offset by changes in the velocity of its circulation, the question would still remain of whether and how this would be transmitted into a lower rate of inflation. The precise connection between money and prices, the 'transmission mechanism' between the two, remains an unconvincing area of monetarist theory.

Hope is mainly pinned on a disciplined monetary policy leading firms and wage bargainers to revise their view about what the future rate of inflation will be, and alter their behaviour accordingly. The theory of 'rational expectations', to which many monetarists subscribe, suggests that the announcement of money supply targets by the authorities and their determination to adhere to them will be translated into the fixing of prices, wages and other costs in line with the lower rate of inflation which should therefore be expected.

Certainly, as non-monetarists would also agree, killing off the notion that prices are likely to rise still faster in the future is an important element in the process of dampening down inflation. Whether this is achievable simply by announcing and subsequently hitting monetary targets is much more debatable. In the event, even if trade unionists for example had modified their wage demands according to the intended restriction in the growth of the money supply, they would have found themselves to be acting inconsistently when the targets

---

3. H. M. Treasury, *Economic Progress Report*, March 1981, p. 2.

4. D. Smith, 'The Demand for Alternative Monies in the U.K.: 1924–77', *National Westminster Bank Review*, Nov. 1978.

were not after all achieved. Secondly, such behaviour would only be rational if they believed that excess money was not only a cause, but the only cause of inflation – and that prices would not therefore rise for other reasons. And thirdly, those firms and groups of workers who ignored the money supply targets altogether would not *all* suffer as a result of their 'irrational' behaviour; the brunt of the consequently higher unemployment that might follow could fall mainly on, for example, school leavers failing to find jobs for the first time.

But it is *only* if control of the money supply leads to direct downward pressure on prices and wages through some mechanism such as the theory of rational expectations that regulation of $M \times V$ results in a fall in P rather than T, i.e. reduces inflation rather than output.

In fact, by 1981 inflation was running at about 12% as compared with 18% in 1980. However, that improvement could hardly be credited to monetarism since, as we have seen, application of the policy was confounded in practice by what should be controlled and by difficulties in controlling it. (Indeed the 1980 rise in inflation must itself be largely ascribed to the increases in indirect taxation which had been imposed, and to wage settlements based on the consequent rise in the cost of living.)

But the impact of *attempted* monetarism was nonetheless considerable. The ways in which the authorities tried to regulate the money supply – through higher interest rates and cuts in public spending – led to a substantial *deflation* of the economy. The money supply was not controlled. Instead, there was Keynesianism in reverse, a severe cutback of demand below its full employment level. It is not surprising that in this process inflation was moderated. There was certainly no 'excess' demand left in the economy; cheap imports as a result of the high exchange rate (see Chapter 5) contributed in keeping down prices; and wage cost pressures in the deepening recession were tempered. (Although deflation itself generates an element of cost inflation through raising unit costs as firms spread their overheads over fewer units of output.)

But the cost was very high. It must be measured not only in terms of the human misery engendered by massive unemployment, but also by the output which was irretrievably

45

foregone as a result of running the economy at stagnant or declining levels of production – with minimal investment and firms operating with idle capacity or being forced out of business altogether. An all-party House of Commons Committee estimated the cost of reducing inflation by policies designed to reduce the growth of the money supply in the following terms: 'after four years a lasting fall in the rate of inflation of about 1% can be achieved at a cumulative cost over four years equivalent to 4% of a single year's G.D.P. and a year's additional unemployment for 2.5% of the labour force.'[5]

That same Committee concluded that by 1981 'It is clear from the evidence that there has been no true "monetarist experiment",'[6] and expressed strong doubt that if there had been, it would have worked. 'We have not been convinced by the evidence of a direct causal relationship from growth of the money supply to inflation.'[7]

5. Treasury and Civil Service Committee, op. cit., p. xcv.
6. ibid., p. xxviii.
7. ibid., p. xciv.

3 / The State Executioner

Of the total expenditure in the economy, the State spends more than four out of every ten pounds. And it continues year after year to borrow huge sums – in 1980, for example, more than £13,000 million. For many people, these facts are extremely alarming and clear evidence in themselves of the need severely to prune the extent of State involvement in the economy and to curtail its dependence on borrowing as the means of financing its activities. During the later seventies increasing emphasis was being laid on restraining public spending, and by the early eighties it came to dominate government economic thinking. A cutback in public spending was presented as the road to greater freedom for individuals and private firms. And a reduction in public borrowing was seen as an essential element in fighting inflation through control of the money supply.

Before discussing the rationale of these policies and the problems of implementing them, we need to see broadly what public expenditure consists of and how it is financed. Where does it all go, and where does it all come from?

The Scope of Public Spending

The great bulk of public spending is in the hands of central government, the major departments of State based in Whitehall. But local authorities, ranging from the Greater London Council to the humblest parish councils, are also important spenders accounting for about a quarter of the total. However, over the years this has been a declining proportion as central government has withdrawn many key types of spending (e g gas, electricity, hospitals, water, community health, and certain aspects of education and housing) from the local councils. And only a relatively small part of local government spending is decided upon by the local councils themselves; most of it is determined by central government, with the local authorities merely acting as agents in implementing those policies.

Fig. 7. *Total public expenditure by programme 1980–81*

	(£ million at 1980 survey prices)
Defence	9,746
Overseas aid and other overseas services	803
Agriculture, fisheries, foods and forestry	1,150
Industry, energy, trade and employment	3,899
Transport	2,824
Housing	4,256
Other environmental services	3,064
Law, order and protective services	2,833
Education and science, arts and libraries	8,909
Health and personal social services	9,076
Social security	19,775
Other public services	941
Common services	1,106
Scotland	4,399
Wales	1,737
Northern Ireland	2,472
Government lending to nationalized industries	2,050

(Economic Progress Report, March 1981)

Fig. 7 shows the main programmes which comprise the chief items of public spending. It can be seen that social security is far and away the largest of these, followed by defence, health and education. In coming to grips with these indigestibly vast totals, it is worth making a number of distinctions.

In the first place, many of the programmes involve the central or local government authorities themselves buying goods and services – for example, in building hospitals and schools or paying the wages of policemen and the armed services. This direct spending can be distinguished from 'transfer payments' which occur as the State shifts purchasing power from one section of the community to another while leaving the recipients free to spend their State-increased incomes as they wish. The main types of transfer payment include pensions, social security benefits like unemployment pay, grants to private industry and payment of interest on the National Debt. As can be seen from Fig. 8, transfer payments of various kinds account for nearly half of total public spending.

Fig. 8. *Public spending categories 1980*

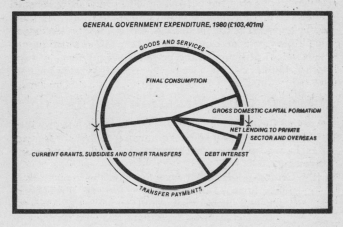

(C.S.O. Economic Trends No. 328, February 1981)

Then again, public spending can be divided into current and capital components. The building and initial equipping of a school or hospital, for example, is capital spending. The subsequent costs of staffing, heating, maintaining and generally running it constitute current expenditure, spending which recurs week after week, year after year. Fig. 8 shows that in 1980 only a very small proportion of the total could be classed as capital expenditure.

A further distinction may be made between those programmes where it is possible for the government, if it so chooses, to impose definite limits in advance on how much should be spent, and others where expenditure is 'demand-determined'. The latter consists mainly of social security bene fits, where the government sets the rate of benefits and the actual amount spent depends on how many people then qualify to receive them. Thus the entitlement to unemployment benefit is fixed by the authorities, but how much has to be paid out is determined by the numbers unemployed. This less controllable element of public expenditure accounts for about one-third of the total.

It also needs stressing that a substantial proportion of public spending goes to provide facilities that are an important element in our material well-being. The provision of schools, medical care, council housing and similar amenities form what can be regarded as the *social wage*. Goods and services which are publicly provided and consumed are just as much part of the standard of living as the private consumption – of cars, clothes, holidays – which we buy for ourselves out of income.

FINANCING PUBLIC EXPENDITURE

In paying for the wide variety of services which it provides, the State draws on four sources of finance: central government taxes, local government taxes, 'trading' and other income, and borrowing.

(i) Central government taxes provide the great bulk of public finance – nearly 90% of total tax revenue and nearly four-fifths of its overall requirements. They fall into three categories. First there are direct taxes on income and wealth. These take the form of individual income tax, corporation tax on the profits of firms, petroleum revenue tax on the North Sea companies and taxes on the transfer of capital. Second, there are 'indirect' taxes which we pay as we spend. About half the revenue from these now comes from V.A.T., with the rest made up of excise duties on alcohol, tobacco, oil and vehicles. And third, there are payroll taxes, comprising the National Insurance contributions paid by employers and employees, which we do not always think of as taxes but which in fact are nearly as important as income tax in producing revenue for the government.

(ii) Local government taxes contribute less than 10% of the State's revenue. *Rates* are a tax on property and as such suffer from a major disadvantage in times of inflation as compared with income and expenditure taxes. The amount received from the latter tends to rise automatically as prices increase in so far as incomes and expenditure grow more or less in line. But although the value of property also generally rises with inflation, its 'rateable value' does not. If they are to protect their rate income from the effects of inflation, local authorities therefore find themselves in the unenviable position of having to announce rate increases year by year.

(iii) Trading and other income of the government stems from ownership of enterprises and property throughout the economy. It consists of any surpluses earned by the nationalized industries, rents from properties leased by the government and the proceeds from any sale of such properties.

(iv) To the extent that these three sources of finance do not provide sufficient revenue for the State to pay its way, it must have recourse to *borrowing* in order to make up any shortfall. This borrowing may be for the central government itself, for the local authorities or for the nationalized industries. Together, the total constitutes what is known as the Public Sector Borrowing Requirement (P.S.B.R.). Fig. 9 shows that in 1979/80 about 40% of this was needed by central government on its own account and about 30% each by the other two elements in the public sector. In that year, the P.S.B.R. represented approximately 10% of total public finance.

Because the size of the P.S.B.R. has in recent years become a highly contentious issue, we shall have more to say about it shortly. In particular we shall be looking at who the public sector borrows from, how it does it and what its likely effects are.

Fig. 9. *Public sector borrowing 1979–80 (£ million)*

Central government (own account)	4,230
Local authorities	2,943
Public corporations	2,727
Total public sector	9,990

Public Spending Cuts

Attitudes towards public spending have changed dramatically over the years. The period following the Second World War saw a vast increase in government expenditure as a result of the establishment of a Welfare State providing a range of social services, the taking over of several major industries into public ownership, the creation of new towns and continued high outlay on defence. Moreover, public spending was seen as a key element in maintaining total demand at a level sufficient to achieve full employment along Keynesian lines. And during the fifties and sixties, the main political parties continued to compete with each other in electoral promises to provide more roads, schools, hospitals, higher pensions and social security benefits – all of which implied increased public expenditure.

However, this did not mean that the State was necessarily taking an increasing proportion of the national cake to improve the quantity and quality of its services, or that they should be paid for out of higher tax rates. It was generally expected that higher public spending could be afforded from the increase in the nation's output of goods and services which was customarily taking place year by year.

This was a period of relatively sustained economic growth, with regular rises in prosperity as the economy's productive ability was increased. At the time, we used to complain that growth was 'only' about 2–3% a year while some of our competitors abroad were doing much better. But this rate of economic growth was sufficient for a doubling of the standard of living every twenty-five years – out of which governments, both Labour and Conservative, agreed that a slice should go in providing more and better public services.

By the mid-seventies the picture was very different. The economy was stagnating, partly as a result of the adjustments which were entailed by the great leap in oil prices of 1973–4, and partly as the view took hold that policies of expansion would only contribute to an unacceptable rate of inflation.

In this new context, restraining the growth of public spending, i.e. reducing future plans to increase it, became the order of the day. This was the process which was featured in many of the 1976–9 budgets. By the eighties it had hardened still further into an objective of diminishing the share of government spending in what was now a declining national total. The new government committed itself to a 4% reduction in the volume of public spending (in real terms) by 1982–3.

It was soon failing to meet its targets, with total expenditure in 1980/81 2% higher in volume terms than in 1979/80. This was 3½% more than it had planned, although 5% lower than the previous government's plans. But within the total, substantial cuts had been made in all the major spending programmes through the setting of reduced cash limits on expenditure; particularly severely pruned was the provision of public sector housing, education and regional assistance. In addition, strenuous attempts were made to restrain local authority spending.

However, against these cuts had to be set increased spending resulting from the impact of the recession – on unemployment benefits, redundancy payments, jobs assistance programmes and help for firms like British Leyland and the British Steel Corporation. The government nonetheless remained 'committed to reducing public spending both to redress the balance between the private and public sectors, and also to control inflation effectively without excessively high interest rates, which damage the wealth-producing sector of the economy'.[1]

THE PROS AND CONS OF PUBLIC SPENDING CUTS

There is one ground for reduced public spending on which everyone can agree. Public spending may be wasteful, involving bureaucratic red tape and other types of inefficiency so that more than is necessary is spent on providing services of any given quality. No one would argue against cuts which mean that consumers of public services get better value for their money.

However, waste of this kind is difficult to identify (which is not to say that it does not exist). Governments pledged for example to reduce the number of civil servants and other administrators often find it hard to do so – perhaps because it is civil servants and administrators whose job it is to implement such decisions. Therefore the practical scope for cutting

1. Economic Progress Report: March 1981, p. 5

public spending in this way turns out to be disappointingly small in relation to the total.

More specifically, the case for public spending cuts rests on two related propositions: (i) that it is desirable or more efficient to extend the area of private choice, and (ii) that the size of the public sector 'crowds out' the private sector.

(i) *Increasing Private Choice*

It is argued that public spending is too high because the State has assumed responsibility in matters which it would be better to leave individuals and firms free to decide about for themselves. Reduced public spending has the attractive appeal that it leaves more money in people's pockets which *they* can then choose how or whether to spend. Spend less on education, for example, and leave it to parents to decide whether to buy extra books for their children or even to send them to private schools. Less on the N.H.S. and let people make their own choice about whether to take out private insurance to cover the cost of a superior service. Stop offering inducements to businesses to set up in particular regions, and allow them to locate where *they* think they can make profits.

Part of the case for spending cuts is that the State now spoonfeeds people with a variety of services regardless of whether or how much they want them. The purpose of encouraging some of them instead to be provided by the 'market' is to reintroduce *prices* as a test of consumer preferences. If consumers want them sufficiently, they will pay for them – and this acts as a signal to private producers then to provide them.

How far governments should assume responsibility in these matters, what the share of public spending should be, is a perfectly proper subject for political debate in which major differences in opinion are bound to arise. The conclusion drawn will ultimately depend on political ideology, on the value judgements of the governing party about the nature of the society which they wish to create. But economic considerations are also relevant in defining the desirable scope of private choice. Part of the argument against public spending cuts is based on doubt that the market *can* be substituted to provide a socially acceptable or economically satisfactory alternative.

In the first place, 'freedom of choice', appealing though it may sound, is in fact not likely to work very fairly given the existing distribution of income and wealth. The market mechanism operates in a manner similar to an election, with consumers casting their votes (spending) for the various candidates on offer (goods and services); these votes are then recast by firms to obtain the shares of resources dictated by the pattern of consumer voting. However, in practice the market is a highly undemocratic way of deciding what should be produced, mainly because the number of votes varies so widely from consumer to consumer. Spending by consumers on low incomes (with few votes) may reflect basic needs; votes cast by those with high incomes may be the expression of trivial wants or whims. The market does not distinguish between them. For example, the private sector building industry is inevitably geared to housing for those who can afford to pay for it rather than for the homeless who lack sufficient voting power to register their needs. Thus the possibility of benefiting from freedom of consumer choice is very much greater for some than for others. The public school system, for instance, is frequently passionately defended on the grounds that parents should have the right to make sacrifices so that their children obtain a superior education. But the truth of the matter is that this 'right' is only meaningful for the relatively few who could conceivably afford to buy what is therefore a privileged opportunity for their offspring.

Moreover, public spending cuts can have an unfortunate cumulative impact on the relative qualities of services which are provided both publicly and privately. For example, less spending on State education or the N.H.S., so that the services fail to improve or even positively deteriorate, increases people's incentives to opt out into the private sector. But the probability is that those who can afford to do so are also those who would have been most vocal and influential in resisting such a deterioration.

And with regard to public spending in assisting industry, there is a similar danger in over-reliance on the market to do the job instead. The market mechanism works on a purely *commercial* basis, with firms producing what is profitable in terms of the costs and revenues which appear in the companies' balance sheets; if they don't earn enough to cover costs, they go out of business. But there may be wider but nonetheless *economic* costs and benefits which do not show up in a company's accounts. For example, if a firm sets up business in a depressed part of the country, this may lead to significant gains – reduced outlay on benefits for workers freshly employed, increased production in other firms servicing the newcomer or selling more to its workers, and reduced congestion in an already more prosperous region where the firm might otherwise have located. On a narrowly commercial criterion the firm may not have chosen to move to the depressed area; on wider economic grounds there may be a good case for a State subsidy encouraging it to do so.

The arguments in favour of public sector spending are partly social, partly economic; but essentially they stem from the limitations or defects of the market mechanism in practice. Cutting public spending therefore represents a reaffirmation of belief in the efficiency of the market *despite* these and other shortcomings which explain why it has failed in the past. It is a belief which must rest either on the view that for some reason it will work more effectively in the future – or on a new definition of what is regarded as an acceptable social and economic outcome.

(ii) *Making Room for the Private Sector*

Apart from the belief in wider private choice as an end in itself, the case for public spending cuts is based on the argument that the public sector has grown to a point at which the development of a dynamic and efficient private sector is inhibited through being starved of resources. In Britain, government expenditure as a proportion of total output (G.D.P.) has grown from 32% to 43% between 1960 and 1979 – and this fact is frequently presented as obvious evidence of the 'burden' imposed by excessive State involvement in the economy. It is also often implied that this is a drag on the economy greater than that suffered by our major competitors.

In fact, as Fig. 10 shows, public spending in Britain is a smaller proportion of G.D.P. than in other European countries. It is also declining, whereas in most of the others it is increasing. However, while the figures refute the notion that public spending in Britain is far higher than elsewhere, they offer no guidance about what the appropriate proportion of government expenditure should be.

On this matter, the view is often put forward that public

Fig. 10. *Public spending as % of G.D.P.*

	1960	1975	1979
Netherlands	35.3	54.5	58.3
Luxemburg	30.5	49.1	54.4
Belgium	30.5	45.5	52.0
Ireland	27.6	48.5	49.3
Denmark	25.0	44.9	47.7
W. Germany	32.5	46.4	46.4
France	35.5	43.5	46.4
Italy	32.1		46.3
U.K.	31.7	47.7	42.8

(E.E.C. Commission: European Economy, November 1979)

spending must be held back in order to avoid the private sector being 'crowded out'. The economy has limited quantities available of land, labour and capital – basic resources. The more that is pre-empted by the State, the less that is left over for the wealth-creating sector of the economy on which public spending is said to depend. The public sector is seen as parasitically living off the efforts of the real producers in the economy.

But quite what is meant by the 'wealth-producing sector'? In political debate it is often crudely equated with private industry (including agriculture and mineral working) which contributes towards production in a way that other economic activities do not. But this is a highly unsatisfactory distinction. In the first place, since production is ultimately the process of satisfying consumer wants, it is only completed when output is made available where and when consumers want to buy it. Thus transport, wholesaling and retailing are just as much part of 'production' as manufacturing is. And consumer wants can also be satisfied by direct services as well as goods – like the provision of haircuts, entertainment or holidays.

Secondly, within the public sector there are anyway large key areas of the economy producing minerals or industrial goods in just the same way as their counterparts in the private sector. Publicly-owned industries are responsible for much of the nation's output of coal, oil, steel, ships and cars. Moreover, the efficiency of the private sector depends to a considerable extent on the provision of goods and services from the public sector. Roads, housing, health and education, for example, all help to maintain or increase productivity throughout the economy. Therefore public spending cuts, far from releasing resources to make the private sector more productive, can instead reduce its efficiency.

What may have a certain usefulness is the distinction which is sometimes made between the output of goods and services which is *marketed* and that which is not. That is, part of production is actually sold to buyers whereas another part is distributed in other ways, e.g. State school or hospital places. Once again, this is not a distinction between public and private sectors since the public sector includes the nationalized industries whose output *is* marketed.

It is certainly important that the marketed output is sufficient to meet the considerable calls which are made upon it in supplying 'the total private consumption, investment and export needs of the whole nation'.[2] And it is true that there has been an alarming tendency for this sector, particularly manufacturing industry, to shrink in recent years. Some claim that this has been because it has been squeezed by excessive growth of the public sector. However, there is an alternative view that it is other factors and policies which have been causing the decline of manufacturing industry, one of the *results* of which has been difficulty in allowing public expenditure to grow as it has in other countries. This is a matter which will be discussed in Chapter 6.

Too often the debate is couched in terms which suggest that the issue is public *versus* private spending in a way which ignores the interrelationship between the two types of spending. Moreover, the argument that public spending cuts are necessary 'to leave room for commerce and industry to prosper' assumes that the resources thereby released *are* then productively absorbed by the private sector. Reduced public expenditure means that labour is shed from the public sector and that it makes fewer calls on other resources. These are then available for re-employment in the private sector, which can increase its output accordingly. But if the slack caused by public spending cuts is not taken up by the private sector, if the

2. R. Bacon and W. Eltis, *Britain's Economic Problem: Too Few Producers*, Macmillan, 2nd edn, 1978, p. 28.

switch of resources does not occur, then the result will simply be higher unemployment.

And this is just what has been happening in recent years. During the period since the mid-seventies when efforts have been made to hold back public spending, private sector invest-ment has *not* risen to fill the gap. This is hardly surprising since there is no mechanism (apart possibly from the rate of interest which will be discussed in the next section) for bring-ing about the switch from one to the other. Private industry will only invest more if it sees the opportunity of profitably selling a greater output. But this is not the likely outcome of public spending cuts. Firms relying on government contracts find their orders directly reduced; more generally, the defla-tion in total demand caused by the cuts (for example, less spending by teachers, civil servants or steelworkers who have lost their jobs) make the prospect for the private sector gloomier. They may see little point in investing in new plant and machinery when they are working well below their exist-ing capacity.

This problem, of ensuring that resources released from the public sector *are* taken up by the private sector, exists even when the economy is working at full employment – and where competition between the two for limited resources is most ob-vious. But when there is *already* large-scale unemployment, when resources are lying idle, it is a very strange argument that further public spending cuts are still necessary to make room for private investment. It is a resurrection of the notorious 'Treasury View' which led among other cuts to a slash-ing of the unemployment benefit by 10% in 1931 – and against which Keynes first mounted his attack against orthodox eco-nomic thinking. 'The Government's programme,' he wrote at that time, 'is as foolish as it is wrong . . . Not only is purchasing power to be curtailed, but road-building, housing and the like are to be retrenched. Local authorities are to follow suit. If the theory which underlines all this is to be accepted, the end will be that no one can be employed, except those happy few who grow their own potatoes, as a result of refusing, for reasons of economy, to buy the services of anyone else .'[3] His argu-ments against public spending cuts at that time, or 'economy'

3. J. M. Keynes, *Essays in Persuasion*, Macmillan, 1931.

as they were then referred to, still apply with equal force. 'What are we releasing resources for today? To stand at street corners and draw the dole. When we already have a great amount of unemployment and unused resources of every description, economy is only useful from the national point of view in so far as it diminishes our consumption of imported goods. For the rest, its fruits are entirely wasted in unemployment, business losses and reduced savings.'[4]

In such a situation, it is *not* the case that more investment means a sacrifice of present consumption, that greater public spending implies less resources being available for the private sector. With resources lying idle and unemployed, it is possible to have more of both. Attempts to impose still more cuts on public spending serve only to depress the private sector further.

Why, then, *does* the government persist in pruning public spending in these circumstances, insisting that such economies are an integral part of its strategy? The answer lies in its adherence to monetarist doctrines and the way in which public expenditure is financed. It is time to look again at a quantity which was outlined earlier – the Public Sector Borrowing Requirement.

The Cost of Public Borrowing

We have already seen that, in financing its expenditure, government obtains revenue from taxes on income, spending, employment and property – together with a trading income from its role as owner of productive assets. To the extent that these are insufficient to pay for its planned programme of spending, the government has to borrow. There are three main ways in which this Public Sector Borrowing Requirement can be financed.

(i) By borrowing from the general public through familiar channels like the Post Office or through deductions from pay – e.g. the Save-as-you-earn scheme, National Savings Certificates either of the conventional variety or Index-Linked, and investment accounts with the Post Office Savings Bank.

4. ibid.

(ii) Through the issue of gilt-edged securities, government bonds sold on the Stock Exchange. These are IOUs issued in £100 units and carrying the promise by the government to pay the holder a fixed sum of money annually. The loans are of varying periods. For example, someone buying *Exchequer 13½ 1994* knows that in that year he will be repaid the £100 face value of the bond and that he will meanwhile receive an annual £13.50 payment of interest.

The stocks are 'gilt-edged' in the sense that payment of interest is absolutely guaranteed by the British government regardless of the general state of the economy (which does affect the level of dividends paid on ordinary company shares). It might be thought therefore that governments would never have any difficulty in finding takers for their bonds.

However, potential buyers have to take into account what they think is going to happen to prices over the future life of the bonds. If they expect inflation to persist, they will realize that £100 in 1994 will buy far less than it does today. They will therefore only buy such a bond if they think that interest earnings in the intervening years (plus any rise in its price above what they have paid for it) will more than compensate for this reduction in its real value. The result is that government stock can only be sold if it carries interest regarded by buyers as at a satisfactory level.

(iii) Through the sale of Treasury Bills. These are short-term (generally 91 day) assets which are offered for tender each week and sold to the highest bidders, who then profit according to the difference between the price they paid for them and the full face value which they receive as the bill matures. Generally these are bought by the discount houses, financial institutions largely dependent on the banks for their funds (known as 'money at call and short notice'). The banks themselves also hold Treasury Bills but generally only for the latter part of their brief lives. Borrowing through Treasury Bills comprises what is known as the 'floating debt' to distinguish it from 'funded debt' which consists of long-term stocks.

MONETARY POLICY AND THE P.S.B.R.

Great emphasis has been placed in recent years on the need to control, indeed to reduce, the size of the P.S.B.R. Thus the planned P.S.B.R. for 1980/81 was set at £8½ billion. This was approximately 3.75% of Gross National Product and the government further aimed at reducing this percentage to 1.5 by 1983–4. One way of doing this would be to increase taxation and thus reduce the need to borrow. But since the government was committed to tax cuts rather than increases, its only alternative was to cut public spending. But why was it felt so vital that the P.S.B.R. should be lowered? Why was this particular quantity elevated to a position of such importance in the government's strategy?

One reason is a further variant of the crowding-out theory, this time expressed in terms of finance rather than physical resources. On this view, a high P.S.B.R. threatens the private sector through its effect on interest rates. The large volume of gilt-edged stock that the government has to sell means that it must offer higher interest rates to induce the necessary sales. Greater public spending is thus at the expense of private borrowing, which is deterred by the increased cost of funds. But this argument can hardly have been uppermost in government thinking when, as we saw in the last chapter, it was deliberately raising interest rates in its attempt to control £M3 through limiting the *demand* for money (a much larger proportion of which stemmed from borrowing by the private sector of its economy).

In fact, it is the possible effects of the P.S.B.R. on the quantity of money which explains the amount of attention devoted to it by the authorities. There are two ways in which £M3 may be increased by the P.S.B.R.:

(a) If it is financed by the issue of Treasury Bills, there is an automatic increase in the money supply as the government in effect obtains bank deposits in exchange for the bills now held by the banks or discount houses. This is what is generally meant by the government 'printing new money' or borrowing from the banking system.

(b) The effect of the P.S.B.R. is to add to the *net wealth* of the private sector in the following slightly complicated way. The government uses the proceeds of its borrowing to make payments to, for example, the unemployed or its own employees (an increase in the money supply). If it sells bonds to finance the P.S.B.R., it receives payments from the general public (a reduction in the money supply). If the two are equal, i.e. the P.S.B.R. is wholly financed in this way, the money supply remains unchanged at the initial stage. But the fact that the private sector as a whole is now holding the same quantity of bank deposits *plus* additional government bonds may cause it to redistribute part of its increased net wealth by generating an extra demand for £M3, i.e. switch part of it to holding money.

However, in practice the government has been successful in funding most of the P.S.B.R. from non-bank sources so that there has been little direct effect on the money supply. And the indirect relationship between the P.S.B.R. and money supply is obscure, to say the least, and may not exist at all. In any case, there is no doubt that the increase in £M3 above the government's targets stemmed essentially from the *private* sector's 'distress' borrowing caused by the effects of the recession.

Moreover, attempts to reduce the P.S.B.R. during a recession by further public spending cuts are almost doomed to failure. Reduced public expenditure deflates the economy and increases unemployment as a result of lower demand. This will not be confined to the public sector; it is estimated that every job loss there causes a similar rise of unemployment in the private sector as well because of its dependence on public spending.

This then feeds back into the P.S.B.R. in two ways: (a) expenditure is increased on redundancy payments, unemployment and supplementary benefits; and (b) there is a loss of tax revenues due to the lowering of incomes, profits and expenditure. The effect of the two together is to defeat the initial object of reducing the P.S.B.R. Official estimates in 1981 suggested that each extra 100,000 unemployed involved a cost to the Exchequer of £340 million (an underestimate of the true amount because redundancy payments were not included in this particular calculation).

It is the operation of these 'built-in stabilizers', unemployment payments, for example, rising in time of recession and preventing demand from falling as much as it otherwise would have done, which largely explain the £3½ million overshoot in 1980/81 in the target P.S.B.R. And although the government subsequently acknowledged that 'there were bound to be factors' causing the P.S.B.R. 'to move up and down according to the economic cycle',[5] the further deflationary twist given by the 1981 Budget may well find the government again chasing its own tail with regard to the actual P.S.B.R. in 1981/2.

Of course, a policy of cutting public spending during a recession (in order to control the money supply) is the direct opposite of the Keynesian solution, which would have been for government to spend and borrow more rather than less. But the government still asserts that 'higher public expenditure cannot any longer be allowed to precede, and thus prevent, growth in the private sector'.[6] And they may claim that this is a consensus view by quoting Mr Callaghan addressing the Labour Party Conference in September 1976. 'We used to think that you could spend your way out of a recession and increase employment by cutting taxes and boosting spending. I tell you in all candour that the option no longer exists, and that in so far as it did ever exist, it only worked by injecting a bigger dose of inflation into the system.'

Whether, or how far this may be true, will be considered later. In the next three chapters, we shall be looking at some further consequences of the present attempt to implement a monetarist strategy.

5. Evidence to Treasury and Civil Service Committee, op. cit., p. liii
6. White Paper on 'The Government's Expenditure Plans 1979–81', Cmnd. 7746, Nov. 1979.

[4] The Lost Bonanza

Oil spells money. We are all familiar with the legendary wealth
of the Middle Eastern sheikdoms and the glossy excesses of
Dallas. And wherever in the world oil is newly discovered, it
is heralded as a passport to higher living standards. That was
certainly how it was generally welcomed in Britain when it first
became clear that the North Sea yield would transform the
existing heavy dependence on foreign producers to self-
sufficiency plus an exportable surplus by the early eighties.
The four-fold increase in world oil prices engineered by the
O.P.E.C. countries in 1973–4 made the North Sea discoveries
seem an even better prospect.

It did not seem unreasonable to expect, as the extent of the
oil and gas bonanza became known, that we would be substantially better off as a result. Not perhaps in the same league
as Kuwait or Saudi Arabia, but a great deal richer than we
would otherwise have been. Britain throughout the post-war
period had been plagued by a cycle of 'stop–go'; every attempt
to expand the economy and emulate the high growth rates
achieved in other industrial countries was thwarted as imports
rose faster than exports and governments had to apply the
economic brakes because of balance of payments difficulties.
North Sea oil and gas seemed to offer the chance of at last
escaping from this impasse and allowing the economy to forge
ahead unconstrained by worries about our international payments position.

How was the new wealth to be used? No one thought that
oil was a total panacea for all our economic problems, and there
was a general awareness that the North Sea reserves would
anyway last only for a few decades. What self-sufficiency in
energy provided was a breathing space in which the opportunity could be taken to strengthen the economy in preparation for the time when the oil dried up.

And yet today, outside Aberdeen and the big oil companies
themselves, who is better off? The economy is in a worse plight
than ever, the dole queues lengthen, output is falling and in-

dustry is in steady decline. So what has gone wrong? Did we deceive ourselves in thinking of oil as a tremendous windfall gain? Or has the benefit simply been lost through mismanagement? Where has the oil wealth gone?

The answers to these questions will overlap into the next two chapters dealing with exchange rates and de-industrialization. For the time being we will first try to identify the potential gains from the North Sea and then discuss the possible ways in which they might have been deployed.

Oil and Growth

The potential impact of oil can best be understood by briefly considering a fundamental problem common to most economies at most times: their inability to produce a quantity of goods and services large enough for all wants to be satisfied. The result is that we are constantly faced with awkward choices between alternatives, with more of one thing implying that we have less of another.

Consumer wants appear, for all intents and purposes, to be unlimited. The appetite of individuals, families, firms and the State itself for goods and services of all kinds has so far been insatiable. They add up to calls on the productive system which cannot all be satisfied at the same time because of the relative scarcity in any economy of the resources which are needed to produce output.

These 'resources' fall into three broad categories. First, there is what economists term 'land'. This includes not just soil and its fertility but all other natural assets like water supplies, climate and mineral deposits. A second element of resources is labour – the stock of human strength, skills, knowledge and enterprise. And third, there is capital, which consists of the man-made elements in the wealth of a community – factories, machines, roads, schools, ports, hospitals – many of which are vital aids to increased production in the future.

To repeat, the stock of these resources in an economy at any given time is limited and insufficient to meet all the wants which it could be used to satisfy. Since resources are also capable of alternative uses, a problem for all types of economy is how to use them best, how to maximize consumer satisfaction in a situation of scarcity.

Fig. 11.

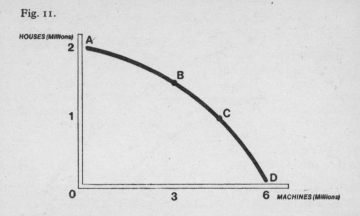

Fig. 11 shows a *production possibility curve* illustrating various combinations of goods which could be produced with the limited resources of an economy. This simple example charts the possible output of just two goods, houses and machines. Point A indicates that if all resources were used only to produce houses, then 2 million of them would be built. In this case, of course, no machines would be produced. Putting all resources to work in manufacturing machines, on the other hand, would mean an output of 6 million machines and no houses (point D). In between are the different quantities of houses *and* machines which it would be feasible to produce, e.g. point B with 1.5 million houses and 3 million machines, and point C with 0.5 million fewer houses and 1.5 million extra machines. Economics has been much concerned with the question of resource allocation, of how to choose between various points like these. Associated with this is the debate about which mix of market forces and government direction is most likely to achieve the best outcome.

But another major area of study, and the one relevant to the oil issue, has been of how to shift the production possibility curve of an economy to the right as in Fig. 12. To the extent that this can be achieved, the problem of scarcity is thereby alleviated. So long as the production possibility curve is static we have to face the fact that more houses means less machines and vice versa. But an outward movement of the production possibility boundary enables more of both to be produced at

Fig. 12.

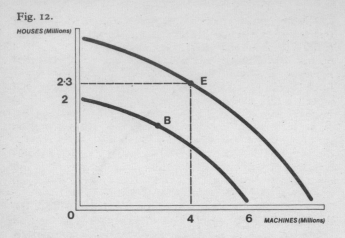

the same time. For example, at point E 2.3 million houses and 4 million machines are produced rather than 1.5 million houses and 3 million machines as at point B.

Shifting the production possibility curve outwards in this way is the process of *economic growth* – the ability of an economy to increase its output of goods and services year by year. Economic growth is an essentially modern phenomenon, a feature of the past couple of centuries, and explains the extraordinary rise in material affluence which has taken place during this period.

Economists have been far from successful in precisely pinpointing the causes of economic growth. Much remains to be understood about why in an economy growth rates have varied over time and why they differ between economies. Although they have not been short of suggestions, economists have not been particularly helpful in offering specific advice about how growth rates could be increased.

But broadly there are two possibilities. The first is that existing resources are combined more effectively, so that a larger volume of output can be squeezed from the same quantity of land, labour and capital. In other words, it may be possible to increase productivity so that the economy runs more efficiently.

The other prospect for economic growth stems from the fact that resources, although scarce and limited in the short run in relation to wants, can be varied to some degree over a period of time. For example, 'labour' can be increased as a result of population growth or by more women joining the paid workforce as they have in very large numbers since the war; and as well as this change in quantity, its quality can be enhanced by greater education and training. Similarly, the 'capital' stock with which labour has to combine in the productive process can also be expanded and improved by new investment; in the the short run this may involve holding back present consumption in order to make room for producing more plant and machinery – a sacrifice today in order to have more jam tomorrow.

And finally, it is even possible to alter the amount of the third basic resource, 'land'. Thus the quantity of arable land can be increased through reclamation, its quality improved by irrigation. It can also be run down by wind, erosion or over-farming into dust bowls; similarly, mineral resources like coal can be depleted. But sometimes an economy can receive a bonus through the discovery of hitherto unknown deposits of mineral resources like North Sea oil and gas. This is a once-and-for-all addition to known natural resources which shifts the production possibility curve to the right as in Fig. 12, enabling more output to be produced than previously. Just how much more, the extent to which the increase in natural resources raises the potential growth rate of the economy, it is difficult to say precisely. Recent estimates suggest that the direct contribution of North Sea oil and gas to the G.N.P. was about 3% in 1980 and may rise above 5% in 1984. This is the value of oil and gas output minus the cost of foreign resources used in producing it and payments of interest, profits and dividends to foreign owners. Even when further allowance is made for the earnings that the capital and labour employed in the North Sea might have made in alternative uses, its direct contribution has clearly represented a substantial bonus when compared with the $2\frac{1}{2}$–3% growth rates achieved by the economy during the most prosperous years of the post-war period. In addition, there was the possibility already mentioned of indirect gains resulting from the greater freedom to pursue expansionary policies without balance of payments difficulties.

However, how far these potential gains are being realized in practice is quite another matter. This is because the exploitation of the North Sea has coincided with the application of monetarist policies which have plunged the economy into a deep recession. In other words, the economy has not been operating at a point like J in Fig. 13 – *on* the production possibility curve, and capable of producing more only by squeezing a greater output from already fully employed resources. Instead, the starting point is, say, K – *within* the production possibility boundary. Thus oil and gas have come on stream at a time when the economy is working below capacity, with resources already lying idle and not being used to satisfy unfulfilled wants. Discovering and bringing into play additional *new* resources in these circumstances obviously loses much of its significance. It is as though a win on the pools goes to an individual who lacks the imagination or interest to spend even his existing income.

Fig. 13.

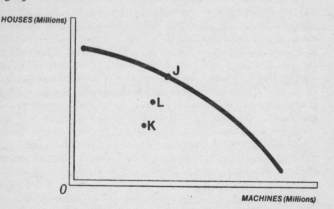

This is the main reason why we are not as well off as we might have expected as a result of the North Sea. The gains that were hoped for have been hidden or wiped out by a recession which has kept overall production stagnant or even declining.

It is possible that the impact of the recession may have been moderated as a result of oil so that we are at a point like L in Fig. 13 rather than K, with output and employment falling less than they would otherwise have done. It is possible that the benefits from the North Sea have simply been postponed – that changes are taking place during the course of the recession which will enable a greater outward shift of the production possibility boundary at a later stage. Whether this is so partly depends on the use to which government revenues from the North Sea are being put. This we shall look at shortly. But it is also possible that because of the way in which it has been managed, the existence of the North Sea resource has made things worse rather than better. That part of the oil story will have to wait till the next two chapters.

Rent from the North Sea

Regardless of by how much, if at all, the economy as a whole gains from the North Sea, there are obvious benefits to those directly or indirectly engaged in the operation of extracting the oil and gas and delivering it to distribution points. Workers in the industry earn wages, salaries and consultancy fees which they might or might not otherwise have received by working in alternative occupations. Further beneficiaries will be those who are engaged in the construction of rigs and other equipment and in the ancillary activities needed to service the oil sector. And a major slice of the gains will go, of course, to the oil companies themselves.

These gains vary widely from company to company. Some have been hugely successful, others much less so. At one extreme we can imagine the relatively unhappy case of Piteus Oil Corporation, which was allocated a number of what have turned out to be distinctly unfavourable blocks of the North Sea area. Their exploratory drillings were mostly fruitless and the few wells that have proved worth exploiting are outlying, low-yielding and geologically awkward to work. The Corporation is disappointed, but nonetheless making just sufficient profit to keep it in business. Piteus is, in other words, a 'marginal' enterprise, decidedly envious of some of its competitors like, for example, Lucky Strike Ltd.

Lucky Strike has found the going easy. Several of its blocks are centred above a major reservoir in relatively shallow water close to the coast. By the standards of the petroleum industry its exploration costs were minimal, and it now has a large number of productive, smoothly operating wells. Its profits are very substantial indeed.

The range of difference in the fortunes of the North Sea companies is of great significance for governments intent on taxing them. This can best be explained by another brief excursion into elementary economic theory, this time using the concept of 'economic rent'. Economic rent is not to be confused with the everyday notion of rents on property, although the two uses of the term are to some extent related.

We have already seen that there are three broad categories of resources, or 'factors of production' – land, labour and capital. Each of them receives earnings for the part it plays in the process of production. Thus labour derives an income in the form of wages and salaries. Capital, too, receives a reward, although a slightly more complex one. Payment for the use of capital is made up partly of interest; and partly it consists of an element of 'pure profit', the amount of which varies according to the riskiness of the conditions in which it is employed.

Economic rent is the comparable return earned by the factor of production 'land'. The amount of land available at any time is an even more fixed quantity than that of the other human or man-made resources, and this relatively fixed supply means that the payment for the use of land therefore depends essentially on the strength of the *demand* for it rather than on its cost of production. Thus if we imagine plots of agricultural land of varying fertility and only a low demand for the crops which could be grown on them, price will settle at a level just sufficient to induce production on some of the more fertile of the plots. If, on the other hand, there is a very high demand for the crops, the price paid must be sufficient to cover production costs on the *least* fertile of the plots now used. But in that case, it will exceed costs (of wages, equipment, seeds, etc.) on the other plots according to the extent to which they are more fertile than the marginal one. This 'surplus' over costs (occurring on all except the marginal plot) is the economic rent which accrues to the landholders.

Put another way, economic rent is a payment to a factor of

production *over and above* that which is needed to keep it in its present use. If it is taken away, if the price paid for the product includes no provision for rent, then output will still continue at its existing level. Thus production will be maintained even if the economic rent earned on the more fertile plots is wholly extracted through taxation: the price, high enough to ensure production on the marginal plot, will be sufficient to ensure that all *costs* are being fully covered.

Exactly the same reasoning can be applied to North Sea oil and gas. In the marginal companies like the hypothetical Piteus Corporation, revenues only just cover costs of production including a 'normal' rate of profit which can be defined as the yield which the capital employed could have earned in an alternative use (with an additional element to the extent that North Sea investment was a use involving higher than average risks). But the oil and gas prices which just keep Piteus in business are at a level which leaves other operators like Lucky Strike Ltd with considerable surpluses after their costs have been met. In other words, the accounting profits declared by the North Sea companies include both the yield on capital as such *and* a rent element stemming from ownership of the 'land' resource of the North Sea deposits. And to repeat the point again, this is a surplus rather than a payment which has to be made in order to induce them to produce. In principle, it can therefore be siphoned off without affecting production levels.

Government policy towards the North Sea companies has consequently been much concerned with identifying this economic rent element in their earnings and in devising ways of appropriating it through taxation. It is not surprising, of course, that private owners of the leases in the North Sea resist such a process and argue that their earnings are the necessary rate of return to capital employed in conditions of high risk. And certainly, the proportion of their profits which can truly be classified as economic rent, and therefore in excess of that needed to keep them in profitable business, is not easy to establish. It can only be tested by seeing whether, after taxation, production does in fact remain at the same level, and by how far they are prepared to invest in further development.

In the case of the U.K., the attempts to capture the rent element of the North Sea for government revenues have taken a number of forms. There are royalties on output associated with the allocation of blocks; Corporation Tax payable by the oil companies on their profits; Petroleum Revenue Tax levied on their overall receipts; and the returns from the British National Oil Corporation (B.N.O.C.) which constitutes the direct public stake in the ownership of the North Sea reserves.

The potential government revenues from these various sources depend on a large number of factors and are extremely difficult to predict. Most obviously, the amount is determined by the extent of the oil and gas reserves which are discovered, by the speed with which they are exploited and by the price levels at which they are sold. Another very important consideration is the ingenuity shown by the oil companies in devising ways of avoiding paying the taxes which are levied.

Government revenues from the North Sea are expected to rise sharply to a peak during the mid-eighties. This is partly because increasing amounts of oil and gas are coming on stream at generally rising prices, and partly because in the earlier years the oil companies were able to offset a large proportion of their vast exploration and installation costs against tax.

In 1980/81, the various North Sea sources produced nearly £4,000 million of government revenue, an amount officially estimated to increase in real terms by about 55% by 1983/4. Other estimates are more optimistic, suggesting that in current prices the yield could be between £15 billion and £30 billion by the mid-eighties, the wide discrepancy between alternative forecasts reflecting the many unpredictable elements that are involved.

Using North Sea Revenues

North Sea revenues are certainly very large, but they need to be kept in perspective by relating them to other large totals. For example, in 1981 they amounted to some 2% of the Gross National Product, a percentage which is likely to rise over the next few years but not much exceed 5%. Nor can they be expected even at their peak to account for more than about 10% of total government revenues. Their effect is therefore likely to be proportionately much less than in the cases of smaller countries like the Netherlands or Norway or Kuwait which have enjoyed similar windfall gains. However, they are large enough to have a significant impact in several important areas of policy-making.

Fig. 14 sets out the simple alternatives for governments in deciding how the revenue should be used.

Fig. 14. *Use of oil revenues*

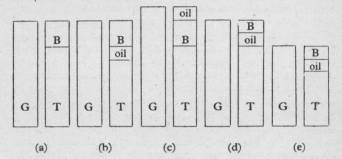

Fig. 14(a) shows the starting point, with government expenditure (G) being financed from taxes (T) and borrowing (B). The first possibility is that the government should hold its spending at a constant level but use the oil revenues to juggle between its sources of finance. Thus in 4(b) spending and borrowing are unchanged, and the additional oil revenue is used to allow cuts to be made in other taxes, e.g. income tax or V.A.T. And in 4(d), spending and taxes are held constant, with the North Sea bonus allowing a reduction to be made in the P.S.B.R. 4(c) illustrates a quite different approach, with existing taxes and borrowing remaining the same, and oil revenues being used to finance an *increase* in public expenditure. On the other hand, government spending could be cut as part of an overall economic strategy, with the revenues from the North Sea thereby allowing an even greater reduction in borrowing and/or taxes.

However, two points need to be made about this way of presenting the alternatives. In the first place, it is a very static way of looking at the choice which has to be made. It implies that there is a simple mechanical relationship between the various categories – spending, borrowing, oil revenues and taxes. But while it is bound to be the case that changes in government spending must be matched by corresponding changes in the amounts derived from the three sources of revenue, this tells us nothing about how the equality between the two is achieved. Thus, alternative 4(e), of cutting public spending and thereby reducing borrowing and/or taxes, sounds a less attractive proposition when the argument at the end of Chapter 3 is recalled. The effect of attempted reductions in public spending may be to lower national income and employment, with the consequence that an increased *proportion* of spending has to be on unemployment benefits and the like; similarly, total tax revenue at existing rates may actually fall as a result of lower incomes so that holding T constant or reducing it would involve *increases* in the *rate* of taxation. On the other hand, increased public spending would have the opposite effect; higher revenue from the increased incomes which would result might allow tax rates (or borrowing) to be *reduced*.

Secondly, Fig. 14 illustrates only the *immediate* options facing governments in deciding how to deploy North Sea revenues. Changes in taxation or borrowing, and increased (or decreased) public spending are not ends in themselves. They are only instruments of policy, means by which a government's economic objectives may be achieved. The key issue which might be expected to dominate the debate about the North Sea windfall is this: should the gains be used, for as long as they last, so that we enjoy a higher standard of living than would otherwise have been possible – or should the objective be to strengthen the economy in preparation for the post-oil era? In either case, there is a further choice to be made about the relative roles of the State and the private sector in achieving the aims of policy.

(i) *Consumption versus Investment*

Consumption means enjoying the fruits of output today – in the form of more goods and services like video recorders, washing machines, cars, summer holidays and social security benefits. Investment is the channelling of part of output into the production of things like factories, equipment, roads and docks which do not yield any immediate satisfaction to consumers but which replace or add to the capital stock of the community. The hope is that the result will be an increased capacity of the economy to produce a larger quantity of consumer goods in the future. More consumption or more investment is one of the classic economic choices which has to be faced up to in most economies.

In a fully employed economy, the choice may be a painful one. Raising the level of investment is only possible by restraining present increases in consumption to leave room for it. A decision is therefore entailed about how as a society we value consumption today, in relation to consumption in the future. It is the sort of question which we can resolve on an individual basis by asking, 'What sum of money would I accept in one year's time, or five year's time, in lieu of £100 today?' The answer reflects our time preference. And exactly the same issue has to be posed for the community as a whole. How far are we prepared to sacrifice increased living standards now for the prospect of higher living standards later?

The North Sea, by providing an addition to the total resources of the economy, offered a golden opportunity of avoiding some of the sacrificial aspects of this basic choice. It should have been possible to have had more investment *without* a cut in consumption, or more consumption *without* reducing investment – or some combination of the two.

In fact, to have concentrated on raising investment would seem to have been the wiser choice, given the finite nature of the North Sea reserves. Just how long they will last is debatable, depending on what fresh discoveries might be made, the level of prices (which determines whether known reserves are commercially worth extracting), and on how rapidly they are depleted. But it seems clear that their benefits will be relatively short-lived, with a tailing off during the nineties and the turn of the century. In the circumstances, there was therefore a very strong case for ensuring that North Sea revenues should have been deployed to restructure the economy in ways making it more capable of functioning effectively when the oil finally runs out.

(ii) *Public versus Private*

Secondary to the choice between consumption and investment are two subsidiary and interrelated issues concerning the form that either of these should take, and the mechanism through which North Sea revenues could be expected to lead to the desired goals. Both of these involve deciding about the relative roles of the State and the private sector.

One possibility is that the government should itself have provided both the instrument and the content in using the revenues. Thus if, for example, it was decided that they should be used to permit higher consumption, then it should have taken the form of higher public spending on education, the national health service, welfare benefits, etc. Standards of living would thereby have been improved by increasing the 'social wage' element.

Or if, on the other hand, increased investment was the aim of policy, then once again this might have been achieved directly by higher government spending – on larger investment programmes by the nationalized industries, provision of improved infrastructure like transport, communications and sewage, on government-built factories in the depressed regions, on setting up new firms and industries through, for example, the National Enterprise Board.

THE NORTH SEA AND DEFLATION

In the event, as we have already seen, the exploitation of the North Sea has coincided with a period in which increasing reliance has been placed by governments on monetarist policies. The resulting deflation has led to rapidly rising unemployment, under-utilization of productive capacity and gloomy industrial prospects. In these circumstances, the choice between consumption *or* investment is no longer of the same relevance. More of *both* can be afforded by the fuller use of already unemployed or under-employed resources. And the bonus of increased output which the additional resources extracted from the North Sea might have provided is more than cancelled out by the loss of potential output caused by the recession.

Far from financing the restructuring of the economy, the new revenues have not even enabled the immediate targets of reduced public borrowing and lower taxes to be achieved. The P.S.B.R. has remained high because of the effects on public spending and incomes brought about by the recession itself: increased outlay on unemployment and redundancy payments, loss of tax revenue, and large-scale financial assistance to both public and private industries to alleviate the problems caused for them by falling demand. And the tax cuts which were to be a vital element in encouraging higher private investment look increasingly difficult to sustain in face of the avowed intent to initiate fresh public spending cuts in the future.

We began this chapter by asking why we are not richer as a result of North Sea oil and gas. The truth is that, during the worse recession since the thirties, many of us have been better off. What has happened is that the revenues from the North Sea have helped to finance large numbers of people out of work and a redistribution of income from those who have lost their jobs to those lucky enough to stay in employment. And instead of providing the basis for expanding the productive capability of the economy, it will be argued in later chapters that the way in which the North Sea has been managed has transformed what could have been a great bonanza into a factor further intensifying the damage inflicted by the recession. British manufacturing has sharply declined, with home-produced goods losing ground to imports at an alarming rate. The immediate cause of this has been the exchange rate, which we begin to examine in the next chapter.

[5] The Price of Pounds

In 1980 one of the most popular holiday destinations was the United States. Sunny Miami was flooded with British tourists seeking temporary respite from not only the weather but also the deep depression which had settled over the British economy. Americans, on the other hand, were finding Britain a very expensive place to visit, with London ranking as one of the dearest capitals in the world. This major turnaround from the situation of a few years previously was mainly due to what meanwhile had happened to the exchange rate between pounds and dollars. In 1976–7, for example, one pound would have bought only 1.60 dollars. By 1980 it bought nearly half as many again. And the number of pounds that Americans could buy with their dollars had fallen correspondingly.

On the face of it this was not just good for the tourists. Surely a highly-valued pound is an indicator of economic strength, a reflection of the confidence of foreigners in the state of the economy? Certainly during the post-war period we have been conditioned to believe that a strong pound is highly desirable; every fall in its international value has been presented as a further nail in the coffin of our national pride. For decades after the war both Conservative and Labour governments defended the pound to their utmost, allowing the exchange rate to fall only when it was absolutely inevitable. And fall it did – from £1 : 4 dollars in 1945 to £1 : 2.8 dollars in 1949 to £1 : 2.4 dollars in 1967 and so down to its lowest point in 1976–1977.

So why when it subsequently rose some 32% by the early eighties were British industrialists, instead of being cock-a-hoop, bitterly complaining that the strength of sterling was making it impossible for them to compete in the export markets of the world, and that at home their sales were being eroded by cheap imports? What in fact determines the rate at which the pound exchanges against other currencies? And what are the effects of changes in its value?

The Value of the Pound

We are all very well aware of how inflation has reduced the value of the pound in our pockets so that a pound today represents only a fraction of the purchasing power that it did twenty or thirty years ago. This is related to, but not the same thing as the *external* value of the pound – the quantities of other currencies which can be bought with sterling. This exchange rate results from the activities of the 'foreign exchange market' – the complex of contacts, mostly by telephone rather than face to face, between all those engaged in the purchase and sale of the many currencies of the world. Thus when as individuals we buy foreign currencies at a bank we begin a chain of processes which ultimately reaches a foreign exchange dealer who matches these orders to buy against orders to sell those currencies by other clients.

The rate at which one currency exchanges for another is set basically by the strength of the demand for it (the quantities which people are trying to buy) in relation to the strength of the supply of it (the quantities which others are trying to sell). In the case of Britain, the demand for and supply of pounds in the foreign exchange market stems mainly from its role as a major participant in international trade. We import a vast range of goods from abroad – industrial raw materials, food and beverages, manufactured goods like machinery, cars and electrical equipment, and we export a similarly wide variety for sale to foreigners.

When we buy imported products in the shops and show-rooms we pay for them in pounds. But those pounds are of no direct use to the foreigner who is the ultimate seller of the goods. He wants payment in his own currency, like deutsch-marks, francs or yen. So if a company imports goods from, say, the United States, it has to acquire dollars in order to settle its account. It buys them with pounds, so that the effect of importing goods is to augment the *supply* of pounds coming on to the foreign exchange market. Likewise when British firms export goods they require payment in pounds. Americans buying such goods therefore have to buy sterling with dollars – so that British exports lead to a *demand* for pounds on the foreign exchange market.

If that were the end of the story, then the rate at which pounds exchanged for dollars would depend on the amount of imports and exports. If for example imports exceeded exports, then the supply of pounds being offered for sale would be greater than the demand for them by would-be purchasers. As with any other commodity, this excess supply would push the price of pounds downwards to the point where demand and supply were just matched. The pound might fall in value, as in Fig. 15(a), from £1 : 2.4 dollars to £1 : 2 dollars.

Fig. 15.

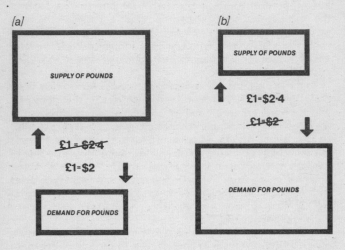

Exports in excess of imports would have the opposite effect. The demand for pounds (from foreigners trying to settle their bills with British exporters) would be greater than the supply of pounds (from British importers buying the foreign currencies which they need) so that the exchange rate would be forced up as in Fig. 15(b). Only if by an extraordinary coincidence total exports and total imports of goods happened to be equal would the exchange rate remain the same.

But that is not the end of the story. The imports and exports of *goods* only form what is termed 'visible' trade. They are transactions involving the transfer of tangible merchandise of one kind or another. But as well as these, there are imports and exports of 'invisibles' which arise from the sale and purchase of services and similar transactions. Among the main categories of invisibles are earnings and expenditure on shipping, airlines, banking and insurance; tourism; maintenance of government embassies and military bases; and flows of profits, interest and dividends.

For example, if British goods are carried by a foreign shipping line, this involves a payment in a foreign currency. It is therefore an invisible import. If Americans spend their holidays in Britain they have to exchange dollars for pounds – for the U.K., an invisible export. A British base in Germany entails expenditure by us in deutschmarks, an invisible import. Payment of dividends by Ford U.K. to their U.S. shareholders represents an invisible import because sterling has to be exchanged for dollars.

All these transactions thus involve the exchange of pounds for foreign currencies as *though* a physical transfer of merchandise had taken place. They therefore have exactly the same type of impact on the exchange rate. Invisible imports (payments by U.K. residents to foreigners) will press downwards on the exchange rate because they are additions to the supply of pounds on the foreign exchange market. And invisible exports (where foreigners have to buy pounds in order to pay British sellers) will push it up because they constitute a further demand for sterling.

When visible imports are set against visible exports, the resulting account is known as the *balance of trade*. It is the latest statistics about these which are generally announced as 'the monthly trade figures'. Adding on to them invisible imports and exports, we arrive at the *balance of payments on current account*, as follows:

	Visible exports
minus	Visible imports
=	*Balance of Trade*
plus	Invisible exports
minus	Invisible imports
=	*Balance of payments on current account*

On top of visible and invisible trade, there is a third very important set of transactions which influences the exchange rate. This consists of international movements of *capital*. Suppose, for example, that oil-rich Arab individuals or governments decide to hold part of their wealth in the form of British bank balances or holdings of British government bonds or British company shares. Then to finance this they will have to switch to sterling, and this buying pressure will make the pound stronger. The same thing will happen if a foreign company like Nissan directly invests in Britain by setting up a subsidiary to manufacture Datsuns here. The immediate result is that the pound is strengthened as they acquire sterling to buy the bricks, mortar and machinery that they need. Later, as they sell their cars, part of their profits are likely to be repatriated into the coffers of the parent company in Japan; interest payments will have to be made on any money they have borrowed from Japanese banks; and Japanese shareholders will expect dividends. This outward flow of profits, interest and dividends on the Nissan investment will have a depressing effect on the exchange rate as it involves the sale of sterling and purchase of yen. Similarly, British investment overseas will initially weaken the pound, but subsequently help to keep the exchange rate up as earnings from the investment flow back.

Long-term capital movements of this kind are based on assessments by investors about the prospects of different economies – judgements about where it is safest to hold wealth or most profitable to set up business. Capital may also flow between countries as a short-term response to interest rate differentials between the major financial centres. If, for example, the rate of interest in London is 15% and only 10% in Paris, French individuals and companies with surplus funds will be tempted to switch them to the U.K. where they will earn a higher rate of return.

Finally, international movements of capital may arise from speculation about the future of exchange rates. If it is commonly believed that the sterling rate will rise, then foreigners will be attracted to buy pounds in the hope of selling later at a profit, i.e. getting more foreign currency for their pounds than they paid for them. On the other hand, fears of an impending fall in the value of sterling will lead foreign holders to sell now while the going is good. In both cases, expectations about what is going to happen may prove to be self-justifying. Thus widespread buying in anticipation of a rise does in fact push the exchange rate up. A run against sterling because it is thought likely to fall causes the selling pressure which brings about just the effect which was feared.

Fig. 16.

The exchange rate for a currency, then, is determined by the supply and demand for it stemming from visible and invisible trade and a variety of capital movements. These upward and downward influences on the exchange rate are summed up in Fig. 16.

Fixed and Floating Exchange Rates

During the post-war period up to 1971 it was the practice of the British government, in company with most others, to prevent the external value of the pound from fluctuating beyond very narrow margins around a 'par value' set in agreement with the International Monetary Fund. Exchange rates were more or less fixed, with changes in par value being allowed under I.M.F. rules only in exceptional circumstances and with the prior consent of the Fund. Such changes were known as 'devaluation' if in a downward direction and 'revaluation' if the par value were increased.

But if exchange rates are determined by supply and demand, how were governments able to prevent fluctuations from occurring? The answer lies in their ability to 'manage' the forces of supply and demand.

Suppose, for example, that the position is the one illustrated in Fig. 15(a), with the supply of pounds exceeding the demand for them so that the exchange rate is headed for a fall. In these circumstances, the government authorities can only prevent this happening by themselves supplementing demand so that it *does* equal supply at the existing exchange rates. It means that they must *buy* pounds with whatever foreign currencies sellers are seeking to acquire. Their ability to support the pound therefore depends on the availability of a stock of such foreign currencies for them to draw upon. These take the form of the nation's 'official reserves' of gold and foreign exchange which have been built up in times when the opposite conditions have prevailed.

This opposite situation is shown in Fig. 15(b), the demand for sterling being greater than the amount supplied so that if nothing is done the exchange rate will be forced up. Such a rise can be avoided by the authorities in this case reinforcing supply, i.e. selling pounds and receiving for them quantities of foreign currencies which are then added to the official reserves.

There are other ways, apart from such direct intervention, in which the authorities may try to alter the supply and demand totals. They can adjust the level of interest rates in the hope of attracting or repelling foreign funds; the flow of international capital can be affected by the imposition (or removal) of exchange control regulations specifying the conditions in which such purchases or sales of foreign currency are allowed to take place; and government may negotiate official borrowing or lending with the I.M.F. or other governments. More broadly, the underlying trading strength of the pound will be influenced by the impact of government policies on the economy in affecting the rate of economic growth, prices and the balance of payments.

During the period 1945–72 sterling was successfully managed by these techniques so that its par value was only changed on two occasions. These were the devaluations of 1949 and 1967. To devalue was seen by the government of the day as a traumatic decision, taken with great reluctance only after it became clear that the pound could not be supported at its previous level without resort to what were then regarded as unacceptable policies (like reducing the excess supply of pounds coming on to the foreign exchange market by severely deflating the economy or imposing import controls so that British spending on foreign goods and services would be cut back).

However, when continued difficulty was experienced in pegging the pound at its lower post-devaluation rate, it was finally allowed to 'float' in June 1972 and find its own level in the foreign exchange market, to begin with largely free from official intervention. The immediate result was a sharp downward movement, or 'depreciation' as it is sometimes called under a flexible exchange rate system to distinguish it from the even more abrupt devaluations under a fixed exchange rate regime. By 1976 it was some 25% below its previous level when compared with other currencies. (Because other countries also adopted a policy of floating, the measure of depreciation itself became more complex. It was no longer sufficient to make comparisons just with the dollar, because the change in the pound's value varied from currency to currency. A new index was therefore compiled giving different weights to changes in the pounds exchanged for other currencies according to their relative importance; this weighted average was labelled the effective exchange rate.)

The fall in the exchange rate between 1972 and 1976 implied that there was a persistent excess of sterling in relation to the demand for it. One cause of the downward float was the current weakness in the balance of payments, particularly after the massive rise in the price of oil which took place in 1972–3, leading to an unprecedentedly large current account deficit in 1974. And secondly, the exchange rate was depressed by speculation based on the belief that it was likely to fall further in the future.

A major cause of both of these downward pressures on sterling was the fact that the British inflation rate was consistently higher than that being experienced by our leading competitors. With a fixed exchange rate, this would have meant that our exports would have become dearer and imports relatively cheaper. A floating exchange rate, on the other hand, allowed British selling prices in home and foreign markets to be kept broadly in line with others despite higher inflation. For example, if Britain's inflation was at 15% and Germany's at 5%, the price at which exports to Germany were sold needed to rise by only 5% provided that the rate at which the pound exchanged for the deutschmark fell by 10%. In other words, the falling pound in effect offset the higher rate of British inflation (although it also pushed up import prices which further fuelled inflation).

However, the relationship between the balance of payments on current account and the exchange rate was not a straightforward one. This was principally because the O.P.E.C. countries, earning vast surpluses as a result of the oil price increases, then 're-cycled' large sums back to the consuming countries. The revenue they earned from the sale of the oil was often far greater than they could spend immediately, and they therefore chose to re-lend the excess funds to the deficit countries like Britain and earn interest on them. This source of demand for pounds prevented sterling from falling as much as it would otherwise have done.

And it was oil which was the most important factor in subsequently changing the picture once again. This time, in the late seventies, the effect on exchange rates came from growing awareness of the significance of Britain's own North Sea discoveries and the anticipation that they would lead to self-sufficiency in oil by the early eighties. To the extent that the balance of payments became more favourable as a result of reduced dependence on imported oil, this meant a smaller supply of pounds (seeking to buy foreign currencies) coming on to the foreign exchange market as compared with the demand for them – with the exchange rate moving up accordingly. And secondly, the expectation that the balance of payments would continue to be strong in the future led to an inflow of foreign capital in search of an investment outlet which was 'safe' in the sense that the exchange rate was not expected to fall. (It is no good investing 1,000 deutschmarks in Britain because the rate of interest is higher there than in Germany if, in a year's time, the amount of deutschmarks that can be bought with the pounds has fallen to 800 because of a depreciation in the exchange rate.)

Between 1976 and 1980 the pound appreciated in the foreign exchange market by more than 30%. In addition to the impact of North Sea oil (and occasional switches by foreigners into pounds and *against* other currencies like the dollar in 1977), part of the rise must also be attributed to the increasingly exclusive pursuit of monetarist policies during this period. These, as we have seen, give paramount priority to the reduction of inflation as an economic objective and are based on the belief that it is only through 'sound money' that this can be achieved. Both the priority and the means are of the kind which are likely, rightly or wrongly, to find favour among financiers elsewhere. The view of Britain as a place where money could be safely deposited was further enhanced.

Other aspects of monetarism have further made for a rising pound. In particular, the setting of money supply targets has made Britain a highly profitable as well as a safe place to hold funds because of the way in which the authorities have concentrated on reducing the demand for money through high interest rates – which provide a greater incentive for foreigners to hold sterling. And the deflationary impact which attempted monetarism has had holds down the level of imports which firms and individuals can afford to buy, so that fewer pounds are sold on the foreign exchange market.

It is difficult to apportion the rise in the pound between these various causes. Even the Treasury admitted that 'Almost all attempts to explain sterling's recent strength leave a significant proportion unexplained ... Many factors have been at work, and there is no way to be sure even of their relative importance in the foreign exchange market.'[1] And the Chief Advisor to the Bank of England expressed mystification about why the pound had risen so high: 'It is very difficult to understand why the exchange rate is where it is now ... It is considerably higher than one might have analytically expected.'[2]

Whatever the precise breakdown between the causes, the upward movement of sterling was such that by 1980 it was back to its 1975 level. The fluctuations in the external value of the pound are charted in Fig. 17 and have now been broadly explained in terms of the changing supply of pounds on the foreign exchange market in relation to the demand for them. But what were the *effects* on the economy of changes in the exchange rate – in particular, of the *rising* pound during

Fig. 17. *Sterling exchange rate 1975–80*

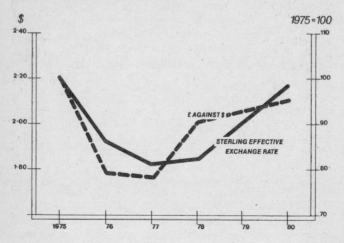

1. Treasury and Civil Service Committee, op. cit., p. lxii.
2. ibid.

the years when monetarist policies were being conducted most vigorously?

Pros and Cons of a Strong Pound

It may seem self-evident that a 'strong pound' is highly desirable, while a fall in the value of sterling is a clear indication of weakness in the economy and that things are going wrong. The terms themselves carry that connotation. And certainly British governments have been biased towards this view for a very long time, dating back to disastrous attempts which were made in the twenties to restore the pre-1914 exchange rate with the dollar. As we have seen, the post-war devaluations were made only when it seemed that there was no other option. And even after 1972 there was a 'dirty float' in the sense that governments did not generally let the pound find its own level, but intervened to prevent it falling further than they thought proper.

However, whether a rising or high pound is in fact preferable to a low or falling pound depends on the economic objectives which a government is trying to achieve, and on the ways in which the economy is affected by the exchange rate. For the rest of this chapter we shall examine the rationale and effects of a high exchange rate. In Chapter 7 we shall return to the question, and look at the arguments put forward by those who advocate a lower exchange rate.

For monetarists, a rising pound *is* desirable and constitutes a vital element in the strategy to control inflation. As the Treasury put it in their memorandum to the all-party Committee on Monetary Policy: 'One of the first effects of a restrictive monetary policy will be the exchange rate. It may improve confidence directly by lowering the expected rate of inflation in the U.K. relative to other countries' and 'higher interest rates also improve the rate of return on sterling, compared with foreign currency assets'.[3] And far from being an unfortunate or unwanted side-effect of the attempt to regulate the money supply, the resultant rise in the exchange rate is

3. Treasury and Civil Service Committee, op. cit., Vol. II, Minutes of Evidence, p. lvi.

seen as a key part of the 'transmission mechanism' by which monetary control brings about lower inflation.

In the first place, there is the direct effect of a high exchange rate in keeping import prices low. Thus an American exporter to Britain wanting 2.4 dollars for his product will have to charge £1.20 for it if the exchange rate is £1 : 2 dollars; if the exchange rate is higher, £1 : 2.4 dollars, then he can sell it for £1. This means that British firms using imported raw materials or machinery or components find that their manufacturing costs are reduced. They therefore have the opportunity of pricing their products more competitively. British consumers, too, benefit from the high exchange rate to the extent that they spend their incomes on imported goods and services. The fact that these are cheaper helps to slow down the increase in the cost of living and may result in lower demands for wage and other income increases. Once again, this helps to keep down production costs.

On the other hand, a rising exchange rate also pushes up the prices of our exports and makes it relatively difficult to sell them. But this may also be claimed to have favourable consequences.

(a) Faced by declining profit margins in export markets (or inability to compete at all and make a profit), British producers are forced to redouble their efforts to increase their productivity in order to restore their competitiveness. It will encourage them to invest in new plant and machinery, to rid themselves of surplus labour and generally streamline their operations so that they are able to sell their goods *despite* the higher exchange rate.

(b) Their exchange rate disadvantage in foreign markets will in particular make it very clear to firms with export business that they will not be able to recoup higher costs of production through raising prices. They will therefore be highly resistant to excessive wage claims. This discipline imposed on employers in the export sector by the need to keep in line with their foreign competitors will then feed through to the rest of the economy, reducing the 'going rate' for wage increases.

(c) Their difficulty in competing on price may also induce British exporters to switch from products and markets where price-competitiveness is vital to others where

quality considerations are of relatively greater importance in gaining markets. Such an 'up-market' move
should be welcomed, it is claimed, because it is on
high-technology, superior quality products that Britain
should be concentrating in the future rather than on
traditional mass production goods where other countries now have the edge.

Critics challenge all of these elements in the case for a high
pound. Cheap imports, they agree, help to keep prices down.
But the cost of doing so is rising unemployment as British
producers, in failing to compete with imports made so competitive by the high exchange rate, are driven to the wall.
There is a danger that permanent damage is inflicted on the
manufacturing sector of the economy, from which it will subsequently be unable to recover. And cheap imports only
benefit exporting firms to the extent that their products
embody a sizeable import content; those which do not simply
suffer the crippling effects of the high pound. Higher export
prices *may* lead firms to seek ways of keeping down their
costs of production, but the simple arithmetic of their plight is
discouraging. The degree to which their competitiveness has
been eroded by the high exchange rate is far too great for
them to offset it through productivity increases. In these
circumstances they are unlikely to undertake new investment
programmes, particularly when their problems overseas are
compounded by a stagnant or declining home market. And
finally, instead of exporters moving up-market in response to
their difficulties in competing on price, they may instead
decide to withdraw from export markets altogether – a process
which it may prove very difficult subsequently to reverse.

The authorities have thus seen the exchange rate as part of
the mechanism by which control of the money supply is transmitted into lower inflation, and have often asserted that they
cannot anyway affect the exchange rate since it is determined
by market forces. From what has already been said in this
chapter, this is clearly not strictly true since governments can
themselves influence and 'manage' these underlying forces in a
variety of ways. Indeed they did so to a limited extent in
1979 by the removal of remaining exchange controls on British
investment overseas. Any resulting outflow (increased supply
of pounds buying foreign currencies) offsets part of the

upward pressure on sterling exerted by the inward movement of foreign capital (demand for pounds). Similarly, a fall in the exchange rate could be expected if interest rates were reduced so that the U.K. became a less attractive repository for foreign funds. And the authorities can counter the pressure of a high demand for pounds by an increase in their supply, i.e. themselves buying foreign currencies as described earlier.

What *is* true, however, is that such options are closed if policy is aimed at strictly regulating the money supply. Lower interest rates might stimulate the demand for money, an increase in bank borrowing which the government is anxious to avoid. And if the authorities were to try to reduce the exchange rate by buying foreign currencies, the sterling they would need to do so could only be acquired by a rise in the P.S.B.R.; if this were to be done without increasing the money supply, higher interest rates would be called for to attract additional holders of government bonds. Since these would act as a magnet for further foreign funds, a government so committed to controlling £M3 is thus caught in a vicious circle.

But even given monetary targets it is possible to bring the exchange rate down by the use of devices like controls on the inflow of funds, the setting of lower interest rates for foreign holders of British assets, or other methods of controlling the money supply like direct controls over the banks. But such methods are unlikely to appeal to a government aiming at minimum intervention in the working of the economy.

In fact by 1981 the exchange rate had begun to fall of its own accord – only slightly against most major currencies but very sharply against the dollar. Interestingly, this was due mainly to the introduction of vigorously monetarist policies in the U.S.A., resulting in extraordinarily high interest rates there which made it an even more attractive haven for foreign funds than the U.K.; in addition, a weakening of world oil prices led to some re-evaluation of Britain's North Sea advantage. However, far from welcoming this depreciation, the authorities saw it as a threat to the counter-inflationary policy which they sought to limit by a degree of intervention in the foreign exchange market and some rise in U.K. interest rates.

There will be more to say on exchange rates in coming chapters. We next look at the combined effects on British industry of the various aspects of monetarist policy which have now been outlined, including consideration of the view that a high exchange rate is the inevitable mechanism by which the structure of the economy is adjusted to accommodate North Sea oil. And in Chapter 7, it will be time to examine the case for a deliberate and substantial devaluation of sterling.

[6]   The Death of Industry

By the early eighties, widespread concern was being voiced at the state of British manufacturing industry – deeply pessimistic about its own prospects in the face of declining demand, high interest and exchange rates, and growing foreign competition. It was a combination of adverse circumstances from which not even the most established companies could remain immune, and to which a government ideologically opposed to such support had to respond by bailing out major enterprises.

A cynic might say that the only novel element in this situation was that this time it might really be true that British industry was in a critical condition. For ever since a freak conjunction of factors led to Britain becoming the first workshop of the world, other countries have demonstrated a distressing ability to catch up or overtake. And ever since, there have been laments about the inadequacy of British economic performance. By the turn of the century, for example, working parties were being dispatched to the United States to discover why productivity was higher there. Blame was variously laid at the door of restrictive practices by trade unions, dilettante management, an outdated educational system, insufficient investment in new technology and other causes still familiar today. Even during the decades after 1945, when Britain was enjoying unprecedented rates of economic growth and material prosperity on a scale never experienced before, observers were commenting gloomily on the continued shortcomings of the economy and offering a range of explanations similar to those of their predecessors. Ironically, this was also the period when the feasibility and desirability of sustained economic growth were first beginning to be seriously questioned.

Some of this doom-mongering has simply been a display of 'econo-masochism', the obsessive British tendency to make unfavourable economic comparisons with what goes on elsewhere. But there is also evidence that in recent years there has been a genuine deterioration of worrying proportions, which policies of the kind already outlined have made worse even if they were not the original cause.

False Alarms?

It is not difficult to assemble collections of statistics which together paint a picture of an economy in long-term decline. And given the fact that Britain is a country which has for the past century and a half essentially depended for its prosperity on the output of its industries, there are trends in the *manufacturing* sector of the economy which certainly at first sight seem to be distinctly alarming.

(i) For more than a century after 1850, the proportion of the workforce engaged in manufacturing production remained more or less constant, peaking at nearly 36% in 1961. Since then, as Fig. 18 shows, it has been persistently shrinking – to 31% in 1975, to less than 28% in 1980 and perhaps little more than 25% today.

Fig. 18. *Proportion of total employment in manufacturing* (%)

1950	34.7
1960	35.8
1970	34.7
1975	30.9
1980	27.5

(Dept. of Employment Gazette)

(ii) Since the working population itself grew from rather less than 10 million in 1850 to the present 26 million, the relative constancy of the proportion occupied in manufacturing means that the *absolute* numbers employed grew enormously. But once again, a substantial fall is now being registered, from a peak of 8.4 million in 1966 to 6.7 million in 1980. That is, within just a decade and a half, no less than $1\frac{3}{4}$ million jobs in manufacturing industry have disappeared.

(iii) Britain was also once the world's leading *exporter* of manufactured goods. By 1880 it was accounting for some two-fifths of the total world export trade in manufactures. Fig. 19 shows just how startling the decline in its share has been both over the period as a whole and in the recent past.

Fig. 19. *U.K. % Share of world manufactured exports*

1881–5	38.1	1950	25.5
1900–05	29.4	1960	16.5
1921–25	23.8	1970	10.8
1931–35	18.4	1980	7.9

(iv) At one time, Britain's pattern of trade with the rest of the world was according to a basic division of labour in which we largely exported manufactures and imported foodstuffs and raw materials. Mainly during the post-war period, that pattern has dramatically changed, with manufactured and semi-manufactured goods growing rapidly to the point where they now comprise nearly two-thirds of our total imports. The speed with which this change is continuing to take place is illustrated by the fact that whereas imported manufactures represented less than 10% of the home market in the early sixties, the proportion had more than doubled by the mid-seventies.

What emerges from figures like these is a view of Britain as a once great economy with its strength gradually sapping to the point where it is now sinking into a state of 'de-industrialization', a dismantling of the manufacturing base on which its health has always depended.

However, this is much too simplistic an interpretation of what has been happening. For example, the declining proportion and numbers of the workforce engaged in manufacturing did not mean by the mid-seventies a fall in manufacturing *production*. It fell as a proportion of national output but national output was itself increasing. Thus manufacturing output rose until this time despite fewer workers being employed. In other words, productivity increased with each worker on average producing more than previously.

Moreover, the falling share in total output contributed by manufacturing was not a uniquely British phenomenon.

Fig. 20. *Manufacturing as % of total output*

	1960	1970	1975
U.K.	31.0	31.7	29.1
France	35.0	38.0	36.0
Germany	39.9	44.5	43.2
U.S.A.	27.4	27.9	26.0

(O.E.C.D.)

Fig. 20 confirms that a similar trend could be observed in many other industrial countries.

The figures probably mainly reflect the stage of development that these countries happen to have reached, following the changing pattern of employment outlined in Fig. 21. Fig. 21(a) shows a typical distribution of the workforce in an under-developed country. Primary production, agriculture and mineral extraction, is the main source of employment and output, and there is also a large tertiary sector made up of relatively under-employed workers in domestic service, petty trading and government offices; secondary production, manufacturing and processing, is relatively unimportant at this stage. As the economy develops, the distribution between the three sectors of the economy changes as in Fig. 21(b), with a relative contraction of both primary and tertiary employment and an increase in manufacturing. What industrial countries may now be experiencing is a third stage, illustrated in Fig. 21(c), with the tertiary service sector of the economy expanding at the expense not only of primary production but also of manufacturing.

This growth of the tertiary sector can be regarded as an indicator of affluence. As a country becomes richer, an increasing proportion of higher spending is channelled into demand for more and better services like leisure facilities, tourism, health and education provision. And in the same way that a vastly larger output of food is now produced by an agricultural workforce proportionately tiny compared with that of the nineteenth century, we might expect a similar development in the future to take place with regard to manufacturing.

Britain's international performance in manufactures also is in some ways not as gloomy as is suggested by Fig. 19. Cer-

Fig. 21. *Distribution of the workforce at different stages of development*

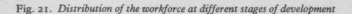
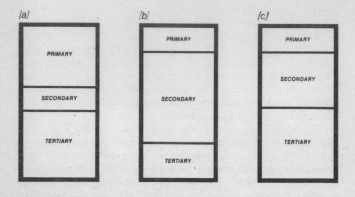

tainly, the U.K. share of world markets in manufactured goods has declined, but it is a share of a total which itself has been greatly increasing. In absolute terms, British manufactured exports have grown at a substantial rate. And nor has the rise in imports of manufactures been peculiar to the British economy over the years. The same trend can be observed in other major industrial countries as world trade has increasingly taken the form of the exchange of manufactures between countries at a similar stage of development. Nonetheless, the evidence does suggest that Britain has fared less well than many of its economic rivals – who have not suffered a relative decline in their overseas and home markets to the same extent, and who have generally enjoyed faster rates of economic growth than Britain. But even this in itself is not necessarily a matter for concern. In the first place, the British standard of living has increased very substantially; it may have risen even more in other countries but that is relevant only to the extent that we are consequently consumed with envy. Secondly, there are technical reasons which to some degree explain the relative disparities in British and foreign performance – for example, an element of 'catching-up' and the fact that until recently many of them had much larger and relatively unproductive rural sectors from which labour could be siphoned off into manufacturing industry to yield a faster overall rate of growth. And thirdly, there are plenty of grounds for doubting that the rate of economic growth is anyway a very satisfactory indicator of the welfare of a community or that its maximization is a desirable goal.

However, this is not to conclude that talk of the crisis in British industry is wholly misplaced and unjustified self-depreciation. Genuine cause for concern does exist in some aspects of Britain's relatively weaker showing, particularly when coupled with the impact of the policies pursued with increasing vigour since the mid-seventies.

De-industrialization

In recent years and particularly since the mid-seventies there have been a number of developments which suggest that, despite what has so far been said, British manufacturing industry is in a seriously deteriorating condition.

(i)   The falling rate at which manufacturing output was growing (some 16% in 1967–70 down to 9% in 1970–74) has recently given way to an absolute decline. Between 1975–80 the reduction in manufacturing output was 20%; in the deep recession of 1981 it was running some 15% below its 1979 level.[1]

(ii) The substantial shedding of labour from manufacturing industry has not been accompanied by a growth in the tertiary sector as it was previously. Instead of workers being displaced as a result of a relative change in consumer preferences in favour of services, they have simply become unemployed rather than re-absorbed in alternative occupations. The scale on which this has happened would have been even greater had the $3\frac{1}{2}$–4% annual increase in productivity typical of the post-war period been maintained. In fact, during the seventies productivity gains were reduced to less than 1% a year.

(iii) There has been a marked worsening in the ratio of British imports of manufactured goods to exports of

1. For the facts on recent industrial decline, see J. D. Hughes, *Britain in Crisis*, Spokesman, 1981.

manufactures. It has already been noted that a rise in the volume of imported manufactures has been common to most of the industrial countries of the world. But in the case of the U.K., the growth of such imports has been at a far faster rate than the growth of industrial exports. For example, between 1973 and 1979 the volume of exported manufactures rose by 20% while that of imported manufactures increased by 55%. The result was that whereas in 1970 exports of manufactures were nearly 50% greater in value than imports of such goods, by the early eighties Britain was at times getting close to becoming a net importer of manufactures.

'De-industrialization' is a fashionable term which is frequently used very loosely. As we have seen, if it only refers to a relative contraction of manufacturing, then that need not in itself be a problem – particularly if it involves the transfer of workers from monotonous assembly line processes in factories to more interesting service occupations. If such a reconstruction of the economy is then termed 'post-industrialization' it may be welcomed as a step forward rather than a matter for concern.

If, on the other hand, de-industrialization is seen as a problem, then it needs to be defined in a way which indicates *why* a relative or absolute weakening of the manufacturing sector is worrying. There are three main grounds for such anxiety. In the first place, the labour disgorged from manufacturing may only become unemployed rather than being absorbed into the tertiary sector. Second, there may be a decline in the incomes generated by manufacturing such as to reduce the government's tax revenues so that it is no longer able to finance a desired level of public services. And thirdly, there may be 'a progressive failure to achieve a sufficient surplus of exports over imports to keep the economy in external balance at full employment'.[2]

These aspects of de-industrialization are interrelated and can be understood by seeing that our demands on the economy fall into four broad categories: for manufactured goods, for

2. The 'Cambridge' definition proposed by A. Singh, 'U.K. Industry and the world economy: a case of deindustrialization', *Cambridge Journal of Economics*, June 1977.

non-manufactured goods (like food and raw materials), for marketed services (like banking or cinema seats) and for non-marketed services (like the N.H.S.).

Thus a fall in manufacturing incomes reduces the size of the tax base from which the government can pay for non-marketed services – unless it is offset by a simultaneous expansion of, for example, the part of the economy providing marketed services. And on the balance of payments front, the *net* contribution of the manufacturing sector (i.e. exports minus imports of manufactures) must be sufficient to pay for the non-manufactured goods and services that we import (to the extent that these are not financed by the export of services). Moreover, this must be possible without just depressing the demand for imports by allowing unemployment to rise to unacceptable levels.

On all these counts, the British economy does seem to be in a process of de-industrialization, with the extent of the underlying problem masked only by the fortuitous bonus of North Sea oil and the artificial restraint on imports which results from mass unemployment. In particular, the net foreign earnings of the manufacturing sector have fallen to the point where they are hardly sufficient to pay for vital imports of foodstuffs and raw materials. And the danger with de-industrialization is that once it is set in motion it can become a cumulative decline. The poor prospects for manufacturing industry lead to even less investment, lower productivity rises and still greater uncompetitiveness in world and home markets so that the import/export ratio of manufactures worsens further – causing it to contract more.

The Nature of Manufacturing Decline

It may be claimed that talk of de-industrialization is misplaced, and that British industry is simply suffering with others from the world-wide slow-down in growth which followed the raising of oil prices in 1973–4 – a fall-off in demand which is affecting all the leading industrial nations and from which, in due course, they will all recover. However, British manufacturing industry has suffered longer and much worse than most others. Between 1973 and 1980, for example, while world industrial output rose by 13%, there was a fall of 10% in the U.K. And when world trade stopped growing in 1980, Britain weathered the storm particularly badly; while other countries were deliberately increasing public spending to temper the effects of the recession, the British government persisted with further expenditure cuts.

This was in accordance with its diagnosis that the cause of British manufacturing weakness was its 'crowding out' by the public sector. On this view, industry at present is not so much in a crisis as passing through a necessarily painful but essentially transitional phase. As we have seen, the chief aims of the current economic strategy are the reduction of inflation through monetary restraint as the pre-condition for future economic growth, and the freeing of resources from the public sector for more productive employment in the private sector. It is argued that once this is achieved, investment will again pick up in a more favourable climate of business expectations created by tax cuts and more realistic wage settlements.

This is a view that has already been considered and criticized in earlier chapters. In the event, the deflationary stance adopted in the attempt to meet money targets and the increases in indirect taxation needed to keep down the P.S.B.R have contributed further to the lack of competitiveness at the heart of the British industrial decline. And instead of public service employment therefore expanding to absorb the longer-term reduction in manufacturing industry's labour requirements, public spending cuts have reduced the demand for private sector output still further, with the consequent underutilization of its existing capacity leading industry to invest even less.

Moreover, North Sea oil, instead of helping to insulate Britain from world recessionary effects as might have been expected, has become as a result of the way in which it has been managed a factor in reducing the ability of industry to compete. As we have seen, it was one of the causes of the capital inflows which forced up the exchange rate by over 25% between 1976 and 1980. British export prices were consequently increased while at home there was growing difficulty in fighting off foreign competition.

Oil and Manufacturing

Some go so far as to argue that a decline in British manufacturing output is an *inevitable* result of the North Sea and the high exchange rate that it entails.[3] Self-sufficiency in oil and gas has meant a massive saving on imports which would otherwise have been necessary. It is claimed that, since the balance of payments must balance, this improvement in the oil element of the balance of payments has therefore to be matched by a corresponding decline in our non-oil trade (which happens to be mostly in manufactures). In other words, this dispiriting view suggests that the benefits of the North Sea can only be enjoyed if there is a reduction in domestic manufacturing output sufficient to accommodate higher non-oil imports.

The argument is outlined in Figs. 22 and 23. Fig. 22 shows the pre-North Sea balance of payments, assuming for simplicity that the current and capital accounts were both in balance to begin with. That is, the inflow of foreign capital is just matched by the outflow of British overseas investment. And the value of exports just equals the value of imports. Imports are made up of two broad categories: (a) foreign oil, and (b) other goods and services – in particular, foreign manufactures.

Fig. 23 presents the picture as it might look after the North Sea has made it possible for us to achieve self-sufficiency in oil. Oil imports accordingly disappear as an item on the debit side of the account. At the same time, there is an increased inflow of foreign funds, attracted by the relative security offered by an economy which now has its own oil. Fig. 23(a) illustrates that on this argument the result will be a fall in exports and a rise in non-oil imports. The effect of both of these will be a reduced demand for British manufactures as less are required in overseas markets and at home they are replaced by imports of foreign manufactures. The manufacturing sector therefore contracts. The mechanism which brings about this switch in

3. This is the interpretation often put on the analysis of P. J. Forsyth and J. A. Kay, 'The Economic Implications of North Sea Oil Revenues', *Fiscal Studies*, July 1980.

Fig. 22.

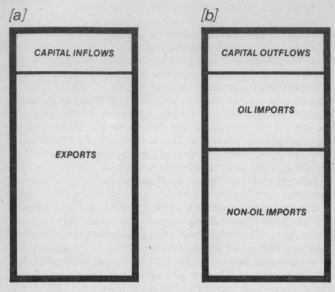

Fig. 23.

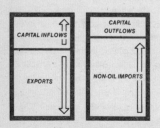
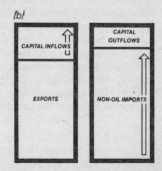

both cases is the exchange rate which rises because of reduced dependence of the economy on foreign supplies of oil and the higher capital inflow that increases the demand for sterling and hence its price. Exports become dearer and imports cheaper. Fig. 23(b) shows that even if British exporters manage to offset this loss of competitiveness by greater efficiency or harder selling, the net result will be the same: non-oil imports will rise to a correspondingly greater extent.

In other words, the gain to the balance of payments caused by self-sufficiency in oil is that we no longer *need* to produce the same quantity of manufactured goods as before. The benefits from the North Sea allow our international payments to be balanced with lower exports and higher imports of foreign manufactures. The bonus of the North Sea is that we can *afford* to pay for manufactures produced elsewhere rather than make them ourselves. And the way in which this adjustment is brought about is through the higher exchange rate.

This is certainly one form in which the benefit of the North Sea could be 'enjoyed' – to use a term which might seem somewhat inappropriate to firms forced out of business and workers who become unemployed as a result of the consequent contraction of the British manufacturing industry. And particularly in view of the limited nature of the North Sea resources and the fact that they will be depleted within a relatively short time, it would be a very short-sighted way of capitalizing on the North Sea advantage. But in the argument as it has been presented so far, the process of reducing the manufacturing sector to make room for the increased oil production appears to be the inevitable outcome.

If this were true, a good case could be made for leaving the oil in the North Sea. Fortunately it is not so, because the need for a decline in manufacturing which is implied only follows if the totals on the credit and debit sides of the balance of payments remain *constant*. Even on that assumption, one way of avoiding the sequence of events as described so far would be if the outflow of capital from Britain were to increase at the same time – so that the exchange rate did not rise to the same extent and imports of manufactures did not expand as much as they would otherwise have done. This indeed seemed to be the purpose of the abolition of exchange controls on British overseas investment which took place in 1980. Higher investment abroad, it can be argued, is desirable in that it builds up a future flow of profits, interest and dividends which will strengthen the balance of payments in the post-oil era. But it has not so far been sufficient to offset the increase in non-oil imports which is taking place, and it also carries the danger of diverting investment from the domestic economy where it is most needed.

In any case, what needs to be questioned is the underlying assumption so far made that the level of output in the economy remains constant during the period when oil is on stream. If that is so, then it does seem to follow that the elimination of oil imports means (a) that foreigners can only continue to buy our exports if they sell more non-oil imports to us; and (b) that domestic manufacturing therefore has to contract to make room for our increased consumption of imported manufactures.

In present circumstances this is not an unreasonable assumption, with output not simply being constant but actually falling so that the situation is made even more acute. However, this is not the inevitable context in which the North Sea has to be exploited but the result of deliberately deflationary policies of the kind already analysed at length. A way out of the impasse therefore lies in an expansion of the economy which could allow *both* British manufacturing industry to grow again *and* a higher level of non-oil imports if required. Indeed, as we have already argued in Chapter 4, it is only in this way that full advantage can be taken of the opportunity offered by North Sea oil. It is only because of the perverse nature of recent economic policies that the North Sea, far from being a great gain to the economy, has been seen almost as an additional problem to be coped with. And the view that oil must be accompanied by large capital inflows and a higher exchange rate is one which we have already questioned and which will be discussed further at a later stage.

Learning from the Dutch

Reference is often made in the debate on de-industrialization to the example of the Netherlands, which has already served as a guinea pig in the process of managing a sudden increase in its natural resources. In the Dutch case, it was the development of natural gas in the late sixties and seventies which led, according to some observers, to a process similar to that just described. The results have been labelled as the 'Dutch disease', from which we too will suffer if greater care is not exercised in the management of the North Sea resources.

The Dutch exchange rate did rise. So also did manufactured imports. And jobs in the manufacturing industry fell by about a third. And in the case of the Netherlands, the revenues from natural gas were largely used to enable consumption to expand; mostly this took the form of boosting public expenditure to provide extensive social services and benefits.

However, the rise in the guilder was only in line with that of other E.E.C. countries, particularly West Germany, to which the Dutch exchange rate was largely tied. The rise in imported manufactures was similar to that which we have already observed to be common among industrial nations in recent decades. And *output* in manufacturing industry (and the Dutch share of world manufactured exports) increased over the period.

The lesson to be learned from the Dutch experience is certainly not therefore that de-industrialization is inevitably accelerated by the exploitation of freshly discovered natural resources. But the experience of the Netherlands does, on the other hand, emphasize the wisdom of using resources which will be shortly depleted in ways that strengthen the economy subsequently. The Dutch by and large opted instead for immediate increases in public consumption which have not been easy to sustain as the gas supplies began to run out.

If this is the lesson that British policy-makers think that they have learned from the Dutch experience, then they have been applying it in an extreme form, to say the least. Recent policy has aimed at cutting rather than increasing public expenditure, in order, it is claimed, to make room for private investment. Part of the strategy, as we have seen, is to deploy the oil revenue to hold back the P.S.B.R and to initiate tax cuts which will later stimulate the regeneration of industry. We have already argued that such a strategy is unlikely to succeed, involving as it does a cumulative deflation in which attempts to cut public spending are offset by reduced tax yields and a growing outlay on unemployment benefits. Private investment is deterred by the combined effects of high interest rates, low demand and a high exchange rate. The potential benefits of North Sea oil are largely wasted.

The real lesson to be learned is the need to ensure that within an *expanding* economy the North Sea revenues are channelled in such a way as to keep the manufacturing sector at the required level and generally to improve the use of resources in preparation for the post-oil period. Even more important than the issue of whether the revenues from the North Sea should be directed towards the private or the public sector is to see that they are used primarily for *investment* rather than consumption.

There is a strong case for setting aside the revenues in a special North Sea Fund so that it is quite clear how they are being used. Generally, governments are not in favour of such 'hypothecation' – for example, using the proceeds of vehicle and fuel duties to finance only road transport expenditure. Such earmarking of taxes is opposed on the grounds that they should be used to promote the welfare of the community in general rather than just those who contributed them. But the North Sea is different in that it yields a once-and-for-all and only short-term boost to government revenues. To channel the tax proceeds through a separate fund would make it possible for more informed public debate, with clearer information available, about their extent and how they were being used. It would provide a constant pressure on policy-makers to weigh up the consequences of alternative uses and justify them according to long-term goals, rather than to allow the revenues to be dissipated in response to immediate financial pressures.

This is not to argue that increased investment in itself would halt the process of de-industrialization. There is ample evidence that in the past it has not simply been too little investment which has caused Britain's relatively weak economic performance, but also that the *quality* of investment has frequently been inadequate – in the wrong sectors or the wrong products (as most obviously typified by Concorde). But where should we be putting our resources in the future? In recent decades, Britain has had an increasing struggle to maintain its position as a manufacturer of conventional products like steel, ships, radios and televisions, and cars. Coming years are likely to see even more intense competition in these now traditional industries from the 'newly-industrialized countries' such as South Korea, Brazil and Taiwan. Nor does a switch to increased output of services offer an easy alternative. In the first place it must be emphasized again that although there is a clear need for greater provision of public services of many kinds, it is a rise in the production of marketable and *exportable* services that would be required to fill any gap left by a decline in manufactures. And secondly, although such 'invisibles' already make a substantial contribution towards the balance of payments (about half the value of manufactured exports), Britain's share of the total world market has been declining here as well.

Thus although it will certainly be necessary to sustain traditional industries while longer-term adjustments are being made, and the relative superiority that is often claimed for Britain in the production of services needs to be exploited to a greater extent, it is ultimately in the 'high-technology' and quality areas of the market that the future must lie.

The problems of encouraging investment in such types of production will be formidable. They also remain academic while policies are being pursued that are so damaging to investment prospects in general. In coming chapters we shall therefore be looking at alternative expansionary strategies, beginning with the views of those who believe that a very substantial devaluation is an essential element in any future development of the economy. For them, it is the persistent over-valuation of sterling for much of the past half century which has been the main cause of the drift towards de-industrialization.

[7] One More Try

During the twenty-five years after the war there was a broad consensus between governments about the objectives of economic policy – full employment, price stability, sustained economic growth and a sound balance of payments. Disagreements between the major political parties were about how they should be achieved. They reflected not only different emphases in political ideology about the sort of society we were working towards but also the inability of economists to provide clear answers to questions about the causes of inflation or growth, or the ways in which policies to achieve the various objectives were interrelated.

By the seventies, a re-ordering of policy priorities had begun, with full employment starting to slip from its former pre-eminence. By 1979 the process was complete, with the elimination of inflation becoming the supreme aim of economic policy to which all others were subordinated. Moreover, in face of conflicting economic advice about the causes of inflation, faith was exclusively placed on the monetarist explanation of why prices rise.

The economy became the experimental laboratory for testing the hypothesis that it is excessive growth in the money supply caused by government overspending which is at the heart of the inflationary problem. But by 1981 inflation had fallen (albeit only to the level from which it had risen after the experiment had begun) *despite* a failure to hold the money supply within the targets set. What instead had been experienced was a massive deflation of the economy, spending cuts which resulted in a dampening of inflation only at a huge cost of lost output and unemployment. And the incidental consequences were the damage inflicted on manufacturing industry and the dissipation of the potential benefits from North Sea oil.

But supporters of the policy continued to argue that in due course a 'natural recovery' would take place in which a vigorous, dynamic economy would emerge as the ultimate vindication of the policies pursued. Constantly, too, they reiterated the view that 'there is no alternative'. It is that view which will be questioned in this and subsequent chapters.

The Case for Expansion

The obvious alternative to deflation is reflation, stimulating the economy into renewed expansion. The case for expansion may be based on three premises. In the first place, mass unemployment is humanly and socially quite intolerable. For school leavers to find themselves unwanted from the start, for older people to be deprived of the means of supporting themselves and their families, must for the majority of the unemployed constitute a humiliating indignity and hopeless frustration which it is morally unacceptable for society to inflict. It is also socially and regionally divisive and may even ultimately threaten our basic social stability.

Secondly, expansionists point to the loss of potential output which has resulted from deflation. The dalliance with monetarism from the mid-seventies and the subsequent attempt at its full-blooded application has resulted in a double loss of output: (a) by the economy being run below full capacity, with unemployment not only of labour but also of productive plant and equipment; and (b) by forfeiting the potential 'growth increment' – the ability of the economy to produce *more* year by year to which we had grown accustomed throughout the earlier post-war period. To try to quantify these losses is a hazardous exercise useful only to give an indication of the order of magnitude involved, but the figure is certainly a large one. With full employment and 3% growth over the past five years, it is possible that we might now be more than 25% better off.

And thirdly, it is claimed that reflating the economy offers the best chance of simultaneously achieving the various objectives of economic policy. Expansion, as well as reducing unemployment, will encourage firms to invest more and workers to cooperate in improving productivity; the result will be renewed economic growth, increased international competitiveness and the creation of an economic climate within which it will be easier to contain inflationary pressures. However, it is on this particular point, about whether an expansion can be induced without leading to a further explosion of prices, that monetarist critics are most vocal.

The basic mechanics of engineering an expansion of the economy are straightforward. And it is not disputed that such an expansion can, at least in the short run, be achieved. All that is required is the application of the familiar techniques which evolved from the Keynesian analysis of the 1930s recession and which were used with considerable success for the quarter of a century after the war.

The Keynesian approach is the opposite of the current policy mix of public spending cuts, balancing the budget and reducing real wages – all of which serve to lower demand and intensify the recession. Instead, demand should be *increased*. A fresh injection of spending into the economy, for example by the government providing funds for more house building, will then have 'multiplier' effects. As construction workers spend the bulk of their increased incomes, further incomes will be created for those whose goods and services they have bought, leading to still more rounds of spending. Firms will therefore find that they are selling more than previously, which will induce them to employ more workers. To begin with they will be able to produce more output by taking up the existing slack in their capacity, but after a while they will begin to see the need for investment in new plant and machinery. And they will be prepared to undertake such investment because rising demand in the economy makes them confident about their ability to sell more.

The government can initiate this expansion either by inducing the private sector to spend more, or by increasing its own expenditure. Private sector spending can be stimulated by means such as tax cuts or lower interest rates or investment grants. Or the State can raise its own level of spending through the nationalized industries or a variety of public works programmes which in turn will expand the demand for private sector output.

The very different forms which expansion could take are illustrated by the views put forward within a month of each other in 1981 by the C.B.I. and the T.U.C. In the C.B.I. discussion paper 'The will to win', considerable emphasis was placed on cost-reducing measures like cutting National

Insurance payments and heavy oil duty, and holding back the prices of nationalized industries. The T.U.C. 'Economic Review' called for much broader spending increases on pensions, social benefits, health and education. But both stressed the need for public *investment* on projects like railway electrification. (The scale of the two sets of proposals, however, differed widely, the C.B.I. envisaging a rate of reflation only about a quarter that demanded by the T.U.C.)

But it is interesting that both bodies should have been pressing for more expansionist policies using what are essentially Keynesian techniques. What, then, are the objections to such measures being used vigorously to the point at which the economy is again working at full capacity on a path of renewed growth? Why is it an option derisively dismissed as 'throwing money at unemployment'? The answer, of course, lies in the fear that it is a recipe for accelerating inflation which in the end would force an expansionary strategy to be abandoned. To see whether this fear is justified we need to look at the short-run and the long-run implications of expansion.

In the short run, a higher level of demand created by public spending or by tax cuts will stimulate greater output. So long as there are ample under-employed or unemployed resources available, increased spending can be matched by a larger volume of goods and services coming on to the market, and prices need not therefore rise faster than they otherwise would have done. Indeed, as expansion takes place, firms will achieve greater capacity utilization of their plant and machinery; this will enable them to spread their overheads over a larger run of output, reduce their unit costs of production, and thus help to hold prices down.

Nor need the financing of expansion at this stage be inflationary even according to monetarist criteria. In the first place tax cuts and public spending would certainly raise the P.S.B.R. as the government deliberately injected more spending into the economy than it was taking out through taxation. But the result, as we have seen, is a multiplied rise in output and incomes out of which a larger amount of taxes on profits, wages and salaries, and spending will be paid. Furthermore, to the extent that workers are drawn back into employment, public spending on unemployment benefit and related items will be reduced.

In other words, expansion would probably be largely self-financing, with the State behaving like the prudent household much admired by monetarists – not by balancing its books but by borrowing and investing to yield a higher income in the future. It is quite probable that in this process the P.S.B.R. would be actually reduced as a proportion of a larger national income.

However, as expansion proceeds, problems do arise at a later stage with the application of simple Keynesianism of this kind:

(i) Bottlenecks may appear which mean that higher demand no longer leads to higher output as it did during the earlier stage. If this happens, with higher spending no longer being matched by an increased supply of goods and services being offered for sale, then prices rise instead. For example, it may be difficult to expand the production of a certain product because of a shortage of components or labour with the appropriate skills being available in the right areas. Such 'supply constraints' can inhibit expansion long before the economy is working at full employment.

(ii) To the extent that higher spending is on imported goods and services, its benefits accrue to foreign producers. Buying imported consumer goods or capital equipment stimulates greater foreign production rather than domestic output. Our own unemployment correspondingly persists and balance of payments problems may arise.

(iii) Private consumption and investment may be stimulated to the point where, together with public spending, total demand in the economy exceeds the value of full employment output. In this case, the result is demand inflation of the kind described in Chapter 1, with prices being pulled up as producers bid for limited resources. And, as we have just seen, this can happen at lower than full employment levels of output if there are supply side difficulties.

(iv) Above all, there is the danger that expansion will give a fresh impetus to cost inflation. With reduced unemployment, free collective bargaining will again lead to wage claims in excess of productivity increases, with firms able to meet them in the knowledge that their buoyant market will allow them to raise prices. And some firms may choose to raise prices and take higher profit margins rather than exploit the growing market by greater output.

These were just the sort of difficulties that were encountered during the lengthy period when governments relied heavily on demand management techniques to regulate the economy. Their response then was to apply the brakes as symptoms of overheating became apparent – often belatedly because the problem was diagnosed too late, sometimes too sharply because of the crudeness of the monetary and fiscal measures which were used.

So why should the outcome be different today? Would an expansionist approach inevitably doom us to a return to the stop–go pattern of the fifties and sixties? Or worse, a return to the situation of high inflation leading to expectations of still higher inflation in the future?

Those who argue today in favour of deliberate government policies to expand the economy, rather than waiting for a natural recovery which may never take place, do so knowing the limitations of naïve Keynesianism. They are aware that demand management is not in itself sufficient, and that it must be supplemented by measures working on the supply side too. They recognize the need not only for supportive policies but also for institutional changes to achieve a *managed* expansion which is therefore sustainable.

Very different views are held about just what these policies and changes might be. There are those who believe that an alternative strategy necessarily entails a considerable extension of specific government intervention in the economy coupled with radical changes in ownership and control. Another school of thought holds that the problems of the British economy can only be solved by providing it with a degree of insulation from the outside world through import controls. We shall be looking at these arguments in later chapters. For now, we consider a third possibility – that what is required is a similar combination of policies to those which have been used in the past, but this time made to apply more effectively. In essence, this boils down to the cause for expansion based on a substantial depreciation of the exchange rate and the implementation of a prices and incomes policy.

Expansion and Exchange Rates

We have already seen that the recent high rate of sterling was mainly due to the inflow of foreign funds resulting from North Sea oil and attractive interest rates. The positive arguments in favour of a high exchange rate are not very convincing; both the level of the exchange rate and the speed with which it was allowed to rise at the end of the seventies and early eighties helped to render British industry uncompetitive to a degree at which their attempt to compensate by increasing productivity was in vain.

'Devaluationists' argue that the high exchange rate was in no way the inevitable consequence of having our own North Sea resources but instead resulted from the way in which they were managed by governments bent on the pursuit of monetarist targets. Moreover, they contend that the rise of the pound during these years was only the latest episode in a long history of persistent over-valuation of sterling. They believe that a very substantial reduction in the exchange rate, by a third or even more, is the vital key to restoring the competitiveness of British industry and replacing the present vicious circle by a virtuous one, as illustrated in Fig. 24.

A depreciation of sterling means that exports can be sold more cheaply in foreign markets and imports become dearer. The result should be a larger volume of exports and imports being lower than they would otherwise have been. However,

Fig. 24.

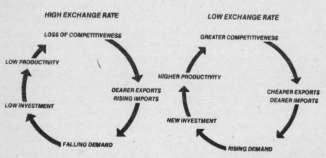

the impact of a lower exchange rate depends on the *extent* to which exports and imports are affected, i.e. on the price elasticities of demand for them. Price elasticity is a measure of how responsive demand is to changes in price. If, for example, a 10% fall in export prices leads to a more than 10% rise in the volume sold, demand is said to be elastic (and the amount of foreign currency earned increases). Inelastic demand, on the other hand, exists if the volume sold increases by a smaller proportion than the price change, say 5% (in which case less foreign exchange is earned than before the fall in the exchange rate).

For the balance of payments current account to be favourably affected by the depreciation, the combined elasticities of demand for imports and for exports must be greater than one. This can be seen by considering the case where the elasticity of demand for imports is zero – where the volume of imports remains unchanged when their price rises. In this case, the amount of foreign currency spent on imports is constant (it is only their sterling price which has gone up), and any improvement in the balance of payments depends on what happens to exports. A lower export price means less foreign currency earned per unit of exports sold; therefore for more to be earned, the rise in the number of units sold must be of a greater proportion than the fall in their price, i.e. elasticity of demand for them must be greater than one. It follows that were the volume of imports at all sensitive to a rise in their price (elasticity greater than zero) the contribution required from higher export sales in improving the balance of payments would be correspondingly less.

It is difficult to calculate just what the relevant elasticities would be in practice. However, there is little ground for pessimism on this score. Studies have been made which indicate that the elasticity of demand for exports might be about two (the volume of exports rising by twice the proportion of the fall in price which caused it), and that of imports at least a half (imports falling by more than 10% in the case, for example, of import prices rising by 20%).

But devaluationists are above all concerned with the dynamic effects which they predict would follow from a lower-valued pound. In the first place, the restoration of international competitiveness provides the basis for expansion of the economy and higher employment levels, as workers and equipment are drawn into use to meet the higher demand from export markets and at home as British goods again become more attractively priced. In these conditions, fresh investment will soon be stimulated which will improve productivity and further increase the competitive edge originally given by the lower exchange rate.

Admittedly, price is not the only consideration in the consumer choice between British and foreign goods. Non-price factors like quality, delivery dates, servicing and salesmanship all play their part. But progress in improving performance in many of these respects costs money, and firms will only be able to spend if they are earning sufficient margins over their basic costs of production. Depreciation widens these margins, and enables producers to contemplate investment in, for example, a better sales and after-sales network – which again reinforces their price advantage over competitors.

Critics of the devaluationist approach offer three main arguments against the policy of substantially reducing the exchange rate. They claim that the expansion which would accompany depreciation might lead to severe balance of payments difficulties. Second, inflation would be greatly increased by the rise in import prices resulting from depreciation. And third, it is not anyway practicable to bring about such a change in the exchange rate.

(i) *Balance of Payments*

Certainly, as we have already seen, expansion in the past has frequently led to imports rising more rapidly than exports with consequent balance of payments problems. And even with a lowered or falling exchange rate, there is likely to be a deterioration in the payments position at least in the short run. Lower export prices will not immediately lead to higher sales – so that foreign exchange earnings may to begin with actually decline and only later increase as foreign buyers adjust to the new situation; similarly imports may rise quite sharply as producers stock up with necessary raw materials and other requirements for expansion, with the rise in import prices only making itself felt at a later stage.

This delayed effect on export earnings, coupled with the fact that in the short run imports were continuing to rise, posed considerable problems during earlier decades. But the situation today is made very different by North Sea oil. The underlying strength which this gives to the balance of payments provides an immediate cushion which allows some increase in imports without causing concern. Indeed it can be argued that an increase in imports with expansion of the economy is necessary to keep the exchange rate down. The main function of the lower exchange rate is not to create balance of payments strength but to restrain imports sufficiently to allow simultaneous expansion of *domestic* output.

One supporter of this relatively orthodox approach therefore concludes that 'North Sea oil can provide the "fat" in the balance of payments to finance the extra import costs of a Keynesian demand-boosting trigger to get expansion under way ... Britain may well be advised to indulge in the luxury of a once-and-for-all Keynesian demand expansion to provide the conditions in which the rate of growth of industrial capacity will adjust upwards to the higher rate of growth of output which is now attainable.'[1]

(ii) *Inflation*

Part of the object of a sterling depreciation is to raise import prices so that home-produced goods are made more competitive. But to the extent that British consumers and firms continue to purchase goods from abroad, inflation is inevitably increased. Moreover, it is likely that there will be further indirect effects. Firms, faced with rising costs of raw materials, imported plant and components, will try to recoup them through higher prices to consumers. Workers, able to point to the increased cost of living resulting from dearer imports, will press for compensating wage rises. They will also be encouraged to demand higher pay if they see firms making greater profits in export markets as a result of the depreciation. The wage-price spiral will be given a fresh twist.

Indeed, some hold the view that it was the 1967 inflation and the later floating of the pound which were the prime factors in the inflationary explosion of the seventies. Under fixed exchange rates, it is not possible for governments to allow

1. W. Eltis in F. Blackaby (ed.), *De-industrialization*, Heinemann Educational Books, 1978, p. 231.

prices to rise much out of line with inflation in other countries. Faster inflation in Britain than elsewhere, for example, would cause difficulty for British exporters and make imports relatively attractive; the consequent deterioration in the balance of payments and fall in foreign exchange reserves would *force* the government into corrective action. But once the exchange rate is allowed to fluctuate, this discipline is removed. The brunt of the adjustment required by higher inflation is instead borne by the exchange rate itself. Thus, it is said, a floating pound can both allow a higher rate of inflation in Britain than in other economies, and at the same time itself be an important element in the mechanism by which inflation is accelerated.

However, the inflationary impetus afforded by depreciation of the pound can easily be exaggerated. First, the price of a large proportion of our imported foodstuffs is governed by our position within the Common Agricultural Policy of the E.E.C. and would not necessarily increase with devaluation (unless the so-called 'green pound'[2] were simultaneously devalued). Secondly, the rise in the price of manufactured and semi-manufactured goods which now comprise the bulk of our imports would only serve to increase the cost of living and the cost of production to the extent that consumers and firms did *not* switch to what would now be cheaper British substitutes. And thirdly, it is not an automatic and inevitable process that higher import prices will trigger off further cost and price increases. Just how far depreciation feeds back into higher inflation depends crucially on the reaction of wage bargainers. To say the least, we lack a sufficient understanding of the behaviour of money wages to make precise predictions about the response to higher import prices in conditions where the *standard* of living is simultaneously rising as a result of economic expansion.

(iii) *Impracticability of Devaluation*

The assertion that it is not anyway possible to effect a substantial change in the exchange rate can be understood in one of two senses. It may be taken to mean that the authorities are

2. An artificial exchange rate set between sterling and E.E.C. currencies for trade in agricultural produce.

technically powerless to bring about a downward movement of the pound in the face of the market forces of demand and supply which actually determine it. Or alternatively, it may express the belief that although the nominal rate of exchange may be changed, the *real* exchange rate will remain unaffected.

It has already been argued earlier that a high pound is closely associated with monetarist policies and that it is only within that framework that governments cannot use the familiar weapons available to them in reducing the exchange rate.[3] An expansionist strategy, on the other hand, would entail the reduction of interest rates which would make foreigners less keen to hold sterling; the short-term deterioration of the balance of payments would be a further factor increasing the supply of sterling in relation to the demand for it; and the strategy would commend itself less highly to foreigners seeking a safe deposit for their surplus funds. For all these reasons, a falling pound would be the highly probable outcome of an expansionist approach. Reducing it to the appropriate level might require a clear statement from the authorities about what they thought that level should be, and they have at their disposal a variety of techniques already mentioned by which they can hope to establish it.

However, it can be claimed that such success would only be illusory. The feedback into higher inflation would soon erode any initial competitive advantage that the depreciation gave, so that we would be back where we started from, with the *real* exchange rate the same as before. Against this, the devaluationists counter by pointing out that any such erosion may take a considerable time. The evidence of past devaluations suggests that improved trade performance can be expected for up to about six years. Moreover, in the past, devaluations have tended to be of a size only sufficient to offset the loss of competitiveness already suffered. A more positive policy of substantial devaluation to give a major competitive advantage would set in motion the cumulatively beneficial effects on the economy already outlined.

It is also generally accepted by those arguing for aggressively reducing the exchange rate that non-inflationary expansion

---

3. Although, as in 1981, they seem prepared to intervene to prevent it *falling* as much as it might otherwise have done.

would require a variety of supporting measures to make it work. In particular, the strategy may have to rely heavily on the implementation of a successful prices and incomes policy.

Expansion and Incomes Policy

Incomes policies have already been introduced on many occasions during the post-war period. The first was the call for restraint in the years 1947–50, the most recent the two attempts in the seventies. Of these, the 1972–4 exercise was in three stages. Stage I consisted of a pay and price freeze, Stage II set a limit to pay increases of £1 a week plus 4%, and Stage III raised this to 7% or £2.25 a week with additional 'threshold' payments if inflation rose above a certain level. 1975–8, on the other hand, saw a policy based on a broad 'social contract', an understanding between the government and the T.U.C. about the need for controlling the increase of incomes within a framework of government policies which made restraint acceptable; on the pay side, increases were limited to begin with to £6 a week, shifting later to percentage guidelines which, when reduced to a call for 'not more than 5%', led to the breakdown of the policy and the fall of the government.

These and the other episodes in the history of incomes policy have a number of features in common. They all originated at times of crisis, when inflation was felt to be getting out of hand. They were all short-lived, three years being about par for the course. And they all failed in the sense that not only did they ultimately collapse but their breakdown was followed by a 'catching-up' phase in which incomes rose rapidly to compensate for the years of restraint.

This history of failure, and recognition of the very difficult problems involved, make the re-introduction of incomes policy in the future an even more formidable task. Its past association with sacrifice, inequity and confrontation make it that much harder to present in a freshly acceptable form. For some it is an idea which is doomed from the start and anyway an unwarrantable interference in the process of free collective bargaining. For others it is the keystone in the process of getting the economy moving again, without which an expansionist policy will court the danger of inflation returning to intolerably high levels.

PREREQUISITES OF AN INCOMES POLICY

Past experience suggests that at least three basic conditions must be met if an incomes policy is to have any chance of success.

(i)   All incomes must be subject to the policy rather than just wages. There has been great resentment that earlier incomes policies have not been applied equitably, so that some groups have been able to evade restraint more easily than others. For example, wage-earners with the opportunity of overtime working, or salaried staff on annual incremental increases, can to some extent cushion themselves against the effects of limits set on basic pay rises. Similarly, it is important that the self-employed or those with earnings from property or capital should not be seen to evade the restrictions which can be more simply applied in the case of wage-earners. This might require a degree of price as well as income control in a supporting role – although a wholly effective income policy would obviate the need for a separate prices policy, since prices are made up of income costs including profits.

(ii) An incomes policy will only work if it is established on the basis of *consensus* about the issues with which it should deal and the broad principles on which it is to be based. This is much more important than the question of whether it should be statutory or voluntary. If there is general agreement about its nature and purpose, it will not need the backing of the law. If the consensus is lacking, attempts at imposing the policy through legal compulsion will only lead to confrontation.

(iii) Incomes policy must be presented and accepted as having a degree of *permanence* in the process of managing the economy rather than as a short-term holding operation which is commonly expected to be short-lived. Otherwise it simply leads to pent-up frustrations which subsequently vent themselves in an explosive fashion. But a permanent arrangement is difficult to achieve, since governments have terms of office of about five years. In this respect, perhaps the most that could therefore be done is for a newly-elected government to introduce an incomes policy immediately regardless of whether inflation is rising or falling, and to make clear its intention that the policy will not be dismantled while it remains in power. Ideally, there would be still greater continuity, with the major political parties agreeing about the machinery through which incomes were to be regulated, while leaving room for the ideological differences between successive governments to be resolved within that framework rather than by rejecting it outright.

PRINCIPLES AND PRACTICE

The aim of incomes policy is to limit the growth of *money* incomes (not real incomes) to whatever level it is decided that the national economic situation warrants. The overall handout which can be 'afforded' in this sense depends on (a) the rate of productivity increase, the extent to which output per worker in the economy is rising; (b) the general state of the economy, whether output as a whole is expanding, stagnant or declining; and (c) the level of inflation which is regarded as acceptable.

Clearly the decision about by how much incomes on *average* can increase is therefore a matter of political as well as economic judgement. *Real* incomes growth is dictated by (a) and (b). But it may nonetheless be decided to allow a growth of money incomes in excess of this on the grounds that, at least to begin with, incomes policy should not be over-ambitious in its attempts to revise past expectations of the 'going rate' for pay rises. It is also obvious that the prospects for introducing an incomes policy are greatly enhanced if the economy is expanding rather than in recession; it is easier to discuss the sharing of a larger cake than one which remains the same size or is even getting smaller.

At this level, of emphasizing that the nation should pay itself no more than it can afford, the objective of incomes policy is non-controversial. The problems arise at the stage of deciding how any given total should be distributed. Here, the essence of the exercise is to eliminate as much as possible of the present 'leapfrogging' competition in which the real gains from extravagant increases in money incomes are largely eroded away as others in the bargaining process secure similar or possibly higher rises.

On the wage front this would be more straightforward if what is commonly asserted were true – that it is in nobody's interest to obtain large pay rises, because they simply lead to higher prices which render them valueless. In fact trade unions, for example, are behaving perfectly *rationally* in seeking high wage settlements. First, those placed early in the annual wage round obtain money wage increases which are only later negated by inflation; in the intervening period, they have secured *real* gains for their members. Second, those further back in the queue can legitimately claim that they are engaged in a necessary catching-up process without which their members' real wages would fall. They will probably also try to obtain larger rises than those who have already settled in order to move a step ahead. And thirdly, the unequal distribution of bargaining strength means that those in a more powerful negotiating position may obtain longer-term gains in real wages at the expense of those not so well placed.

A major problem is therefore what has been termed the 'competitive sectionalism' of the way in which pay is determined, i.e. that frequently we only become better off by temporarily or permanently reducing the real incomes of other groups in the economy. Perhaps the biggest breakthrough which could therefore be made in achieving an alternative rationality in pay bargaining would be to secure agreement that major wage claims should be presented more or less simultaneously so that the extent to which they are simply bidding against each other can be identified and moderated accordingly. That this is not a wholly impracticable possibility is suggested by the experience of the late sixties when the T.U.C. was very close to establishing its own wage-vetting procedure along not dissimilar lines.

However, even if such a forum could be established, the fundamental question would still remain of the criteria according to which pay increases would be judged acceptable. One such criterion would be to link pay closely to changes in productivity industry-by-industry, allowing increases only to the extent that output per head has also risen. If this were done throughout the economy, the basic objective of incomes policy would be achieved in that the overall growth of incomes would be matched by higher output, thus avoiding any inflationary pressure. But in practice, applying this principle would have results which might be regarded as unfair, and it would any-way be only partly practicable. There are many ways in which productivity (output per worker) can be increased, but the main one is by new investment which gives workers more or better quality equipment to work with. However, the scope for applying improved technology is far greater in some industries than in others, and it seems inequitable to reward or penalize different groups of workers in a way which has little connection with their own efforts or factors that they themselves can control. On top of this, there is the problem of deciding the justifiable rate of pay increase for those in occupations where changes in productivity are difficult or impossible to measure. Mostly these are employed, like teachers or nurses, in pro-viding services.

Another possibility would be that everyone should receive the same flat rate increase, thus guaranteeing an equal share-out of whatever is available in total. But this egalitarian approach comes up against the stumbling block that it in-volves the erosion of existing differentials between various groups. Its effect is to reduce the gap between the lowest and the highest paid and to squeeze everyone between the two closer together. There are many who think that this would be a very good thing in itself. But the fact of the matter is that, justifiably or unjustifiably, strong views are held about what differentials are appropriate; a large part of the pay bargain-ing process is essentially concerned with attempts to maintain or adjust existing differentials. Therefore unless a broad agreement is achieved about the desirability of a more equal distribution of incomes, the flat rate criterion will inevitably cause resentment amongst those whose relative position in the income scale is adversely affected. Ultimately, this may cause the policy to collapse.

Practically, it may be that no more can be achieved than the acceptance of a 'norm' or 'guideline' for percentage increases in pay. Securing such an agreement, if coupled with the avoidance of leapfrogging, would represent a great step forward in reducing the 'going rate' for increases in money incomes (and by containing inflation, facilitate greater rises in real incomes). But past experience suggests that machinery would be needed for considering exceptions to the general rule. An incomes policy lacking flexibility is unlikely to succeed. The trouble is, of course, that all groups of workers see themselves as exceptional in one way or another. Any pay bargainer worth his salt should certainly be able to put forward such a case on behalf of those he represents. There would therefore have to be supplementary criteria for judging whether an increase above the norm or outside the guideline is acceptable or not.

It is at this point that the question arises of whether incomes policy should be related to wider issues than simply checking inflation. It is at this stage, for example, that 'fairness' can be appropriately introduced as an element in the fixing of pay. Such matters, whether one group of workers is 'worth' more than another, cannot be reduced to simple economic terms. They involve consideration of the relative values which, as a society, we attach to the contributions made by its various members. It can be argued that an important function and benefit of a comprehensive incomes policy is that such values would have to be openly discussed, with the government of the day being forced to make its own position explicit.

However, to use it as a means of discussing and bringing about changes in the distribution of income in this way may be to burden incomes policy unduly and entail inpracticably detailed intervention in the pay-fixing process. It is this sort of fear which leads others to suggest that an incomes policy should be only modestly ambitious if it is to have a chance of succeeding. Professor Meade, for example, proposes[4] a policy which would only be activated when the ordinary processes of bargaining lead to disputes; in such cases arbitration would take place, with judgements being made solely on the grounds of whether employment would be increased as a result.

Between these extremes, a wide range of proposals has been put forward about the form which an incomes policy might

4. J. Meade, 'The Fixing of Money Rates of Pay', Ch. 6 in D. Lipsey and D. Leonard (eds.), *The Socialist Agenda*, Jonathan Cape, 1981.

5. See F. Blackaby (ed.), *The Future of Pay Bargaining*, Heinemann, 1980.

take.[5] But even this simple outline of some of the main issues that are involved illustrates the formidable problems which will be encountered if and when a further attempt is made in this direction. For the time being, any such intervention is, of course, anathema to a government wedded to a belief in monetarism and the efficiency of market forces; and the confidence of trade unions in dealing with government is badly shaken as a result of the deliberately severe recession which has been experienced. On the other hand, it is possible that all concerned may ultimately be more receptive to the virtues of an incomes policy coupled with expansion as a result of having seen what the alternative may be.

But doubt remains about whether, even given renewed expansion of the economy and a positive approach to the introduction of incomes policy, its inherent problems can be solved without a radical change in attitudes. It is this doubt about the ability of incomes policy to contain the inflationary pressures that may be generated by reducing the exchange rate which leads some to conclude that import controls would therefore have to be an essential part of an expansionist strategy. This is the view which is considered in the next chapter.

[8]   A Siege Economy?

With mass unemployment in Britain it becomes harder to buy foreign goods without a twinge of guilt, but we do it nonetheless on a very large scale. Sometimes the decision is made easier by the lack of home-produced substitutes; it is difficult, for example, to track down a British-made transistor radio. Sometimes we do it in ignorance of where the product originated – is the Ford made in Britain or Belgium or Spain, and where did its components come from? Sometimes we buy foreign simply for cheapness, or because of better quality, and sometimes it may be considered smarter to do so.

There is nothing new about this; Britain has always been heavily dependent on foreign trade with more than a quarter of its output being exported to pay for imports of one kind or another. And, as we have already seen in Chapter 6, the declining share of Britain in the world trade in manufactures – from about 30% at the turn of the century to the 9% in recent years – is not in itself proof of a long-term problem; a falling share of a growing total may represent a satisfactory performance in view of the emergence and development of many other manufacturing countries.

However, the changes which have been taking place over the past decade *are* disturbing. During the seventies, while British exports of manufactured goods increased by 50%, imports of manufactures rose by no less than 140%. Fig. 25 shows the significance of this for several major industries in the consequent increase in the degree of 'import penetration' – the proportion of home sales met from imports.

Aspects of the balance of payments shown in Fig. 26 are also matters for concern. These show that a large current account deficit as in 1975, caused mainly by massive fuel imports, had been transformed by the North Sea into a substantial surplus by 1980. However, meanwhile the position with regard to non-oil trade had been growing steadily worse. In particular, imports of manufactures as a proportion of exports of manufactures rose from 69% in 1970 to 79% in 1975 to 89% in 1980.

Fig. 25. *Import penetration*

	1970	1979
Construction equipment	40%	73%
Office machinery	51%	99%
Watches and clocks	53%	79%
Electronic computers	51%	90%
Motor vehicles	8%	39%
Textiles	16%	33%
Footwear	14%	33%
Chemicals	18%	30%

(Overseas Trade Statistics of the U.K.)

Fig. 26. *Items in the balance of payments 1975–80*

	1970	1975	1980
Current Account balance (£m)	779	− 1674	2737
Fuels (£m)	− 748	− 3489	− 491
Manufactured imports (£m)	4672	12567	31240
Manufactured exports (£m)	6808	16033	34814
Manufactured imports as % of manufactured exports	69	79	89

(National Institute Economic Review)

It is trends like these which provide the background to the growing clamour in recent years for protection of British industry by the imposition of controls on imports. Support for such measures has come from diverse sources – from both the T.U.C. and producer associations, from particular trade unions and management in the worst hit industries, from the Labour Party (especially the left wing) but also from some members of the Conservative Party. Often the arguments which are put forward are simply pleas for first aid for ailing sectors of British industry. But there is also a case to be considered that future expansion of the economy will not be possible along the course outlined in the last chapter, and that import controls are a prerequisite of an expansionist strategy.

However, before examining the pros and cons of the protectionist case it is worth recalling the basic rationale of international trade as presented in traditional economic theory.

Nature and Benefits of International Trade

Within countries the prime cause of us becoming materially so much better off over the past couple of centuries has been the extension of specialization or the 'division of labour'. Instead of trying as individuals or families to be self-sufficient and produce all our own needs, we have increasingly concentrated on just a part of production – specializing first by product and later by process. Most people today are engaged in a tiny part of the business of production; at the end of their week's work they have nothing to show for it in terms of what they could consume themselves. But the economies which result from this specialization, the reduced production costs which are made possible, are enormous. Not only do we become more efficient and adept by concentrating on particular types of work; it is the breakdown of production into a great number of relatively simple processes which has facilitated the introduction of mechanization at every stage.

The implication of a high degree of specialization is interdependence. We rely on others to produce the goods and services on which we spend the incomes earned from our own specialist contribution to output. Specialization necessarily entails exchange, with output being produced for sale in the market and money incomes soon replacing barter as the means by which the exchange takes place.

The basis of the specialization within an economy is that individuals largely concentrate on doing what they are best at. A doctor spends all his time practising medicine; a secretary specializes in typing. However, there is a little more to it than this because the doctor may also be a better typist than his secretary. But even if this is so, it will still pay him to confine his energies to medicine. That is because his superiority is even *more* marked in medicine than it is in typing. He is *absolutely* more efficient in both occupations, but he is *comparatively* more efficient in medicine.

Specialization is thus according to the comparative rather than simply the absolute advantages which individuals have in particular occupations. The basis for international trade and the benefits which result from it are exactly the same. International trade is an extension of the division of labour to countries. By each of them specializing in types of production in which they have a comparative advantage over others, total world output is correspondingly increased. When they subsequently exchange that increased output through international trade, they all find that they are better off than they would have been had they pursued self-sufficiency.

This was the theory elaborated in the first place by David Ricardo in the nineteenth century. It follows from the theory that world resources will not be put to their best possible use and world output will not therefore be maximized if countries impede the process of specialization by placing restrictions on international trade. Tariffs, duties levied on imports, distort the underlying costs and make imports more expensive than they would otherwise have been. That encourages countries to produce goods which they can obtain more cheaply by importing them – and paying for them by the export of goods in the production of which they have a comparative advantage.

The theory therefore pointed to a policy of free trade, allowing the international exchange of goods and services to take place entirely without interference. It also suggested that all the partners in international trade would benefit from it, whether they happened to be rich or poor, secondary or primary producers, developed or less developed. Take, for example, country X which is better at producing *both* food and manufactures than country Y. It will still pay country X to specialize in the production of manufactures if that is the sector in which it has a comparative advantage (i.e. where its superior efficiency is the greatest). In doing so, it will be able to get its foodstuffs more cheaply from country Y by exporting manufactures to it than it will by producing its own food requirements.

Of the many qualifications which need to be made to the theory as outlined so far, there are three of particular relevance to the current debate on import controls. First, free trade only leads to the best use of world resources if specialization is genuinely according to the comparative advantages of the countries involved. For this to be so, prices must reflect the true costs of the resources which go into production. If this is not so, if prices are in fact distorted by, for example, monopoly profits or State subsidies, the division of labour which ensues may lead to less rather than more efficient production. Secondly, although the theory predicts that all the partners engaged in international trade will benefit from it, it does not say how the gains will be distributed between them. In practice, it is likely that the major proportion will go to those which are already better off and that weaker economies gain relatively less. The latter might therefore benefit more from limited rather than maximum trade – even though the 'world' gains would thereby be diminished. And thirdly, a textbook exception to the free trade rule is generally made in the case of 'infant industries'. This refers to a situation in which a country may have a potential comparative advantage in a certain type of production, but unless it is allowed to protect producers in the short run the advantage may never become clear because meanwhile they will have been destroyed by competition from already established producers.

Free Trade versus Protection

For most of the last century and a half Britain has adopted a basically free trade stance. During the latter part of the nineteenth century following the repeal of the Corn Laws, Britain greatly benefited from cheap imports of food and raw materials and unrestricted access to markets for manufactured exports. With a headstart in industrialization, free trade was very much in the British interest. It is no coincidence that while Ricardo was elaborating his free trade theory in Britain, a quite different economic theory justifying protection was developed by Frederick List in Germany – at that time lagging behind. But by the twentieth century, as other economies had caught up and foreign competition was becoming more intense, 'tariff reform' became a major issue dividing the major political parties. However, it was not until the 1930s that Britain introduced import controls on a significant scale.

During the post-war period, learning to some extent from the experience of the inter-war period when the volume of international trade had been greatly diminished, the leading industrial powers again opted for a largely free trade approach under the auspices of the General Agreement on Tariffs and

Trade (G.A.T.T.) by which they sought through successive rounds of negotiations to dismantle the trade barriers between them. For Britain, membership of the E.E.C. was a further move in this direction since it entailed the complete elimination of trade restrictions against other members (although coupled with the establishment of a common external tariff against non-members).

But now there is a renewed call for movement away from free trade. From some quarters this takes the form of a plea for selective import controls aimed at protecting specific industries or stemming the flow of imports from particular areas. Others argue the need for *general* import controls, imposing across-the-board restrictions.

SELECTIVE IMPORT CONTROLS

Where an industry is faced with rapidly increasing import penetration, arguments for protection can be put forward on a number of grounds: to save British jobs, to provide breathing space in which home producers can become more competitive, and as a defence against 'unfair' competition from foreign producers.

Free trade proponents would argue that protection of employment in declining industries by import controls misses the basic point of international trade. Paradoxically, it is only by running down certain types of home production that the benefits of international trade are achieved; what should happen is that resources which are being used inefficiently in certain industries (which is why they are failing to cope with foreign competition) should be diverted into other uses where a comparative advantage exists. Protection therefore simply perpetuates a wasteful use of resources and penalizes home consumers who are forced to buy more expensive or inferior British goods rather than those imported from more efficient foreign producers.

However, this classical argument against protection rests on the assumption that there is full employment in the economy to begin with. If there is not, it hardly makes sense to release further resources from their present uses for redeployment elsewhere. In making better use of resources, the obvious priority is to ensure that those which are now unemployed should be put to productive use. But in that case, it seems more logical to argue for reversal of deflationary policies which are at the heart of the growing unemployment problem in Britain today rather than to quibble about the home/ foreign shares of a total market which is smaller than it need be.

The 'breathing space' argument for import controls is based on the infant industry case which has already been mentioned – that temporary protection is needed in order for industries to achieve full competitiveness. Sometimes, the industries quoted as suitable cases for such treatment are genuine infants – for example, micro-chip production. More generally they are geriatric, industries in which Britain may once have had a comparative advantage which has subsequently been eroded away. The reasons for the loss of competitiveness in the first place need to be carefully examined before concluding that it will be restored with a temporary respite from foreign competition.

Similarly, the call for protection against 'unfair' competition is a dubious one if it is interpreted to mean competition from countries with lower wage costs. The question that needs to be asked is why lower wages are paid there. Wages are low in developing countries not just because of exploitation in the absence of strong trade unions – but also because such countries generally have an abundance of labour. And international trade is based on the fact that different countries have varying quantities of land, labour and capital. We import bananas from areas which are endowed with more favourable climatic conditions, and we export to countries with less capital equipment than we have. It is only an extension of this commonly accepted division of labour that we should also import manufactures in the case where a plentiful supply of labour gives an overseas competitor a comparative advantage. If we restrict imports on the grounds that they are made with 'cheap labour' we should beware that the same argument is not used against us by countries richer than we are.

A more justifiable case for selective import controls is where it can be shown that competition from abroad is unfair in the sense that foreign producers are in receipt of subsidies or other forms of assistance from their governments. It is estimated that some 15% of trade in manufactures between the major industrial nations is now supported to some degree or other. When it can be clearly demonstrated that others are not playing according to the rules, it is unreasonable to expect British producers to do so.

However, the great danger with selective import controls is that they will be concentrated in declining industries which are not the ones to be positively encouraged in an attempt to improve general efficiency and competitiveness. Protection can simply lead to more resources being put to inefficient use, rather than to changing the economic structure in a constructive fashion. And there is no guarantee that the breathing-space afforded by temporary import controls will lead to increased efficiency. Industries may indeed become still less efficient as the need to compete against foreign substitutes is reduced.

There is also the question of whether other countries would be content to accept British restrictions on the amount they were able to export to us, or whether they would be induced

Fig. 27. *Composition of U.K. imports of manufactures by area 1979 (£m)*

E.E.C.	12,103
Rest of Europe	5,488
North America	3,501
Rest of World	4,935

(Overseas Trade Statistics of the U.K.)

to retaliate to an extent which would wipe out the possible gains. Since it is the stronger economies, like the U.S.A. or the E.E.C. countries, which would be more likely to retaliate, the probability is that selective controls would be mostly introduced against weaker countries. But as Fig. 27 shows, it is from economies richer than our own that most of the increased foreign competition has come. It is not the case that Britain has been flooded with imports from the Third World.

Apart from neutralizing unfair competition, the case for specific import controls is therefore not a strong one. Rising unemployment in a particular industry or high import penetration may be a clear indication of long-term decline and a signal for the need for appropriate adjustment policies to divert resources into alternative uses. Or the industry could mainly be suffering from the combined effects of depressed home demand as a result of deflationary policies, high interest rates and an over-valued pound.

In either case, selective import controls are at best a propping-up operation which is no substitute for dealing with the real underlying problem, of which import penetration is a symptom rather than the cause. In this respect the arguments for protecting particular home producers against foreign competition must be distinguished from the case for generalized protection as part of a strategy alternative to monetarism.

Expansion and General Import Controls

The case for general import controls as an essential part of a policy to deal with the current economic crisis has been developed mainly in the Department of Applied Economics at Cambridge. From there, since the mid-seventies, the Cambridge Economic Policy Group (C.E.P.G.) headed by Wynne Godley has issued a regular series of doom-ridden bulletins about the future prospects for the economy if existing policies continue to be pursued. Thus at the beginning of the present decade they were suggesting that we were heading for a fall in industrial output of 10% by 1982, substantially more than occurred during the 1930s. And they were talking in terms of unemployment approaching the 5 million mark by the end of the eighties. So far the predictions from their model of how the economy works have unfortunately proved to be more accurate than any of the others that have been made.

Their analysis is based on the view that the British economy is now in a state of chronic uncompetitiveness. 'The reason for this appalling result lies in the policies adopted by the last government and enforced with increased vigour by the present government.'[1] 'The policies of the present government have for nearly two years been perverse. The government, in our view, has now gone so far in the wrong direction that the situation is much more intractable than it was before.'[2]

1. University of Cambridge Department of Applied Economics, *Cambridge Economic Policy Review*, April 1981, p. 1.
2. ibid., pp. 4-5.

The criticisms offered by the C.E.P.G. are along the lines already outlined in previous chapters – that the high interest and exchange rates associated with policies based on money supply targets have led to a process of de-industrialization in which North Sea Oil 'has not merely been wasted, it has been used to destroy our economic base'.[3] In this and their advocacy of an expansionist strategy as the means of escaping from the vicious circle caused by deflation, they share common ground with the devaluationists.

However, they differ in their view of the scale of the problem and how therefore it can be tackled. As the C.E.P.G. sees it, 'Industry is now so weak that a major reflation would lead straight to huge balance of payments deficits and a collapse of sterling. Devaluation of sterling, accompanied by reflation, would accelerate inflation and could not halt growing unemployment this side of three millions.'[4] Their doubts about the devaluationist approach, which they nonetheless regard as preferable to existing policies, are threefold – the consequences for the balance of payments, its effect on prices, and whether it is feasible.

(i) *Balance of Payments*

The C.E.P.G. argue that devaluation will not succeed because the underlying trends of imports and exports have now become so adverse. They estimate that the British income elasticity of demand for imports is both peculiarly high compared with that in other countries, and also higher than the income elasticity of demand for British exports. Income elasticity of demand is a measure of how demand changes in response to a change in income. Thus the Cambridge view is that an expansion of demand would lead to a much sharper rise of manufactured imports than in exports. On top of this, there would be the usual upsurge in imports of raw materials as producers increased output and used up existing stocks. The C.E.P.G. predict that the result would be a massive current account deficit of the order of £10 billion after a year or so of reflation.

Devaluationists, as we have seen, agree that their policy

3. ibid., p. 1.
4. ibid.

would lead to a short-term weakening of the balance of payments, but anticipate that it would be of manageable proportions given North Sea oil. And in the longer term, they are more optimistic that the marked improvement in the competitiveness of British goods caused by a more realistically-valued pound would reverse past trends favouring foreign products.

(ii) *Inflation*

The C.E.P.G. is also sceptical about the possibility of containing the inflationary pressures which devaluation would generate, and predict that prices would again be rising at 20% within two years of such a strategy being adopted.

(iii) *Feasibility*

The C.E.P.G. does not share the view of the monetarists that it is impracticable to reduce the exchange rate. On the contrary, their fear is that once a reduction in the pound is initiated as the key mechanism in reflation of the economy, it will be very difficult to prevent its fall from acquiring an exaggerated momentum. As Professor Kaldor has put it: 'once international speculators realize that the pound is on a downward trend a tremendous bear speculation could develop which would be difficult to halt. Our reserves are limited and, in the absence of exchange control, there is nothing to prevent a sterling outflow.'[5]

The Cambridge school therefore see the imposition of general import controls as the only way out. In fact it can be said that such controls already exist, in the form of the present 3 million unemployed whose ranks are likely to be increased still further in the future. It is the artificially low spending power of the unemployed which is keeping the imports down. As the situation deteriorates, more formal import barriers will be needed if unemployment is not to rise steadily higher.

It should be stressed that the C.E.P.G. do not see import controls as a way of featherbedding the inefficient but as the necessary condition for expansion through which competitiveness can ultimately be restored. What they propose is that imports should be limited to their present level, any further

5. *Guardian*, 9 March 1981.

increase being allowed only to the extent that the growth of exports might permit. The purpose is not therefore to cut imports to make room for inefficient British producers and thereby force British consumers to buy dearer or less attractive home-produced output. The aim is to stop imports from rising further so that future growth of demand is mainly channelled into higher domestic production leading, hopefully, to increased profits, investment and employment.

They therefore present the choice for British consumers as between: (a) the existing or perhaps even lower level of imports coupled with an economy in which unemployment has to rise persistently in order to keep the balance of payments under control; or (b) the same level of imports but with falling unemployment and a growing economy in which there would be a greater availability of British-produced goods.

The effect of such a strategy on prices depends on the form which import controls might take. The C.E.P.G. originally advocated the use of import *quotas*, i.e. quantitative limits set on various classes of imports. More recently, however, they have advocated the use of tariffs. These would be imposed at various rates: 30% for manufactured goods, 20% for semi-manufactures, 15% for services like tourism, and nil for food and raw materials. Concessions might also be made in the case of manufactured or semi-manufactured goods from certain Third World countries. This would certainly cause a substantial increase in the price of many imports (which is the object of the exercise). But it is argued that the exclusions from the higher rates will mean that there will not be a substantial feedback into higher wages and prices, and that anyway the revenue from the tariffs can be used to minimize any additional inflationary pressure.

Critics regard the Cambridge approach as a retreat into a siege economy which would inevitably result in retaliation from other major industrial countries, causing a shrinkage of world trade like that experienced during the thirties. But supporters of import controls point to the rapid economic growth which followed British abandonment of free trade at that time. They also argue that retaliation need not necessarily take place, since foreign suppliers would recognize that there was a greater long-term advantage for them in a British economy which was buoyant and expanding rather than one which was becoming progressively weaker. But certainly it is difficult to envisage negotiating an agreed imposition of import controls within the framework of present British membership of trading arrangements like G.A.T.T. and the E.E.C.

Moreover, the effect on the efficiency of British producers of import controls is highly debatable. It is possible that confidence from gaining a higher proportion of a growing home market would induce substantial productivity improvements through higher investment and greater economies of scale. It is also possible that the benefits of protection would instead be taken mainly in higher profits secure from attack by foreign competition. The outcome would partly depend on how permanent it was felt that the tariff barriers were to be. Pressure for their removal might serve to keep British producers on their toes but at the same time create uncertainties about the future, reducing their willingness to invest. On the other hand, the expectation that protection was here to stay might induce a sluggishness leading to a widening gap between British and foreign efficiency. Some admission of this danger seems to be implicit in the Cambridge view that by 1990 the tariff rate on manufactures might have to rise as high as 70%.

But, as some critics have pointed out, 'with tariffs at this level the British economy would be almost totally isolated. If a 70% tariff were needed to keep out foreign manufactures, this would imply that British industrial costs were at about 170% of the world level. In these circumstances, British industry could hardly be expected to export anything at all. Indeed, it is doubtful whether, if we were in this predicament, we could even afford to buy in the food, fuel and raw materials essential to keep the economy operating.'[6]

This is an extreme statement of a general point which can be made in favour of devaluation rather than import controls. Both have the effect of making British goods and services more competitive in the home market when compared with imports. But devaluation at the same time stimulates the growth of *exports* by reducing their price, while any increase in exports under the import control strategy would arise only

6. B. Gould, J. Mills and S. Stewart, *Monetarism or Prosperity*, Macmillan, 1981, p. 169.

to the extent that British producers become more efficient and dynamic in their outlook because of their increased security in the home market. However, it is possible to improve export prospects, as in some variants of the Cambridge strategy, by a combination of *both* devaluation and import controls.

The devaluationist and the import control strategies agree in emphasizing that improvements in competitive efficiency are only likely to be achieved within a growing economy. Both stress the importance of a high and steadily increasing level of demand. But while this might be a *necessary* condition for faster productivity growth, it may not in itself be sufficient. Both approaches may therefore be limited in relatively neglecting the need for positive *supply-side* measures to improve efficiency. The extent to which taking these into consideration may involve more radical intervention by government rather than reliance on market forces is a topic which will be taken up in Chapter 10. In the coming chapter we shall be examining the general technological context in which our economic problems will have to be managed during the coming decade.

[9] Work without Workers

The trade cycle of alternating ups and downs in the level of economic activity has been with us for a very long time. Such fluctuations were acute during the latter part of the nineteenth century and during the first half of the present century. They persisted even during the period from 1945–70 when Keynesian policies enjoyed their heyday, although in these years the cycle was greatly dampened down. But regardless of the policies currently in vogue, recession has always finally been followed by recovery, with employment rising again as the economy moves out of its previous trough.

The situation today is novel in two respects. First, it is by no means certain that there will be an automatic recovery so long as monetarist policies in their present form continue to be applied. As we have already seen, they work perversely in intensifying rather than alleviating the recession. The conditions on which it is hoped a natural recovery will be based – tight control over inflation, lower interest rates and tax cuts – may prove difficult to achieve and anyway insufficient to mend the damage which has meanwhile been inflicted on British industry.

The second consideration which is new in the present situation is the doubt that recovery would any longer reduce unemployment to its earlier low level. Even with the abandonment of monetarism and its replacement by reflation based on some combination of the alternative strategies which have been outlined, there can be no guarantee of a speedy return to full employment.

It may be that in the initial stage of expansion, employment would pick up rather more quickly than usual because the severity of the recession led employers to disgorge labour which they might in the milder downturns of the past have 'hoarded' in the knowledge that they would soon need it again. But against this must be set the fact that 'overmanning' may have been reduced to a greater extent than in the past and that many firms will have disappeared altogether – so that a high proportion of the unemployed cannot expect to find themselves back in their old jobs. But most serious of all, the problem of re-establishing full employment will have to be solved in what promises to be a period of dramatic technological change. As renewed expansion leads, as it should, to higher investment and growth of productivity, it can be expected that this will increasingly be in the form of applying the 'new technology'. This will not only reduce the extent of job creation needed for any given level of output; it will also threaten existing jobs. In this context the restoration of full employment will be a formidable task, involving not only the creation of 3 million jobs for those at present out of work, but also an additional 160,000 a year for those entering the labour market for the first time (over and above the number retiring from it), plus alternative work for those who will be displaced in the future.

In this chapter, we shall be looking at these employment implications of the new technology, and also at the way in which it is likely to affect the distribution of incomes. To begin with, we briefly review the extent to which it is likely to be applicable throughout the economy.

Applications of the New Technology

The nature of the new technology is by now fairly familiar. Essentially it consists of a microelectronic revolution as a result of which information can be stored and used to a startlingly greater extent than before. The revolution is based on the microprocessor, a small computer in a silicon chip. This tiny computer can store and process vast amounts of information through the thousands of electrical circuits which it carries. The potential scope for its use in automating the production of goods and services is enormous.[1]

1. The following section draws heavily on C. Hines, *Work and the Microprocessor*, Trade Union International Research and Education Group, Ruskin College, Oxford.

PRODUCING GOODS
WITH THE NEW TECHNOLOGY

Microprocessors have potential applications at every stage in the production of manufactured goods.

(a) *The production of industrial raw materials* in oil refineries, power stations, chemical, pulp and paper, and steel works will increasingly use microprocessors for monitoring and measuring temperature and other key variables which can then be fed into a centralized computer. Thus an already highly automated section of manufacturing will become even more so.

(b) The production of *machines and parts* today still retains considerable craft elements requiring a skilled workforce in the design, machine setting and control of the production of the small batches of parts which comprise a substantial proportion of the output of the mechanical engineering industry. Most of these jobs are now technically capable of replacement by microprocessors.

(c) The *assembly of industrial products* is the area where greatest manufacturing job loss is likely to occur during the coming decade. It will result from two applications of microprocessors: first, their use in the final products themselves – replacing a multiplicity of parts which previously required considerable labour to produce; and second, they are increasingly to be found in robots which directly displace workers in the assembly process.

For example, one automatic sewing machine on the market today 'uses a single microprocessor to control the sequence and pattern of stitches, and replaces 350 gears and other components'. Other important products where a similar level of microelectronic sophistication is being achieved include washing machines, television sets, ovens and cars.

The actual assembly of products by microprocessor-controlled robots is still in its relative infancy, but the rate at which the technology is improving is very rapid. The Mini Metro is being automatically welded by robots, which is estimated to allow B.L. to produce an extra 342,000 cars a year with 70% fewer workers. And as robots become equipped with vision and touch sensors they will be able to take over an increasing proportion of the assembly lines tasks.

SERVICES AND THE NEW TECHNOLOGY

Those engaged in providing services may find in the future that their jobs are threatened by microprocessor computerization to an even greater extent than in manufacturing industry. It is estimated, for example, that 100,000 petrol pump attendants have already lost their jobs as a result of the introduction of self-service petrol pumps based on the new technology.

In retailing, the need for shop assistants can be greatly reduced by the use of tills containing mini-computers and connected to scanners which automatically register and count up the price of items indicated by bar codes on the products; control of stocks can be performed by computers which automatically watch their level and re-order from warehouses; ultimately there is no reason why the processor should not be directly linked to banks.

But it is in office work that the impact of the new technology is likely to be greatest. Offices are essentially concerned with the handling and communication of information, and it has been estimated that at present some 40% of the total workforce is engaged in such work. A large proportion of current office practices will be rendered potentially obsolete by the microprocessor.

The word processor is an electric typewriter with a visual display unit (V.D.U.) and a computerized memory enabling it to perform a wide variety of tasks with greater flexibility and speeds than traditional methods; it is claimed that one word processor can do the work of up to five typists. And as the use of word processors within an organization becomes more widespread, it will become possible to link them into a central computer to enable storage and communication of information in a way which will eliminate much of the need for filing, memoranda, letter-writing and other secretarial tasks.

Thus the potential employment impact of the new technology is very wide indeed, with the scope for its application extending to every sector of the economy. More occupations are likely to be affected than not, because the microprocessor can be applied both in the making of equipment *and* in its subsequent use.

Unemployment and the New Technology

It must be emphasized that only a very small proportion of our present unemployment is so far due to the microelectronic revolution. The rest is the consequence of Britain's declining competitiveness and the drastic reduction in domestic demand that has resulted from deflationary policies. The difficult question to answer is just how far the new technology would impede the restoration of full employment in a phase of renewed economic expansion.

The impact on employment of the new technology depends on four main factors. First, the speed of developments within the field of microelectronics, the cheapness and the possible range of applications of the processes which are evolved. Secondly, how quickly they are brought into general use. Thirdly, the degree to which the new technology is employment-creating as well as employment-destroying. And fourthly, the way in which the notion of 'full employment' is itself to be interpreted and achieved.

(1) The growth of technical knowledge in microelectronics has certainly been staggering. The pace of technical progress has been extremely rapid, as measured by the reduced size, increased reliability, possible uses and price of microprocessors. For example, in its most popular everyday use, the application of chip technology has reduced the price of pocket calculators from £40 to £5 within five years, and it is now possible to buy a home computer for less than £100. More generally, a graphic estimation of the rate of change suggests that if the car industry had been able to reduce its price and size of product, and increase its efficiency at the same speed, a Rolls Royce would today cost £1.45, would do 3 million miles to the gallon and six of them would fit on a pinhead. And we have already seen how extensive are the possible applications of the technology in both the manufacturing and service sectors of the economy

(2) Invention does not automatically lead to innovation. There is bound to be a time-lag between any breakthrough in technical knowledge and its general adoption. Just how quickly fresh technical knowledge is applied depends on many factors, like whether or not firms are currently replacing or expanding their existing plant and machinery, the receptiveness of management to new ideas, the resistance which may be expected from trade unions to technical change, and the availability of appropriate skills to operate the new methods of production. It is the unpredictability of these factors which partly explains the widely differing estimates which have been made of when the impact of the new technology will be felt. There are contrasting views – for example, that 1984 will be the year of the 'information revolution'; or that its introduction will be spread over a very much longer period. The latter opinion, that the introduction of the new technology will be relatively gradual and therefore manageable, is that expressed in the 1979 Report[2] of the Department of Employment Study Group, which seems to be the basis for current official thinking.

Nor is it easy to decide what would be the most desirable speed at which the new technology is introduced. The slower it is adopted, the less threat of technological unemployment it poses, with workers being displaced by more automated production. But on the other hand, if it is applied more rapidly elsewhere, there is the possibility of increased unemployment arising from a further reduction in Britain's competitiveness. So far Japan in particular has been quick in achieving a widespread adoption of the new techniques.

(3) The third consideration determining the way in which employment is affected by the new technology is that as well as displacing existing jobs it is also likely to create new ones. Its overall impact therefore depends on the balance between the two effects.

2. Department of Employment, *The Manpower Implications of Micro-Electronic Technology*, H.M.S.O., 1979.

The economic history of the past couple of centuries has been littered with gloomy forecasts of the mass unemployment which would be caused by the latest advances in technology. In the past economists have generally argued, along the lines illustrated in Fig. 28, that such pessimism was unwarranted. Admittedly, improved technology might lead to immediate unemployment of those working with more traditional methods which were now rendered comparatively inefficient. But this would be temporary and transitional. The new techniques would reduce costs and prices and encourage the output of different products. Demand would thereby be stimulated, and because more goods were being sold employment would consequently rise again.

Fig. 28.

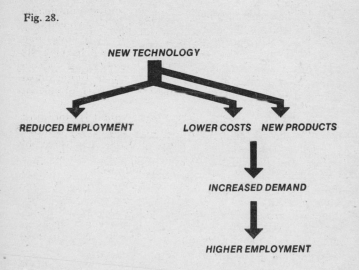

And in the past economists have generally been proved right. But do the same arguments apply in the case of microprocessors? We do not know, but there are reasons for thinking that the current technological revolution is of a quite different order from those experienced before. The pace of change is unprecedented. So also is the comprehensive scope of its possible applications, extending as we have seen throughout most sectors of the economy. And it is *highly* capital-intensive, replacing labour by capital to a remarkable degree. In addition, there is an international dimension to be considered. The new technology will be available simultaneously throughout the world. Its relatively small labour requirements will leave multinational enterprises still freer to locate where they please, so that there is no guarantee that British workers, for example, will maintain their share of any jobs-expansion which results from their new investment.

The key issue is therefore whether the economists' simple arithmetic of job creation matching or exceeding job destruction will apply in this case. How far this will be so depends on (i) the new technology generating demand for entirely new products which will thereby create completely fresh employment opportunities; and (ii) the extension of the demand for existing products (e.g. video tape recorders, TV games, home computers) via cost and price decreases. These will be the main compensating features of the new technology to set against the obvious job loss where existing products and processes are displaced.

Grave doubts must exist about whether they will be enough to offset the fact that the investment embodying the new technology will require such dramatically smaller amounts of labour. And secondly, there are the unknown but possibly very substantial time-lags which will occur between the displacement of labour from traditional occupations and any subsequent re-employment in expanding industries. It is this doubt which makes it vitally important to consider the fourth element in considering how the new technology can be accommodated within a full employment objective. That is, a reassessment of the notion of full employment itself.

Redefining Full Employment

The notion of 'full employment' from which unemployment is a shortfall is not as straightforward to define as it might at first appear. Quite what is meant by it can vary from time to time and society to society. It is based on certain conventions or norms which in the short run we take as given, but which are in fact capable of being reformulated if we choose to do so.

Full employment in Britain means that there should be work available for all those seeking it. Today that means about 26 million people. That is a huge increase in comparison with the thirties workforce of some 20 million, and the rise is mainly due to the much larger proportion of women who have entered the labour market in the post-war period. Apart from this, the total has also varied according to whether the number joining the workforce has been larger or smaller than those withdrawing from it into retirement.

However, the total number involved is only one dimension of what is meant by full employment. The next aspect is the question of how *much* work there should be for each of them. In the first place, this depends on what we conventionally accept as the average length of an individual's working life – the ages at which he or she enters and then finally leaves the labour market. This will be determined by factors like the statutory school leaving age, the ease and scope of further education opportunities, the level of retirement pensions and the age at which they become payable.

Again, the volume of work which is needed to ensure full employment depends on what is regarded as a normal rate of working – the tempo at which people are expected to operate, the number of hours worked per day, how many days a week, how many weeks a year. At the moment we tend to think broadly in terms of a fifty-year working life, forty-eight weeks a year, forty hours a week.

We know from experience that it has been possible for demand to increase sufficiently for jobs to be provided for the vastly larger numbers of women who have joined the paid workforce during the post-war period. But whether full employment defined in the conventional fashion will remain attainable with the enormous economies in the use of labour made possible by the new technology is highly debatable. Not only might it be impracticable, but the scale of investment, output and consumption which would be required to do so may not be desirable in themselves. The question of how much further we want to proceed along the road of ever-increasing material affluence, and how far it is even possible to do so, will be touched upon in Chapter 10.

There is, in any case, an alternative approach to the new technology. Instead of seeking ways of achieving full employment based on conventional norms within the context of the coming technological revolution, we could revise those norms in such a way that the breakthrough on the technological front presents an opportunity of increasing, rather than a threat of diminishing welfare. The ability to produce similar or even growing levels of output with reduced human effort offers the possibility of a major redistribution between work and leisure.

Through the new technology, many unpleasant, dirty or dangerous jobs may be eliminated altogether. In other cases, there will be scope for a substantial reduction in the proportion of peoples' lives which they have to spend on work which affords them little or no satisfaction. The advantages already enjoyed by a few could be spread to the many. A shorter working week, longer holidays, regular sabbaticals for retraining or further education – are all ways in which increased leisure could be shared among the community.

Given such attractive prospects, why is the new technology more commonly regarded as a looming danger rather than as the opportunity to enhance the life-styles of the majority of people? It is because we have not so far evolved the methods for ensuring that the new technology leads to these desirable results – that the work, income and leisure which it generates will be equitably distributed. It is because of the fear that technological change is proceeding at a rate far more rapid than our social and political ability to adjust to it.

Sharing the Benefits of the New Technology

Application of the new technology will, as things stand, be introduced through the process of free collective bargaining between enterprises (private firms or nationalized concerns) and trade unions representing the workers involved. Nearly always the interest of the two parties will be in conflict, and the compromise reached will depend on relative bargaining strength. What we are concerned with here is whether the general outcome of these many negotiations is likely to be a satisfactory one.

From the point of view of enterprises, the new technology has several attractions. In some cases it may offer the scope for moving into new product areas, and more generally it leads to a simplification of the processes of production and hence easier management. But above all it is labour-saving – offering the possibility of both cost-reductions and reduced reliance on a potentially disruptive workforce. Even the least adequate managements can generally achieve tolerable industrial relations with machines. Much of the gain of the new technology for enterprises therefore accrues in the form of increased profitability brought about by labour costs lowered proportionately more than its capital costs are increased. How far the enterprise chooses to pass on some of the benefits to consumers in the form of lower prices depends on its competitive position and marketing strategy. If, for example, it is one of many producers simultaneously applying the new techniques, the competition will tend to keep prices lower than if the innovating enterprise has a degree of monopoly over its market. And enterprises may also have the option of relatively small but highly profitable sales of a new product, or larger sales at a lower price with a narrower profit margin.

Trade unions, on the other hand, will be concerned mainly with defending the jobs of their members by resisting the attempts of management to substitute capital for labour. And secondly, they will be trying to get the best deal they can in terms of wages. Generally they will start from the disadvantage that it is management who decide the timing of innovation and who have access to all the relevant information. An important part of the trade union response to the introduction of new technology is therefore to maximize the release of information by management and to become as involved as possible in the preliminary decision-making process.

Enterprises and workers thus have contrasting objectives. The outcome of the inevitable conflict between them is difficult to predict and bound to vary from one situation to another. All that we can do here is look at a few illustrative cases to show the sort of problems which are likely to arise.

Case 1. In introducing automated microelectronic processes, management seeks to reduce the labour force through

voluntary or compulsory redundancies. The unions representing the workforce vigorously object. But the enterprise claims
that in view of the competition it is facing, it will otherwise be
driven out of business. It may even try to circumvent complex
bargaining with the workers by threatening to shut down a
plant completely and open up elsewhere, perhaps in another
country if it is a multinational.

In the end, the union may be reduced to negotiating about
the scale of redundancies, their timing and the level of com-
pensation which is offered. But in this case, existing jobs are
lost, and the possibility of their subsequent replacement in
other enterprises depends, as we have seen, on whether
demand is stimulated sufficiently by lower prices and new
product ranges.

Case 2. To avoid industrial trouble, management may aim at
a more gradual introduction of the new technology without
the need for redundancies. The enterprise offers to maintain
its present workforce even though it is in excess of its requirements, and reduce it only through 'natural wastage', i.e. by not
replacing workers who reach retirement age or choose for some
other reason to leave its employment. Nobody therefore gets
the sack. But jobs overall will in due course be lost as the
total workforce contracts. The victims will be school leavers
who might otherwise have expected to obtain employment.
Trade unions will have protected their existing membership,
but only at the expense of their future potential members.

Case 3. It might be that the enterprise introducing the new
techniques does so at a time when it is confidently expecting
increasing sales because of some combination of its own pricing policy, new product range or general reflation of the
economy. In this instance, it is possible that investment using
the new technology can take place without job loss through
either redundancy or natural wastage. But even in this most
favourable case, employment will suffer in the sense that fewer
of those who are already jobless will be drawn back into
employment as a result of expanding demand than had the new
technology not been applied. Certainly, the great part of
present unemployment in the U.K. has so far been due to
deflation of demand and loss of competitiveness rather than to
technological change. But the effect of applying the new technology may be to convert unemployment which was originally

created in this way into permanent structural unemployment in the future.

Case 4. In an attempt to minimize possible unemployment, the trade unions propose a shorter working week. If they ask for fewer hours for the same weekly wage, the result for jobs will depend on what happens to productivity.

(a) If output per man remains the same, then the firm will have to employ additional workers. But it will also find that its labour costs per unit of output have risen. Either it will absorb these increased costs in lower profits, or, more probably, it will try to recoup them through higher prices. In this case the effect will be to reduce *real* wages elsewhere as consumers find that their money incomes now buy less. Employment will have increased, but only at the cost of lower real incomes.

(b) Instead, the shorter working week may be accompanied by an increase in productivity due to the more advanced technology being used or because of more sustained effort on the part of the workers. No extra employment is therefore created, and the incomes of the workers employed in the enterprise are also protected by taking part of the productivity gain from the new technology which might otherwise have been passed on through lower prices to create additional jobs.

These cases are just examples of the many possible ways in which the impact of the new technology might be felt as a result of its introduction through the process of free collective bargaining. But they do suggest two broad conclusions that might be drawn about its likely effects.

In the first place, negotiations between workers and management in the normal fashion will not ensure that employment opportunities are spread among all who want them rather than concentrated among a few. Piecemeal attempts to introduce work-sharing through shorter hours will not automatically lead to an equitable distribution of the potential benefits of the new technology. And secondly, if work-sharing is to be effective, it implies *income*-sharing as well. For example, consider the introduction of the new technology in an economy where output is constant, so that it can now be produced with a smaller quantity of labour. In these circumstances, providing work for everyone who wants it cannot be achieved merely by reducing the hours per worker put in during the course of a year. It also entails a fall in average real wages of those who are already employed to leave something over for those being brought into employment.

In an expanding economy, the problem becomes less acute. Depending on just how fast the growth of output is, real wages need on average be reduced by less, or not at all, or even increase. But the problem will still remain of bringing about a relative redistribution from those already in work to those freshly finding jobs. This means holding back the rise in real wages which higher productivity in the new technology occupations might seem to justify – in order that instead prices can be reduced, demand increased, and new employment opportunities thereby created.

The great danger is that this will not happen. Instead there will be a redistribution of income in favour of those directly involved with the new technology and against those unfortunate enough to work in occupations where it is least applicable – and the growing numbers of unemployed. This could take the form of a double shift, from wages to profits as capital becomes increasingly substituted for labour; and within the wage-earning group, towards those in a particularly strong bargaining position where workers remaining in employment can command high differentials over others.

We would be experiencing Professor Meade's nightmare of the Brave New Capitalists' Paradise: 'Wage rates would thus be depressed; there would be a large expansion of the production of the labour-intensive goods and services which would be demanded by the few multi-millionaires; we would be back in a super-world of an immiserized proletariat and of butlers, footmen, kitchen maids and other hangers-on.'[3]

The new technology is bound to make the task of restoring full employment more difficult, although it will help in providing an impetus for increased investment within the framework of an expansionist strategy. The essential problem is how to harness the new techniques so that their potential benefits are equitably distributed rather than dissipated in further

3 J E. Meade, *Efficiency, Equality and the Ownership of Property*, Allen & Unwin, 1964, p 33.

unemployment. If manufacturing is revitalized into a competitive 'high technology' sector, it can provide the basis for a range of other productive activities of which there is no shortage of candidates. The provision of leisure facilities, better education and medical care, and improving the general infrastructure of the economy are some of the many examples of socially useful production which can enhance the quality of life, part of which may be enjoyed in the form of increased leisure itself.

The alternative, that the fruits of the new technology will consist of the production of new generations of electronic gadgetry for the benefit of the relatively high-paid who escape the growing ranks of the unemployed, is not a very attractive one but is the likely outcome of reliance on market forces to determine the distribution of income and the composition of output.

It is possible to conclude optimistically, as does the Department of Employment Special Study Group, that 'The pace of change is likely to be such as to make possible an ordered and considered response. It is not necessary at this point to make radical policy changes designed to meet a future technological order that is by no means certain.'[4] But if they are wrong, we may shortly find ourselves faced with problems which could only have been solved by an earlier awareness and recognition of their extent.

4. Department of Employment, op. cit., p. 103.

[10]   Which Way Out?

Keynes once suggested that every practical politician is, in fact, on closer inspection, a 'slave of some defunct economist'. Recently the influence of economists has been even more explicit than this, with monetarist thinking providing the day-to-day justification for policies which have profoundly affected the lives of millions of people. In this sense, economics really does matter and cannot be dismissed as abstract theorizing irrelevant to 'ordinary' men and women who find economic issues confusing and difficult to understand.

The economic events and discussions of recent years amply illustrate the nature of such confusion and difficulty. So far we have looked at the theory of monetarism and at some of the practical consequences that have followed from the way government has tried to implement it. And we have considered some alternative approaches. The intention now is not to come down firmly in favour of one or another of them but rather to outline some of the problems involved in deciding how we would like to see the economy run.

In the first place, this means understanding the nature of economic controversy to show the limited extent to which economists can be expected to provide answers to the questions of most general concern. Secondly, it is a matter of clarifying what sort of society it is which we hope will emerge in the future; that will indicate some of the main economic problems on which attention needs to be focused. And finally, we have to decide within which broad economic framework these problems are most likely to be solved.

Sources of Economic Controversy

'If all the economists in the world were laid end to end', said George Bernard Shaw, 'they would not reach a conclusion.' Jokes like this about the inability of economists to speak with a single voice are legion. And if their disagreements were only about harmless trivia they would provide non-economists with a source of innocent fun that would contribute in a minor way to the general well-being of the community. Frequently, however, their arguments are about major issues which are of interest to us all – like unemployment, the standard of living, the distribution of income and the level of prices. It is on key matters such as these that the divisions between economists are deepest and most acrimonious. Yet these are the issues about which policy-makers are most anxious to receive clear advice from economists and on which policies based on economists' advice are most likely to affect our everyday lives.

Unfortunately, economists have not generally proved to be very good at dealing with big questions. The plain truth of the matter is that they do not *know* precisely what causes inflation, or what the relationship is between prices and jobs, or why some countries become richer than others. That does not inhibit many of them from speaking as though they did know. The trouble is that their different views have in common only the degree of firm conviction with which they are put forward.

The nature and sources of economic disagreement are well illustrated by the current controversy about the relationship between money and prices. Is inflation caused by too much money and therefore controllable only by strict regulation of the money supply? Or is it the result of too much spending in the economy, spending which to some extent can vary regardless of what is happening to the stock of money? Are rising prices due to the upward pressure of costs which is the outcome of the way in which incomes and prices are determined by enterprises and trade unions? Or is it some combination of all of these, and perhaps other factors as well, which causes prices to go up?

There is a basic divide between monetarists and non-monetarists in their interpretation of the same set of facts. Monetarists argue that the evidence points to a clear causal relationship between money and prices. Non-monetarists question how closely the two are correlated, and anyway whether that would prove that it is the money supply which determines inflation rather than the other way round. And within each school of thought there are smaller but still highly significant areas of disagreement. For example, monetarists dispute among themselves about which is the relevant 'quantity of money' to be controlled, whether it is its demand or the supply which should be regulated and how this should be done, what is the precise 'transmission mechanism' through which monetary policy feeds through into lower inflation, and whether monetarist measures should be applied abruptly or introduced only gradually over a number of years.

Economic controversy is founded on two main sources of difference between economists – about facts, and about values. Usually, arguments contain elements of both.

Facts present awkward problems at every stage of the economist's work. Typically this consists in the first place of formulating a *hypothesis* – for example, that there is a close link between the money supply and the rate of inflation. Next comes the process of testing the hypothesis against the evidence of the past, which may point to either its rejection as being untenable or its refinement into a *theory* which seems to be well supported and can therefore be used to *predict* how in the future prices will be affected by changes in the money supply. For the theory to be *applied* as economic policy requires that the government is not only convinced that it is correct but also agrees about how it should be implemented. Finally, the implementation of the policy enables the theory to be *evaluated* and discarded, modified, or gain stronger acceptance according to how it has worked in practice.

Throughout, economists are generally dealing with data that are outdated, incomplete or unreliable and have often been collected for some other purpose. And when on the basis of this unsatisfactory raw material they do produce a hypothesis, its subsequent testing is complicated by the economists' lack of laboratory facilities. Here the physical scientist is at a great advantage. If he has a theory that X causes Y, he is then more or less able to set up an experiment in which X is varied so that he can see what the effect on Y actually is. To do this he must eliminate all other possible influences on Y so that he can be sure that what he measures is the isolated effect of X only. In other words, what he examines is how Y changes when X changes while everything else meanwhile *remains constant*.

The economist's laboratory, on the other hand, is the highly complex real world. This means, first, that he has to wait for the 'experiment' to occur as part of the course of events rather than simply set it up for himself; and second, that the *ceteris paribus* (all other things remaining equal) assumption of his economic model will generally only exist by chance. In these circumstances, factors A, B, and C may also be changing when X changes so that it is very difficult to be sure just what the effect of X was on Y. For example, consider the case of two non-monetarist theories of inflation, one that it is caused by excess demand and the other that it is the result of wage-push. A government may hedge its bets by both deflating the economy and pursuing an incomes policy. If inflation then falls, both camps will claim that their theory has been vindicated although in fact the impact of the two types of policy may be impossible to disentangle.

These are the general difficulties under which economists labour. In contrast, the years 1979–81 seemed to offer a quite exceptional opportunity for testing a major economic theory in conditions closer to those of a scientist's laboratory than perhaps ever before. This was because of the total commitment by the government to the monetarist approach and its exclusive reliance on controlling the money supply as the regulator of the economy. Here, it seemed, was the chance to establish once and for all just what the relationship was between money and prices.

However, as we have seen, the authorities failed to meet their monetary targets during 1979 and 1980. Despite this, the rate of inflation did fall (if only back to the level from which it had risen as a result of the government's own measures). Such an ambiguous outcome is capable of many interpretations. Monetarists can claim that their theory remains untried because the authorities over-emphasized £M3 as the critical monetary quantity and tried to regulate the demand for it rather than its supply; some would argue that much tighter monetary discipline was needed for the policy to be effective, others that it should have been applied far more gradually. Anti-monetarists, on the other hand, can conclude that control over the money supply may be impracticable as well as irrelevant, and that costs of attempted monetarism have been appallingly excessive.

How such costs are viewed introduces the other main source of economic disagreement. As well as disputing about technical matters, economists are divided because of the different *value* premises on which they base their arguments. Like other mortals, their opinions are coloured according to their moral and political standpoints.

Thus even if it could be proved beyond any doubt that inflation was caused by too much money, *and* that its control depended on reduced government spending, there would still be great scope for controversy:

(a) About where public spending cuts should be concentrated – on, for example, the purchase of Trident missiles or on local authority provision of housing? and

(b) About what increase in unemployment would be an acceptable price to be paid for reducing inflation. While they might agree about the desirability of greater price stability, various economists would rank it differently in relation to other policy objectives like full employment.

Or, to take a more specific case, consider the continuing dispute between monetarists and non-monetarists about the effects of increased public expenditure on the level of employment. At one extreme it is argued that greater public spending would lead to higher prices but no new jobs because it would only be at the expense of lower private spending which had been crowded out. Others would claim the opposite – that it would create additional employment with no increase in prices. In between is the view that increases in public spending may 'reduce the growth of output per head even if they increase employment'.[1] In this case there is both a disagreement about the facts of the matter, what the actual effects of higher public spending on output and employment would be – *and* a potential difference of opinion between economists according to how they weight the maximization of growth of output per capita against the growth of employment. In practice, the two may be difficult to distinguish.

The present rift between economists about monetarist policies is reminiscent of the so-called Great Debate which took place about British entry into Europe. On that occasion, it may be remembered, a letter to *The Times* was signed by no less than 153 economists opposing British membership of the E.E.C. A few days later a further letter was published

1 Professor Alan Budd in a letter to the *Guardian*, 28 May 1981.

supporting British membership and signed by 141 professional economists.

This time, following the March 1981 Budget, it was 364 university economists who issued a signed statement[2] of their conviction that:

'(a) There is no basis in economic theory or supporting evidence for the Government's belief that by deflating demand they will bring inflation permanently under control and thereby induce an automatic recovery in output and employment;

(b) Present policies will deepen the depression, erode the industrial base of our economy and threaten its social and political stability;

(c) There are alternative policies; and

(d) The time has come to reject monetarist policies and consider urgently which alternative offers the best hope of sustained economic recovery.'

The fact that on this occasion there was no mass response from supporters of government policy does not necessarily indicate a newfound unanimity amongst economists. The statement certainly represented a formidable condemnation of the current strategy by an unprecedented number of economists prepared to make their views public. But two points need to be borne in mind. First, only a quarter of university economists were signatories to the statement; it is possible that an equal number (particularly perhaps including those working in business or banking) might hold the opposite view. Secondly, the wording of the statement was sufficiently general to make it possible for economists of widely differing opinions to subscribe to the overall criticism. It is stronger in rejecting existing policies than in detailing the 'alternative policies' which now offer the 'best hope of sustained economic recovery'.

We have been looking at what some of these alternatives might be. And enough has been said to show that there also exists considerable disagreement among those opposed to the monetarist approach – for example, about the effects of a lower exchange rate or the practicability or effectiveness of incomes policy and import controls.

2. As reported on 30 March 1981.

However, to catalogue these areas of controversy is not to decry either economics or the economics profession. It is simply to emphasize the limitations as well as the usefulness of the subject, and to warn against those practitioners who claim for it more than it is capable of delivering. It is also to suggest how dangerous it is for a government to subscribe so exclusively to a particular school of economic thought, as has happened with the monetarists, when the risks of an inconclusive or even failed experiment may have far-reaching consequences for millions of the workforce and the future development of the economy.

Back to Economic Growth?

The attempt to apply monetarist policies has been criticized on many grounds. It has proved difficult to implement, the causal relationship between money and prices remains highly dubious, and even if such a link exists it is clear that the transmission mechanisms which connect the two work in a slow and clumsy fashion. But above all, the attack has been mounted on the grounds of the destructive waste involved – the re-emergence of mass unemployment, the loss of potential output, the erosion of the manufacturing base, and falling investment.

The alternatives that have been put forward all stress the need to get the economy moving again – first, back to full capacity and then into a renewed expansion which offers the opportunity for reversing the decline in Britain's competitive position. And that, after all, is also the long-term aim of the monetarists, who differ only in thinking that the present painful deflation is a necessary transitional process before a natural recovery takes place.

Thus there is common ground that a successful Britain in coming years will be one that is internationally competitive and marked by falling unemployment, inflation under control and renewed economic growth. The various schools put different emphasis in particular on the relative importance of jobs and prices, and fundamentally disagree how the goals should be achieved. But there is no major argument between them that the ultimate objective is to create an economy capable of

regularly increasing its ability to produce goods and services
year after year.

In other words, there is a common desire to get back to
the situation of the fifties and sixties, but this time without
the pressures on the balance of payments and on prices which
then accompanied attempts to increase the rate of economic
growth.

And yet in the period when Britain did enjoy regular
economic growth, dissatisfaction was being widely voiced.
From some quarters, it was complained that Britain was faring
less well than its main competitors, and the question was how
our growth rate could be increased into line with theirs. More
basically, the objective of maximizing the rate of growth in the
economy was itself increasingly being challenged.[3]

Critics of 'growthmania' pointed out that all that was meant
by economic growth was an increase in the real Gross National
Product, the collection of goods and services of all types which
the economy produced over a year. As an index of economic
progress, which was the way it was frequently used by politicians and commentators, it was highly inadequate because of
the questions on which it failed to throw much light.

(a) Increase in *which* goods and services? Wasteful prestige
    projects like Concorde which could only be expected
    to benefit the few? The output of machines and equip-
    ment which would improve the productivity of British
    industry? More low-cost housing? More electronic
    games and video-recorders? The aggregate growth
    figures tell us nothing about the *composition* of output,
    although this is clearly a relevant consideration in
    deciding whether the standard of living or the quality of
    life is improving or not.

(b) Higher incomes for whom? Economic growth means a
    rise in incomes as well as output. But once again, the fact
    that the economy grows at, say, 3% does not necessarily
    mean that everyone is that much better off as a result.
    It may be that the growth is achieved with rising un-
    employment so that the increase in incomes is con-
    centrated among those lucky enough to keep their jobs.

3. See, for example, J. K. Galbraith, *The Affluent Society*, 3rd edn, Penguin,
1979; E. J. Mishan, *The Costs of Economic Growth*, Penguin, 1969.

It may be that the distribution of income has become markedly less equal. Or more equal. The overall growth rate gives no indication.

(c) At what cost? Gross National Product is a hotchpotch record of all the goods and services produced in the economy during the course of a year. But instead of them all being counted as contributing towards greater prosperity, part of this output should more properly be regarded as a *cost* of increasing affluence. These costs may be difficult to quantify but are nonetheless real. If we are trying to measure the improvement in well-being, there is a good case for *deducting* from G.N.P. items like the employment of resources in cleaning up pollution or manufacturing tranquillizers or providing more facilities to deal with road accidents or industrial diseases.

More generally, the view used to be expressed that economic growth tended to lead to a distortion between 'private affluence and public squalor' – that the growth ethos made it difficult to achieve a proper balance between increased personal consumption and the provision of public amenities that made it possible for individuals to enjoy that consumption. And there was the still more fundamental argument, stemming from concern about the depletion of global resources, that it was simply not practicable to expect output to grow as it had for the previous century and a half without threatening the very future of mankind. It was also clear that the levels of consumption (particularly when measured in terms of energy and raw materials) enjoyed in the rich industrial nations could never be emulated by Third World countries; in this sense, one third of the world was living off the backs of the other two-thirds.

Single-minded pursuit of economic growth therefore increasingly came to be questioned from a variety of standpoints. And as well as those who argued that economic growth was in general an undesirable economic objective there were some who suggested that an implicit recognition of this was reflected in Britain's relatively low growth rate. As one foreign observer put it: 'Few Britons would join the cult of zero growth; like others in the post-war world, most want and expect ever higher levels of income, an increasing stream of goods and services

But Britains have also reached a collective, barely conscious decision of how much extra effort they will invest in the pursuit of more things.'[4] Thus, the slower rate of British economic growth was the product, not of some peculiar malaise, but 'an attitude, a life-style, a choice. It is a preference, at an historically high level of income, for leisure over goods.'[5] The same observer concluded that Britain was 'moving hesitantly towards a more civilized life',[6] and was in the van of those seeking a new post-industrial identity.

However, recent years have given us further experience on which to draw, with a slow-down and then cessation of economic growth, which demonstrates that this in itself does not, of course, improve the composition of output. On the contrary, what we have seen is a reduction in a wide range of social amenities and services, an increase in public squalor, at a time when the stresses of recession have made them even more needed. However, low or zero growth has been accompanied by increased inequalities, human distress and social dissatisfaction. Far from leading to a more equal sharing out of a national cake which has been of constant or even declining size, what has happened is that the burden of adjustment has fallen on to the rising numbers of unemployed, the lower income groups, those in most need of public help, those least able to cope for themselves. There is certainly no evidence of a general preference for the present situation to that of the earlier post-war period.

None of this is surprising, since the recent failure of the economy to grow has not been the result of a decision on the part of the British people, conscious or subconscious, or of government policies deliberately designed to correct a past over-emphasis on economic growth as a policy objective. And to argue now for a strategy of renewed expansion is not necessarily to favour a return to the indiscriminate maximization of G.N.P. but rather to advocate restoring a climate in which explicit choices about the way the economy should develop are more likely to be made. In this respect, the growth *versus* anti-growth controversy is of only limited role

4. B. D. Nossiter, *Britain. A Future That Works*, André Deutsch, 1978, p. 90.
5. ibid., p. 89–90.
6. ibid., p. 200.

vance because of the extent to which it obscures the key issues. The important matters are what is produced, the way in which wealth and incomes are distributed, the sharing of work and leisure, and the general life-style of which economic activity is only a part. Whether satisfactory solutions to issues such as these happen to result in a higher Gross National Product or a lower Gross National Product is largely incidental.

Demand or Supply?

One of the many differences between the monetarist approach and that of the alternative strategies so far outlined is the emphasis which each places on what may be termed the 'demand' and 'supply' aspects of the British economic problem. A major criticism which is put forward of monetarist policies is that they have involved a massive deflation of the economy, with demand being held back by public spending cuts, high interest rates and foreign incursions into the domestic market. Both the devaluationist and import control strategies, in contrast, stress the importance of expanding demand. For the devaluationists, a lower exchange rate leading to increased competitiveness is the main instrument for bringing this about. The C.E.P.G., on the other hand, argue that this would be inadequate, and that there must be substantial protection of British producers if they are to take advantage of rising demand. And since most devaluationists also recognize that there would be a need for their policies to be supplemented by some form of control over prices and/or incomes, neither is subscribing to a crudely Keynesian view that unemployment can be eliminated and prosperity restored *simply* by pumping more spending into the economy.

Increased demand is nonetheless for them a *necessary* condition for such goals to be achieved. Both argue that it is *only* within an expansionary context that more and better investment, higher productivity, restraint of money incomes to permit greater increases in real incomes, less restrictive practices and more enterprising management can be expected to develop. Thus, rising demand is not just the means by which existing over-capacity can be fully used but the mechanism through which greater productive efficiency is achieved.

Monetarists are highly sceptical of such arguments, claiming that the outcome will inevitably be higher inflation. Moreover, they argue that the restoration of British competitiveness depends essentially on prior changes being brought about in attitudes and behaviour. In other words, they stress the importance of transforming the supply side of the economy *before* any renewed expansion should take place. In this respect the monetarist package has three elements: (i) the elimination of inflation, involving a permanent revision of expectations about future income and price increases; (ii) reduction of public spending to avoid the private sector being crowded out; and (iii) increased incentives through tax cuts, particularly on personal incomes. Once these conditions are established the economy will automatically recover and the subsequent expansion will be one capable of being sustained.

In its emphasis on supply-side economics, this essentially 'right-wing' approach shares common ground with the proposals emanating from those on the political left. They, too, question whether British industry is capable of responding positively enough to such a stimulus. While agreeing that increased demand is a necessary basis for regenerating the economy, they doubt if it is sufficient in itself. Higher demand creates the conditions in which greater investment, productivity growth and competitiveness may result, but it is no guarantee that they will. Past performance casts doubt on the ability or willingness of producers to take full advantage of such an opportunity. It is argued that halting the process of de-industrialization will require radical changes which therefore can only be brought about by greater selective State intervention in the working of the economy and increased worker participation in economic decision-making. Examples of the measures that might be introduced in such an approach include:

(i) Planning agreements for the hundred or so major enterprises in the economy, in both the public and private sectors. These would involve for each of them tripartite decisions being hammered out between management, workers and government on matters such as future investment, location and export plans, and their implications for employment. The nature of these agreements would be that government financial support and tax concessions would then be related to the performance of enterprises in fulfilling these plans.

(ii) Extension of public ownership where necessary to key enterprises within industries where performance was particularly unsatisfactory. This might be undertaken by a body such as the National Enterprise Board and would aim at stimulating activity along the lines indicated by the broad planning strategy.

(iii) Greater control over the financial system, especially of the massive flows of savings now being generated by the pension funds. The purpose would be to ensure that these provided a greater quantity of 'risk capital' for investment in the more dynamic sectors of the economy rather than being channelled into financial investment here or overseas in pursuit of maximum commercial rather than economic gain.

It is claimed that this selective approach relating policy to particular enterprises and making State support *conditional* on their response would give governments the degree of control missing under conventional Keynesianism, which relied on general and permissive measures in the *hope* that the appropriate response would be forthcoming. And like those at the other end of the political spectrum, the left also are concerned with bringing about changes in attitudes more conducive to the solution of Britain's existing economic problems. But in their case, these would result from greater participation by workers in the decisions which shape their futures, and a breaking down of the 'us' and 'them' dichotomy that is endemic in unregulated capitalism.

The choice between these two very different emphases on the importance of supply-side factors is thus an expression of the perennial issue of whether it is more or less government intervention that is required. Today it is presented in a sharper focus than for many decades (during which governments of both parties agreed on the need to 'manage' the economy and differed mainly on questions of how this could best be done). The resurrection of monetarism by a government pledged to restore the market mechanism to its former eminence is a stage in the polarization of the debate, with the alternative increasingly being presented as a fundamental change in the parameters of ownership and control within which the market can then perform its role in an economic and human way.

Of the two, the case for minimal intervention seems so far to have been intuitively more appealing to the mass of British people than the radical alternative which is so easy to paint as the imposition of an East European greyness, loss of individual freedom and over-bureaucratization. It is an appeal that business should be controlled by businessmen who understand it rather than by civil servants or politicians who do not. It is an appeal to return responsibility and freedom of choice to individuals. It is based on the belief that government should limit the economic role to the provision of a sound financial framework within which businesses and individuals can then find full expression for their capabilities.

The left have found it difficult to counter what sounds like the commonsense of these propositions by communicating the failures of the unrestricted market in practice – the fact that market forces work in a disequalizing, unfair, slow and frequently uneconomic fashion. That is, to the extent that they work at all. Today the basic economic structure is not, and never again will be, remotely akin to the market models of the economics textbooks. Instead it is a world of workers organized into large unions and production that is mostly concentrated in a small number of giant firms. The economy has become, as Sir Robert Shone once put it, a game in which the players are 'powerful enough to adjust the goalposts or move the touch-line'. This is a far cry from the assumptions of price and wage flexibility on which, as we have seen, the monetarist model is based.

This is the way the world is, and this is the way the world is likely to develop still further in coming decades. During these decades, too, the problems which will have to be faced will be essentially human ones. To repeat what was said earlier, the questions to be dealt with will not be of how to produce more for the sake of producing more – but what to produce, how many people should be involved in its production, and what satisfaction they derive from their working and leisure lives. They will be questions about what constitutes a fair and acceptable distribution of wealth and income, not just between individuals but between different parts of the country and between different countries of the world.

These are matters which the market mechanism was not designed to resolve or is capable of resolving when left to its own devices. Monetarism as it has been practised in recent years does not even begin to come to terms with such issues; it seems unlikely even to deal with inflation except at a massively unacceptable cost. It will be interesting to see, if this proves to be the case, whether the outcome will be a reversion to the policies of the centre which provided the basis of con sensus political economy for the twenty-five years after the war - or whether the electorate as a result of this experience will endorse a shift to the left towards economic policies which have not as yet been fully tried but which at least claim to be relevant in dealing with the problems of the future.

Index

arbitration, 129

Bacon, R., and Eltis, W., 58n.
balance of payments, 89, 105,
    131–2
    devaluation's effect on, 140–41
    import controls and, 141–2
    North Sea oil effect on, 105–8
    on current account, 83, 88, 118
    problems, 21–2, 25, 120–21
balance of trade, 83, 102
bank
    balance sheet, 38–9
    cash reserves, 31–2, 39–40
    credit, 31–2
        substitutes for, 42
    deposits, 31–2, 38–9
        government control of, 38–
        40
    liquidity ratios, 40
Bank of England, 37, 39
banks, commercial, 38
Blackaby, F., 121n., 129n.
borrowing, 28, 42–3
    see also public borrowing
British Leyland, 147
British National Oil Corporation
    (B.N.O.C.), 74
Budd, A., 164n.
building society deposits, 32

Callaghan, J., 64
Cambridge Economic Policy
    Group (C.E.P.G.), 139–44,
    170
capital, 72, 172
    international movement of, 84,
        88–9, 104, 106–7, 118
cash limits, 53

cheques, 31
competition, unfair, 136–8
competitiveness, loss of, 137, 139
Confederation of British Indus-
    try (C.B.I.), 114–15
consumer
    preference, 54–5, 120
    spending, 14–15
consumption v. investment, 76–9

deficit financing, 17–18
deflation, 64, 89, 109, 112, 137
    North Sea oil and, 78–9, 108
deflationary gap, 16, 17
de-industrialization, 101–3, 108–
    111, 140
demand
    aggregate, 15
    deficiency, 16, 21
    expansion strategy, 170–71
    management, 18, 21, 25, 38,
        117
    stimulation, 17, 114–17, 121
depreciation of currency, 87–8,
    118–24
devaluation, 86, 91, 117–18, 122–
    124, 140–41, 143, 170
division of labour, 133–5, 137

economic data, 162
economic controversy, sources
    of, 160–66
Economic Progress Report, 44n.,
    53n.
Eltis, W., 121
employment
    created by new technology,
        151–2, 157–8

employment – *cont.*
White Paper on, 1944, 18
see also full employment
Employment Department
Report 1979, 150, 159
European Economic Community, 136, 143, 164–5
Common Agricultural Policy, 122
exchange control, 87
abolition of, 93–4, 107
exchange rates, 80–86, 140
expansion strategy and, 118–123
fixed and floating, 86–91. 121–122
foreign trade and, 81–6, 92–3, 118–22
government management of, 86–7, 122–3, 141
see also devaluation; pound, value of
expansion of economy, 166, 169–174
case for, 113–17, 140
exchange rates and, 118–23
import controls in, 130, 132, 139–44, 176
inflation and, 115–17, 120–22, 130
new technology in strategy for, 158–9
exports
decline in U.K. share of, 97–8, 100
elasticity of demand for, 119, 140
manufactured goods, 97–8, 100, 101–2, 131
prices of, 28, 92–3

fiscal policy, 17–18, 20, 114
Fisher equation, 33
floating debt, 61
foreign exchange market, 81
see also exchange rates

foreign trade, 15
exchange rates and, 81–6, 92–93, 118–22
forecasting, 20
inflation and, 28–9
see also exports; free trade; imports; manufacturing; trade, international
Forsyth, P. J., and Kay, J. A., 105n.
free trade, 134
v. protection, 135–9, 142
full employment, 25, 136, 145
budgeting for, 19–20
government's role, 13, 16–18
inflation and, 22, 24
microprocessors' impact on, 146, 149–52
redefining, 152–4
rise and fall of, 10–13
spending and, 14–18, 20, 22–3

Galbraith, J. K., 167n.
General Agreement on Tariffs and Trade (G.A.T.T.), 135–6, 143
gilt-edged securities, 61, 62
Gould, B., Mills, J., and Stewart, S., 143n.
government
conflicting objectives of, 21
management of exchange rate, 86–7, 122–3, 144
revenue, 60, 102–3
from North Sea oil, 73–8
role of, 13, 16–18, 37–8, 54, 117, 171–3
stock, 61, 62
see also industry, government aid to; public borrowing; public spending
Gross National Product (G.N.P.) 168–9
growth, economic, 21, 25, 52, 68–69, 96, 101
criticism of, 167–70

growth – *cont.*
  forfeited, 113
  see also expansion

Hines, C., 146n.

import controls, 9, 117, 135
  expansion and, 130, 132, 139–144, 176
  selective, 136–9
import quotas, 142
import penetration, 131–2, 138–139, 170
imports
  elasticity of demand for, 119, 140
  manufactured goods, 98, 100, 101–2, 110–11, 116, 131, 138
  oil or non-oil, 105, 107–8
  prices of, 28, 92–3
income, 30–31
  differentials, 128
  distribution, 28, 55, 173–4
incomes policy, 117, 124–5, 127–129
  aims of, 126–7
  prerequisites for, 125–6
industry
  crisis in, 93, 96–104
  government aid to, 53, 55–6, 96, 132, 137–8, 172
  see also manufacturing
inflation, 141
  causes of, 24–5, 29, 36, 45, 121, 140, 161, 164
  cost-push, 23–4, 29, 116
  demand-pull, 22–4, 29, 116
  effects of, 27–9
    on pound's value, 88, 121–2
  expansionary strategy and, 115–17, 120–22, 130
  government policy on, 26–7, 35, 174
  monetarism and, 44–6, 91–2, 112, 161–2, 174
inflationary gap, 22

innovation, 150, 155
interest rates, 16–17, 21, 140
  money supply and, 35, 41–2, 62
  value of pound and, 84–5, 89, 94
International Monetary Fund (I.M.F.), 86–7
investment, 14–15, 17, 20, 59–60, 107–8
  consumption *v.*, 76–9
  interest rates and, 16–17, 22
  prospects, 110–11, 113
  stimulation of, 114–15, 120, 172

Keynes, J. M., 59–60n., 160
  approach to unemployment, 13–18
Keynesianism
  abandoned, 25–6
  criticism of, 18–19
  recession and, 114–17

labour supply and price, 137
land, payment for use of, 72–3
liquidity, 31, 32–3, 39
List, F., 135
local authorities' expenditure, 47, 50–51

manufactured goods
  exports, 97–8, 100, 101–2, 131
  imports, 98, 100, 101–2, 110–111, 116, 131
  by areas of origin, 138
manufacturing
  decline in, 101–4
    North Sea oil as factor in, 104–11
  employment in, 97–8, 101–2, 107
  percentage of total output, 98–99
market mechanism, 54–6, 173–4

marketed output, 58
Meade, J., 129, 158
microprocessors, 146–59
Minimum Lending Rate
    (M.L.R.), 41–2
Mishan, E. J., 167n.
monetarism, 19, 25–6, 33, 36–7,
    40, 94, 160–63, 171, 173–4
    alternatives to, 166, 169–74
    effects of government strategy,
        41–2, 45–6, 104, 112, 118,
        139–40, 145, 163, 165–6
    pound's value and, 89, 91, 93–
        94, 123
monetary policy
    Keynesian, 16, 20
    North Sea oil and, 70, 78–9,
        109
    Public Sector Borrowing
        Requirement (P.S.B.R.)
        and, 62–4, 78, 109
money
    at call, 39, 61
    circulation of, velocity of, 43–4
    nature of, 30–33
    prices and, 29–30
    quantity theory of, 33–6
    regulation of demand for, 40–
        42
    supply, 31–3, 37
        control of, 37–44, 62, 163
        definitions of, 37, 163
        inflation and, 44–6, 91–2,
            112, 161–2, 174
        interest rates and, 35, 41–2,
            62
        P.S.B.R. effects on, 62–3
        targets affecting prices, 44
mortgages, 28
multinationals, 152, 156

National Health Service
    (N.H.S.), 55
National Insurance contribu-
    tions, 50, 114–15
nationalization, 39, 172

nationalized industries, 51, 53,
    57
Netherlands, 108–11
North Sea oil, 65–6, 89
    companies' profits, 71–4
    economic growth and, 66, 69–
        71, 121
    government revenue from, 73–
        74
        separate fund for, 110
        use of, 74–8, 110
    manufacturing decline attri-
        buted to, 104–11, 140
    monetary policy and, 70, 78–9
    potential gains from, 66–70
    recession intensified by, 79,
        104
    rent from, 71–4

oil price increase, 52, 65
    see also North Sea oil
Organization of Petroleum-Ex-
    porting Countries (O.P.E.C.),
    65, 88

par value, 86–7
pension fund investments, 172
pensions and inflation, 28
Petroleum Revenue Tax, 74
planning agreements, 171–2
pound sterling
    over-valuation of, 118
    value of, 80–86, 90
        depreciation of, 87–8, 118–
            124
        interest rates and, 84–5, 89,
            94
        management of, 86–7
        monetarism and, 89, 91, 93–
            94
        rising, 89–95, 104, 118
        see also devaluation; exchange
            rates
price elasticity of demand, 119
prices, 10, 34, 54, 134–5, 155

prices – *cont.*
 and incomes policy, 117, 124–5
  see also incomes policy
 money and, 29–30
 output and, 44–6
 rising, 23–4, 27–9, 116
 stability of, high employment a
  threat to, 22, 24
private choice, increasing, 54–6
private sector
 'distress' borrowing, 63
 v. public sector, 56–60, 62–3,
  77–8, 104
production, 57–8
 bottlenecks, 116
 foregone through monetarism,
  45–6, 113
 microprocessors applied to,
  147–8
 possibility curves, 67–8, 70
productivity, 101, 113, 143, 157,
  171
 in incomes policy decisions,
  127–8
protection *v.* free trade, 135–9,
  142
public borrowing, 47, 51
 cost of, 60–64
Public Sector Borrowing Requirement (P.S.B.R.), 51,
  60–61, 115–16
 monetary policy and, 62–4, 78,
  109
 reduction of, 47, 62–3, 104
public spending, 16–18, 36, 47–
  50, 52–3, 115
 by programme, 1980–81, 48–9
 capital and current, 49
 cuts, 41–2, 52–3, 63–4, 104,
  112, 164, 170
  pros and cons of, 53–60, 75–
  76
 financing, 50–51
 increase in, 76, 78, 114, 164,
  170
 percentage of G.D.P., 56, 57

White Paper on, 1979, 64n.
public works programmes, 114–
  115

quantity theory of money, 33–6

rates, 50–51
rational expectations theory, 44–
  45
recession, 64, 169
 causes of, 79, 145
 Keynesian approach to, 114–
  117
 severity of, 130, 145
reflation, 113, 140, 145
rent, economic, 72–3
reserves, official, 86
resource allocation, 67
resources, scarce, 66–9
Retail Price Index (R.P.I.), 28
revaluation, 86
Ricardo, D., 134, 135

savings and inflation, 28
scarce resources, 66–9
services
 effect of new technology on,
  148–9
 growth of, 99–100
 marketable and exportable,
  needed, 111
Shaw, G. B., 160
Shone, Sir Robert, 173
Singh, A., 102n.
Smith, D., 44n.
social security benefits, 49–50, 53
 see also unemployment benefits
social wage, 50, 78
specialization, 133–4,
speculation, currency, 88
spending and full employment,
  14–18, 20, 22–3
 see also public spending
standard of living, 52, 77–8, 100,
  122

'stop–go', 25, 65, 117
supply
    constraints on expansion, 116
    deficiency, 21
    expansion strategies, 171–2

tariffs, 142–3
taxation, 17, 50–51, 79, 110
    indirect, increases in, 45, 104
    of North Sea oil profits, 73–4
technology, new, 10, 21, 111, 128
    application of, 146–8
    collective bargaining on, 154–9
    employment creation by, 151–
        152, 157–8
    services and, 148–9
    unemployment and, 147–52,
        156–8
    welfare benefits from, 154, 159
trade
    cycle, 145
    international, 133–5
    visible and invisible, 82–3, 111
    see also balance of trade;
        foreign trade; free trade
trade unions, 130, 132, 154–9
Trades Union Congress
    (T.U.C.), 114, 127, 132
transfer payments, 48, 49
Treasury and Civil Service Com-
    mittee, 41n., 46n., 64n., 90, 91
Treasury Bills, 39–40, 61, 62

unemployment, 11, 93, 136–7,
    164
    benefits, 49–50, 79
        reduction of, 59

checking inflation, 24, 141–2,
    164
combating, 164
Keynesian approach to, 13–19,
    114
manufacturing industry, 101–
    102, 107
mass, 113, 131, 151
microprocessors and, 147–52,
    156–8
1931–81, 10–12
1981, 12–13, 45
non-Keynesian, 20–21
post-recession, 145–6
in private and public sectors,
    63
Public Sector Borrowing Re-
    quirement effect on, 63–4
regional, 11, 12, 20–21
school leavers, 9, 13, 156

value-added tax (V.A.T.), 50

wage bargaining, 127–9
wage–price spiral, 23–4, 121
wage settlements, 45, 116–17,
    122
wages
    excessive, 13
    low, 136
wealth, 32–3
wealth-producing sector, 57
welfare and technological pro-
    gress, 154, 159
Welfare State, 52
word processor, 148
work-sharing, 157–8

More About Penguins
and Pelicans

For further information about books available from Penguins please write to Dept EP, Penguin Books Ltd, Harmondsworth, Middlesex UB7 0DA.

In the U.S.A.: For a complete list of books available from Penguins in the United States write to Dept DG, Penguin Books, 299 Murray Hill Parkway, East Rutherford, New Jersey 07073.

In Canada: For a complete list of books available from Penguins in Canada write to Penguin Books Canada Ltd, 2801 John Street, Markham, Ontario L3R 1B4

In Australia: For a complete list of books available from Penguins in Australia write to the Marketing Department, Penguin Books Australia Ltd, P.O. Box 257, Ringwood, Victoria 3134.

In New Zealand: For a complete list of books available from Penguins in New Zealand write to the Marketing Department, Penguin Books (N.Z.) Ltd, P.O. Box 4019, Auckland 10.

GUIDE TO THE BRITISH ECONOMY

In the first part of this introductory guide, Peter Donaldson – who has revised and updated this edition – is mainly concerned with explaining matters of finance, including the stock market. After a full examination of industry, labour and trade, he goes on in the final section of the book to a general discussion of economic theories, their scope, and their limitations.

'Excellent . . . a most lucid and absorbing survey of the British Economy for the intelligent layman or for the beginning student of economics. It really cannot be faulted in either its scope or its exposition' – Professor Lomax in the *Economic Journal*

ECONOMICS OF THE REAL WORLD

Peter Donaldson describes here how a mixed economy is managed and (given the underlying market mechanisms) what can and what cannot be the subject of economic policy. More basically he argues that economics itself is strangely remote from the urgent problems of ordinary people and that policy-makers confuse ends and means. What matters, in his view, is not growth, but growth of what, for whom and at what cost; not full employment, but the nature of work; not just more wealth, but its more equitable distribution.

For *this* is the real world – a world of values and people – neglected by orthodox economics and evaded by policy-makers. Why? Because, suggests Peter Donaldson, if the real issues are to be tackled, there has to be a revolution in our whole outlook on economics and society.

ALMOST EVERYONE'S GUIDE TO ECONOMICS
J. K. Galbraith and Nicole Salinger

'Economics preempts the headlines. It bears on everyone's life, anxieties and, if more rarely, satisfactions.'

Believing that 'the state of economics in general, and the reasons for its present failure in particular, might be put in simple accurate language that almost everyone could understand and that a perverse few might conceivably enjoy', Professor Galbraith has collaborated with Nicole Salinger in an entertaining dialogue.

She leads him through a step-by-step explanation of economic ideas with such clarity that all can understand the basic nature of classical, neo-classical and Marxian economics, the role of money and banking, the modus operandi of fiscal monetary policy, the part played by multinationals, the reasons for simultaneous inflation and unemployment and the causes of the present crisis in international economic and monetary affairs.

THE GALBRAITH READER
J. K. Galbraith

Here is the best of his writing, including selections from *The Affluent Society, The Great Crash, The New Industrial State*, and *Money*; together with more personal items, excerpts from his *Ambassador's Journal*, and letters to President Kennedy describing a nation and a world moving towards crisis. Here is a glittering prose mosaic of the Galbraith style, a portrait of a great man for ever challenging the beliefs of his generation.

'A singular delight . . . the delight of consistent good prose, and of a thinking man thinking' – *The New York Times*

A selection of Edward de Bono in Pelicans

LATERAL THINKING
FOR MANAGEMENT

Creativity is so essential a part of management equipment that it can no longer be left to chance or to the gifted amateur. Pioneer in the use of lateral thinking, Edward de Bono shows here how he sees creativity and lateral thinking working together in the process of management to develop new products, new ideas and to generate new approaches to problem-solving, organization and to future alternatives in planning.

By removing the mystique of creativity and learning to treat it as a definite process which can be learned, practised and used with the aid of specific techniques, he demonstrates how traditional education and management methods (which focus on logical sequential methods) can be brought together to achieve astonishing results.

OPPORTUNITIES
A HANDBOOK OF BUSINESS
OPPORTUNITY SEARCH

'An opportunity is as real an ingredient in business as raw material, labour or finance – but it only exists when you can see it.'

Everybody assumes that he or she is opportunity-conscious – but is frequently only conscious of the *need* to be opportunity-conscious. For often what looks like an opportunity isn't one after all.

Opportunities is a handbook which offers a total, systematic approach to opportunity-seeking at both corporate and executive levels. It is Edward de Bono's most significant contribution to business since he developed lateral thinking – and it should have just as much impact. Remember: 'Just before it comes into existence every business is an opportunity that someone has seen.'

Published in Pelicans by Darrell Huff

HOW TO LIE WITH STATISTICS

'Round numbers', pronounced Dr Johnson, 'are always false.'

But not, of course, the precise and scientific calculations of trained statisticians, with their decimals and percentages. The computer, like the camera, cannot lie. Not without help, anyhow.

In this Pelican Darrell Huff introduces the beginner to the niceties of samples (random or stratified random), averages (mean, median, or modal), errors (probable, standard, or unintentional), graphs, indexes and other tools of democratic persuasion.

John Connell, in the *Evening News*, called this famous study 'wildly funny, outrageous, and a splendid piece of blasphemy against the preposterous religion of our time'.

But don't let that depress you. Figures prove that there's always something to weep about – whether it's cancer, the cost of living, crime, or just the Chinese population. Yes, more and more people are dying every day. It's the trend.

HOW TO TAKE A CHANCE

What's your favourite gamble? Viewing the antics of molecules on an electronic computer, or just whiling away the long winter evenings with Russian Roulette? Dice, dogs, pool, poker, medical research and meteorology – it's all the same. You're flirting with Madame Fortune, and she's seldom pure.

ADVENTURES WITH YOUR POCKET CALCULATOR
Leonard Rade and Burt A. Kaufman

What do you do with your calculator when you have checked your bank statement?

In this lively, entertaining, and non-trivial book two mathematicians introduce you to twenty fascinating and sometimes puzzling areas of real mathematics via the kind of pocket calculator that you probably own already. Random numbers, prime numbers, elementary probability theory, magic squares, the Golden Section – all these can be yours, for fun.

WHAT IS THE NAME OF THIS BOOK?
Raymond Smullyan

'The most original, most profound and most humorous collection of recreational logic and maths problems ever written. It contains more than 200 brand new puzzles all concocted by the ingenious author, interspersed with mathematical jokes, lively anecdotes and mind-bending paradoxes, and culminating in a remarkable series of story problems that lead the reader into the very heart of Kurt Gödel's revolutionary work on undecidability' – Martin Gardner in the *Scientific American*

FREE TO CHOOSE
Milton and Rose Friedman

In a bestselling book which has sparked off controversy among economists and in the media, Milton and Rose Friedman explore the relationship between economics and freedom. With tremendous verve and wit, they dissect the role of government over the broad field of economics and society; they conclude that interventionist governments, no matter how well-intentioned, have almost invariably done more harm than good; they make a compelling case for the free market and the benefit it confers.

'A brilliantly lucid explanation of how a market economy works . . . should be read by anyone who wants to know what banks do, by economists inclined to forget what their numbers mean, by politicians who confuse technical mumbo-jumbo with talking sense' – *Spectator*

THE MEANING OF CONSERVATISM
Roger Scruton

Roger Scruton challenges those who would regard themselves as conservatives, and their opponents. Locating the system of beliefs that make up the conservative outlook, he argues that these have little in common with the creed of liberalism and are only tenuously related to the doctrine of 'market economy'. The evils of socialism, he maintains, lie precisely where its supporters find its strengths, and he goes on to reject the political vision that has made the conservative position seem outmoded and irrational. His book presents a new and striking challenge to Marxism, pointing out that the Marxist conceptions can be used to formulate conclusions diametrically opposed to socialist dogmas, and offers new perspectives on the prevailing liberal theories of law, citizenship and the state.

THE MULTINATIONALS
Christopher Tugendhat

In recent years vast international companies have developed which dominate the 'commanding heights of the economy' throughout Western Europe and North America. Firms like Alcan, IBM, Ford, Shell and Bayer have annual sales as large as the gross national products of many countries, and their rate of growth is much faster. Inevitably there are tensions between the companies and governments who see control of a vital sector of the economy slipping from their grasp.

In this illuminating book, which won a McKinsey Foundation Book Award in 1971, Christopher Tugendhat examines the multinationals and the political implications of their position and influence.

REASON BY NUMBERS
Peter G. Moore

How do you allocate your time and money? Your hunch won't win you much on the fruit machine, but it achieves even less if you are organizing a tea-shop, a factory or the NHS, or choosing a savings-scheme, or devising an appointments system for the office.

Guesswork, however inspired, is no substitute for a sound working knowledge of probability, sampling, decision analysis, risk profiles – in a word, for numeracy. In this Pelican Peter Moore looks at the ways of gathering, presenting and interpreting information and explains the essential arithmetic of resource allocation, planning and decision theory. His examples, and the exercises at the end of each chapter, are based on typical problems encountered in industry, commerce, medicine, economics and agriculture, and in the many areas of public administration.

Also published in Pelicans

THE HIDDEN PERSUADERS
Vance Packard

In a new epilogue to his classic study of the American advertising machine, Vance Packard reveals that, far from losing ground as the innocent Fifties grew into the sophisticated Seventies, its power has grown accordingly: an $8 billion business has turned into a $40 billion industry. Their technologists now include brain specialists, neurophysiologists, hypnotechnicians, voice-pitch analysts. Their victims are the new stereotypes; the liberated woman, the independent man, the militant mother, the chic suburbanite, the swinging New Waver.

Whether or not we fall into such categories, we are all to some extent persuadable – Vance Packard definitively and entertainingly explains why and how.

WHO'S WATCHING YOU?
BRITAIN'S SECURITY SERVICES
AND THE OFFICIAL SECRETS ACT
Crispin Aubrey

The security services, invisible, unaccountable, surrounded by a mystique of dark glasses and turned-up collars, have grown steadily in size; so too has their expenditure on the most sophisticated techniques of mass surveillance.

Their net falls on trade unionists, students, anti-nuclear protesters, Welsh Nationalists, investigative journalists and a host of possible 'subversives'. Crispin Aubrey stumbled into this web one dark and rainy night in 1977, was arrested by the Special Branch and charged under the Official Secrets Act. His subsequent trial, the 'ABC trial', attained a legal significance and had political repercussions far beyond the facts of the case.

'What are you doing, Adam?' Sienna asked fiercely when Ethan was out of earshot. 'If you think spending money on him is the answer, think again. He wants you, not your money.'

'You're incredibly sexy when you're angry—do you know that, Sienna?'

'This isn't about you and me.'

It was like water off a duck's back. Adam smiled, completely unperturbed by her words.

Sienna's heart drummed an age-old rhythm, each beat building up her senses, and when Adam's lips claimed hers she was totally ready. It was like much needed rain after a dry summer. It was like finding water in the desert. It fed her inner needs, and against her better judgement she returned his kiss.

Born in the industrial heart of England, **Margaret Mayo** now lives in a Staffordshire countryside village. She became a writer by accident, after attempting to write a short story when she was almost forty, and now writing is one of the most enjoyable parts of her life. She combines her hobby of photography with her research.

MARRIED AGAIN TO THE MILLIONAIRE

BY
MARGARET MAYO

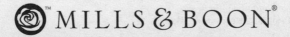

MILLS & BOON

All the characters in this book have no existence outside the imagination of the author, and have no relation whatsoever to anyone bearing the same name or names. They are not even distantly inspired by any individual known or unknown to the author, and all the incidents are pure invention.

First published in Great Britain 2010
Harlequin Mills & Boon Limited,
Eton House, 18-24 Paradise Road, Richmond, Surrey TW9 1SR

© Margaret Mayo 2010

ISBN: 978 0 263 87781 6

Harlequin Mills & Boon policy is to use papers that are natural, renewable and recyclable products and made from wood grown in sustainable forests. The logging and manufacturing process conform to the legal environmental regulations of the country of origin.

Printed and bound in Spain
by Litografia Rosés, S.A., Barcelona

MARRIED AGAIN
TO THE
MILLIONAIRE

CHAPTER ONE

SIENNA'S heart pounded as she stood outside the prestigious residential development, which was set in its own park alongside the Thames. Only the very rich could afford to live there. And the last time she'd seen Adam he'd definitely not been in that category...

When no one answered the intercom system, and it appeared that she had wasted her time, she felt strangely relieved. It had taken a lot of courage to come here and she was just about to leave when she heard Adam's well-remembered voice.

'Sienna?'

It was like velvet over steel. From experience she knew that it could be as soft as molten chocolate or as hard edged as a razor blade. She had felt both sides of his tongue, and as she stood there now Sienna gave an involuntary shudder.

She'd had no idea that a video camera was monitoring her presence. The thought that Adam knew she was there and that he had probably been watching the expression on her face as she waited chilled her blood.

Forewarned was forearmed, and she was at a definite disadvantage.

'Adam!' Was that really her own voice sounding scratchy and nervous when she had been determined to be strong? And why the hell was he keeping her standing here instead of allowing her entrance?

Was he taking some sort of perverse pleasure in it? Unless he didn't want to see her! After all, it had been over five years. 'I—I need to speak to you.' Her mouth had gone suddenly dry, swallowing became impossible.

'After all this time? How interesting. You'd better come in.' Again his deep, dark voice scraped over her nerves and as the barrier to the landscaped gardens lifted Sienna made her way slowly to the main entrance door of the complex where she was confronted with yet another see-your-visitor system. With a sigh she pressed the appropriate button and waited—and waited.

After what seemed like several minutes, though was probably only one, Adam's voice reached her ears again. 'You look impatient, Sienna.'

'Are you playing games with me?' She heard the sharpness in her tone but was uncaring any longer. Her anger was building and she was beginning to wish that she had never decided to approach Adam.

'I've been trying to work out why you're here.'

'And unless you let me in, you'll never know. In fact, don't bother, I've changed my mind.' She swung on one of her ridiculously high heels, heels she had donned to give her the height and the confidence to do what she was about to do, and was about to march back the way she had come when he spoke again.

'Wait!'

And she heard a click as the door opened.

'Top floor, penthouse suite. The lift's to your right.'

With his curt instructions echoing in her ears, Sienna approached the lift. It whooshed her swiftly and silently to the top of the building and she emerged in an entrance hall lined with beech panelling and lit by discreet, inset spotlights. Beneath her feet were exquisite tiles in varying shades of bronze and olive green. Glossy-leaved plants stood in corners and a mirror was directly opposite.

She looked, thought Sienna, petrified. Her wide blue eyes were burning like coals in her pale face, her chestnut hair awry, despite having taken care with it before she had left home. And having nervously nibbled her lips while she had waited to gain entrance, her lipstick was non-existent.

This was not the image she wanted to portray and she stood there a moment taking deep steadying breaths, pulling herself together, forcing a smile. She combed her hair, reapplied her lipstick and was popping the tube back into her bag when a door opened and Adam strode towards her.

Sienna took in a sharp breath. The change in him was dramatic. He'd gone from being almost too thin to broad-shouldered and well muscled. She could actually see his muscles rippling beneath the silk of his shirt. His waist and hips were still slender but he had powerful thighs, barely hidden beneath fine linen trousers.

Where had all this body development come from? she wondered. It looked as though he worked out on a major scale and yet from what she knew of him, and what she'd read in the press, he didn't appear to have time for exercise. Work was still his ethos. If there had been more than twenty-four hours in a day he would have worked most of them.

His strong jaw with its cleft beneath sculpted lips was

firm. His eyes, which were a dark, dark blue, were riveted on her face. Thick black brows jutted over them. The only thing that hadn't changed was his black, curling hair, which was as awry as it had ever been. It touched his shirt collar and looked as though it desperately needed trimming and combing.

'So—Sienna, I wondered if I'd ever see you again.' His deep voice rumbled into the open space. 'Actually, I'm intrigued. How did you know where I lived?'

Sienna allowed her fine brows to rise. 'You're in the news these days. A few enquiries and I had your address.'

Over the years it had been easy to keep tabs on what he was doing. He had gone from being a simple property developer to someone who bought ailing businesses, turned them around, and then sold them off at a huge profit. He had been voted businessman of the year on more than one occasion. To give him credit, he did a lot of charity work as well.

Wide shoulders shrugged. 'I always knew that I would make it.'

'Such modesty,' she flashed. 'But at what cost?' His driving force, his need to make millions, was one of the reasons she had left him.

Adam's lips thinned. 'Are you here to discuss my success? Or is it a share of my money that you're after? Is that why you've never asked for a divorce, so that you can lay claim to half of my worth? Well, I hate to tell you, Sienna—'

'That is not why I'm here,' Sienna said defensively, though in truth she could understand why he thought that. There were women who would go for the jugular under similar circumstances but she was not one of them.

She had struggled these last few years but she would never have asked Adam for a penny, not a single penny. She had her pride. And as for a divorce, she had liked the idea of being a married woman.

If she had met and fallen in love with someone else she might have demanded her freedom, but there had been no one, and clearly Adam hadn't wanted to remarry either—which hadn't surprised her. He enjoyed his life the way it was.

Inside his luxurious suite she stood for a moment looking around her. The large open space was entirely fronted by glass, which led out onto a wide balcony with a riven slate floor, studded with potted plants and cushioned cane furniture. It looked more like a courtyard than a balcony and the view over the Thames was stunning, but she had no time to give it more than a cursory glance before her attention was taken up with the room she was in.

The furniture was minimal. Chunky brown leather sofas and glass topped tables. A massive television screen on one wall. Everything in muted natural colours and the open-plan kitchen at the far end was to die for. Sienna couldn't help wondering whether Adam cooked for himself or sent out for food, or even used one of the restaurants she had seen along the riverside walk.

'Please—sit down.' Adam indicated one of the leather chairs but Sienna shook her head.

'I'd prefer to go outside.' Although the space was immense, she felt suffocated by Adam's presence. Strange when she had known him more intimately than any other man before or since.

'As you wish,' he said, leading the way. 'Would you

care for something to drink or would you prefer to say whatever it is that you came for?'

There was harshness in his voice and Sienna shivered. Adam had changed. He had always been a driven man, working hard, collapsing with exhaustion at the end of each day, but there was a hard edge to him now, a cutting edge. He clearly hadn't got where he was without being utterly devoid of emotion and manically ruthless.

Thank God she had got out in time.

'I'd like a drink, thank you.' Something to lubricate her still dry throat. This was going to be far harder than she had envisaged.

'Tea? Coffee? Maybe something stronger?'

'Yes.' Something strong and intoxicating, something to relax her tense muscles because otherwise she would walk out of here without telling him her reason for coming.

She had not imagined when she set out that Adam would be this coolly controlled man who had her at a disadvantage. She had known it would be difficult, she had rehearsed her little speech a thousand times, but this new Adam was making it ten times worse. She felt that he was toying with her, waiting for the right moment to throw her out and tell her that whatever it was she had come for he wanted nothing to do with it.

A dark eyebrow rose. 'Yes to all three?'

'I mean, I'd like…something stronger.'

His lips twitched but he didn't comment. 'Wine perhaps? Or brandy? How great is your need?'

His sarcasm wasn't lost on her and Sienna lifted her chin, her light blue eyes meeting his darker ones. She had almost forgotten how amazingly good-looking he was and for one small moment she felt a rush of heat between her thighs. Banished in an instant, deeply horrifying.

That part of her life was over. Not once since she'd left him had he tried to find her, proving that he hadn't been particularly disappointed or even worried. In essence it had given him a clear field to work even longer hours. To amass his fortune. She found it difficult to understand why anyone would let money be their god. There was surely more to life.

This apartment, for instance, was nothing more than a status symbol. Why would one man live by himself in a place like this? Unless he used it as a love nest. Did he invite lady friends here? Actually, she had not once seen him in the press with a female on his arm. He was either very careful or working his socks off was still his way of life.

'Wine would be perfect, thank you.'

Left alone for a few minutes, Sienna closed her eyes, wishing she hadn't felt the need to seek Adam out after remaining silent for so long. If she had any sense, she would blurt out her reason for coming here and then run.

Except that good sense seemed to have deserted her. All she could think about was the way she had looked into his eyes and felt an emergence of the hunger and longing she had always experienced when they were together. He had been an amazing lover, setting her whole body alight with a fire she had thought would never die.

But after their marriage Adam had quickly gone from being her knight in shining armour to working so hard, coming home so late, that he'd barely had time to speak to her before falling asleep each night.

'Here we are.'

Grateful for Adam's interruption, Sienna shot her eyes wide. As they cannoned into his she felt a further body blow. He was still devastatingly sexy, causing wave after wave of hot desire to flood her veins. Damn! All these years she had told herself that she hated him, so why was this happening now?

It had to be pure sexual hunger that she felt, it couldn't be anything else. She certainly didn't love him any more. How could she possibly love a man who thought more about his job than he did his wife?

The wine looked deliciously cool and inviting. Sienna watched as Adam poured the pale golden liquid, watching it swirl and then settle. Almost instantly a fine film of condensation formed around the outside of her glass and as she picked it up she stroked her finger down its side.

Adam watched her through narrowed eyes, making her wish that she hadn't done it because he was looking at her as though she had made some kind of erotic gesture. As though she was stroking *him*!

Heat fizzed through her and she took a long swallow, amazed to discover when she set her glass down that she had drunk almost half its contents.

'Is it such an ordeal coming to see me?'

The gruff tone in his voice sent her head jerking in his direction. She saw lips that were grim and eyes that were as cold as ice.

'Why don't you just spit out what's wrong and get it over with?'

How could she? They needed to be at ease with each other first. And getting drunk wasn't the answer!

'It's a very fine place you have here,' she said instead. 'Do you have someone to share it with?'

'If you're asking whether I have a girlfriend, the answer's no. You should know me better than that, Sienna. I have only one lover, and that is my work.'

'So you haven't changed.' Sienna let her eyebrows rise. 'You still work all the hours God made! Why, when you have this?' She spread her hands, taking in their impressive surroundings.

'It's precisely why I work, for security, and to have nice things around me.' His dark blue eyes watched her closely. 'I also have a pied-à-terre in France and an apartment in New York. It gives me a feeling of great satisfaction.'

'Or is that you have so much money now you have nothing else to spend it on?' Sienna queried, unable to keep the distaste out of her voice. It was as though he was deliberately throwing his wealth in her face, showing her what she had missed out on.

'If you've come here to question my lifestyle, I suggest—'

'It's not that,' cut in Sienna quickly. But she wasn't ready yet to disclose her real reason for being here. It was such a delicate subject that she had to get Adam into the right mood. 'It simply seems odd that you have these other places to live and no one to share them with.'

'Are you putting yourself forward?' He smiled grimly and his eyes locked with hers, sending a fresh scurry of feelings through her veins.

She had thought that over the years everything she had ever felt for Adam Bannerman had died. She didn't want to feel anything for him, she despised him and she wouldn't be here now if it wasn't entirely necessary.

There was ice in both her voice and her eyes when

she spoke. 'I've had a taste of what it's like living with a workaholic. It's no fun, I assure you, and I'm not entirely surprised that you haven't found another woman to share your life.'

'Are you suggesting that I should? Is it a divorce you're after? I occasionally wonder why you've never filed for one.'

The deep sarcasm in his voice scoured over her already tense nerves like sandpaper.

'I could say the same about you.' She held her head high and met his eyes. For several long seconds they challenged each other, Sienna not wanting to be the first to turn away.

'I've never had the time or the inclination,' he drawled, his eyes still not leaving hers. 'I knew that one day, when you were ready, you would start proceedings. What I didn't expect was that you would visit me in person. It's quite a surprise.'

'And a mistake,' she snapped before she could stop herself. 'I really think I should be going.' There was no way on this earth now that she could broach the subject that had made her come here. Adam was doing a very good job of letting her know that he liked his life the way it was. He wanted nothing to spoil it. She pitied him. He would become a lonely old man one day if he kept putting work first.

'You're not leaving until you tell me what brought you here,' he said, his tone sharp and authoritative. 'Why don't you finish your wine?'

Sienna glared at him, but she picked up her glass and downed the rest of its contents in one swallow. 'There, finished.' And she stood up.

Adam followed suit and Sienna was glad that she had worn high heels because they made her almost as tall as he was. She lifted her chin and looked into his eyes— and felt a wave of something she dared not think about pass over her. The word began with S and ended in X.

Why was this happening now, when she needed to be strong and in control? Was it the fact that he was the first and only man she had ever fallen in love with? Had her body retained those feelings even though she had been convinced that they had not?

Hell, what a situation to find herself in. Especially as Adam showed no sign of returning them. She couldn't believe how cold he was. It was as though she had never meant anything to him.

'So why are you here?'

Sienna closed her eyes. It looked as if there was no escape. And if the truth be known, she had to do it. She owed it to Adam, to herself, to— She stopped her thoughts there, drew in a deep breath, and bluntly and coldly stated the facts.

'I'm here to tell you that you have a son.'

CHAPTER TWO

ADAM felt as though he had been poleaxed. The words that had just left Sienna's lips sent him reeling across the courtyard.

She was saying he had a son!

A son!

A son who would now be…four years old!

And in all the time they'd been apart she had never had the decency to tell him!

The blood roared through his head like a hurricane and he wanted to hit out at her, shake her, ask her what the hell she had thought she was doing, keeping him in ignorance. This was a scenario he had never envisaged, not in his wildest dreams. It was something he was finding difficult, if not impossible, to take in.

He had never wanted a family, he was happy doing what he did. Happy, for goodness' sake! He didn't want a child in his life, disrupting his routine. The big question was, why had she told him now? Why not when she found herself pregnant?

His eyes blazed as a bigger scenario hit him. 'I'm not the father, am I? Why in heaven's name would you wait this long to tell me if I were? You're after money.

You're trying to take me for a fool. Get out of here, Sienna. *Get out!'*

Never in his life had he been so angry. If Sienna had thought she could pull this stunt on him, she was very much mistaken. If the baby really had been his, she would have wasted no time in coming back. She would have made him face up to his responsibilities. Even if she hadn't, no woman in her right mind would bring up her baby alone without seeking maintenance from the father. She would have insisted on that. She had to be lying.

Sienna's back straightened and her fantastic blue eyes flashed with indignant fury. She looked like a tigress protecting her young. 'He is definitely yours.'

'So you say.' He was not going to be so easily fooled. Words were easy. He had heard of women who did this sort of thing, who tricked their former partners or husbands into believing someone else's child was their own.

'Do you want proof?' she demanded. 'It can be arranged.'

Her eyes locked into his and held, and in that moment Adam saw nothing but blazing honesty. His brief suspicion was reluctantly relegated to the deepest recesses of his mind. Maybe it would resurrect itself. Maybe. Perhaps if he saw the child, he would know at once whether he was his or not. He'd had a strong resemblance to his own father so there was every reason to believe that he would see something of himself in this boy.

Adam folded his arms and looked hard into the blue of her eyes. *'If* the boy is mine, why have you waited so long to tell me about him?' He was aware that his voice was still harshly condemning, and filled with more than a little suspicion, but, hell, she couldn't drop a bomb-shell like this and expect no reaction.

His heart felt as though it was trying to escape from his chest and he was afraid to stand any closer to Sienna because he felt like shaking her. Why, for pity's sake, had she kept her secret all this time? Why?

She looked stunning in a black and white top and stylish black trousers, which hid none of the curves of her sexy bottom. Her black high-heeled sandals gave her added height, even though they looked dangerously dif-ficult to walk in. And her rich chestnut hair, which had always been her crowning glory, was cut in a short, chunky style that suited her elfin face.

She certainly didn't look like the mother of an ener-getic four-year-old. She was dressed to kill. She had come here to drop her bombshell—and she had cer-tainly done that. It was a wonder it hadn't exploded and brought the whole apartment block down around their feet. Above them the sky was blue and serene but inside his body a war was raging.

'My first instinct, when I discovered that I was pregnant, was obviously to tell you,' she said, her eyes holding his.

Intense blue eyes, eyes that he had once felt himself drowning in. Eyes which now warred with his but were extremely beautiful nevertheless.

'But as you'd told me enough times that you didn't want kids, not for many years anyway, I knew it would cause another unholy row between us.' Sienna lifted her shoulders and let them drop again. 'So I decided to bring Ethan up on my own.'

And still she looked unswervingly into his eyes.

Ethan! The boy's name was Ethan! He rolled the name experimentally on his tongue. 'So why are you here now?' he asked harshly, ignoring the unease he felt at her words. It was true he had never wanted children and he hadn't been afraid to say so. But he would never have ignored a son or daughter. They would have been given his love and he would have adapted his lifestyle. He would have had to.

Could he truly have done it, though? He hated himself for admitting that he would have been truly angry that his well-ordered life had been so rudely disrupted.

'You said it wasn't for money.' He pushed his thoughts to one side for the moment. 'What other reason can there possibly be?' He did not understand her, not one little bit. The shock still hadn't worn off and despite the fact that he didn't drink he felt as though he could do with a generous slug of brandy. He needed something to restore his equilibrium.

'Because,' she began hesitantly, for the first time lowering her lids and looking slightly uncomfortable, 'Ethan's been ill, very ill.' Then she looked at him again, a proud tilt to her head, trying to hide the pain in her eyes. 'He had meningitis and I thought I was going to lose him. I realised that if he had died and you'd never even known you had a son, I would have done you an injustice.'

Adam felt a hand tighten around his heart. He felt physical pain. His son had been close to death and he had known nothing about it! The blood roared in his head and he quickly closed the space between him and Sienna, taking her shoulders, gripping them so hard that he saw her wince. But he did not care.

'What sort of a mother are you,' he growled, 'denying your son his father? Especially at a time like that. How could you? I'm presuming that he's all right now?'

Sienna nodded and swallowed hard but she did not try to pull away from him. She stood there and looked sadly into his eyes.

He saw tears, big fat tears that welled and escaped and rolled slowly down her cheeks. One half of him wanted to brush them gently away with the tip of a caring finger, the other half, the angry half, wanted to shake her to within an inch of her life.

In the end he did neither. He released her and, pulling a handkerchief from his pocket, pushed it into her hand. Then he turned away, contemplating the London skyline instead. Not that he saw anything. His eyes were blinded by fury, by disappointment, by the knowledge that his son, his own flesh and blood, had lain at death's door and he had been left in ignorance.

Adam felt a lump in his throat and an odd feeling he could not put a name to. He was not usually an emotional man, keeping an iron control over his feelings. He had a ruthless work ethic and it often crept into his home life as well. And yet Sienna had found a chink in his armour. She had hit him hard with this fresh piece of information.

Accepting the fact that he had a son had been bad enough, but to hear that he had almost died knocked him for six. How long he stood there staring into space he didn't know. It was not until he heard Sienna's tentative voice behind him that he snapped himself back to the present and turned to look at her.

Her eyes, which were sometimes more turquoise than

blue, were incredibly pale at this moment. 'I'm sorry.'
And her voice was so low as to be almost inaudible.

'Pray tell me,' he growled, breathing hard and looking
fiercely into her face. 'Would you have ever told me if—
if my son—' he wanted to say the name Ethan but he
couldn't get his head round it yet '—hadn't fallen ill?'

'I don't know,' answered Sienna quietly, still not
taking her eyes away from his. 'I honestly don't know.
But your reaction tells me that I did the right thing. You
still don't want children, do you? You still put your
work first.'

Adam didn't answer. She was so damned right that
he felt guilty.

'Ethan would have had no father figure to look up to
if we had stayed and lived with you. He'd be in bed when
you got home and you'd have left for your office before
he rose each morning. Not an ideal life for a child.'

She paused but he still didn't answer, he couldn't
answer. Every word she spoke was the absolute truth.

'But,' she continued, 'I think he should know who his
father is. Just as I think you should meet Ethan. We can
still carry on living our separate lives.'

'In other words,' he growled, hating the scenario she
had described, even though it was probably true, 'you
will now be well within your rights to claim money
from me. Just as I thought.'

'Damn you, Adam Bannerman! I want nothing from
you except a father's love for his child. I might have
known it was too much to expect.' Her eyes glittered as
she swung around on her dangerously high heels.

The next second he heard a sharp crack and Sienna
stumbled as one of her heels snapped off. He moved like

lightning and caught her before she hit the floor, wrapping his arms around her and jerking her hard against him.

He had forgotten what she felt like. And what she smelled like. A summer's evening after rain. A delicate fragrance that briefly drugged his senses. She had grown into a beautiful, sensual woman.

He felt himself grow hard and quickly thrust her away from him. Damn! Sienna had just devastated him with her news. He should be hating her, not feeling raw hunger.

Neither did he want her to know that she still had the power to arouse him in case she used it to her advantage. He still wasn't entirely sure that her sole reason for coming there was to tell him about Ethan's illness. Why do something like that after the event? There had to be more to it.

Sienna felt stupid. If she hadn't moved so quickly she wouldn't have broken her heel. What was she to do now? Walk home barefoot? Hobble? Call a taxi—which she could ill afford?

She had borrowed the shoes from a friend, now she would have to pay for a new pair. But not only had she ruined a shoe, it was her dignity as well. She should have known it was a bad idea. Adam had reacted in exactly the way she had expected him to.

She glared at him as she slipped off her other shoe and marched indoors. She did not want to spend another minute in his suffocating presence.

'Where do you think you are going?' Adam's harsh voice sounded over her shoulder.

'Home.' That one single word was as much as she could muster.

'And how far are you going to get without shoes on your feet?' he wanted to know. 'Don't be ridiculous, Sienna.'

'So what am I supposed to do?' she asked angrily, turning to face him. 'Perhaps you'd like to pay for a taxi?'

'I could do that,' he said slowly. 'Or I could take you myself. And meet this boy I am supposed to have fathered.'

His eyes met and held hers but Sienna saw red. 'Supposed?' she queried, her eyes flashing hot sparks. 'Thanks for your offer, but no thanks. If and when you two ever meet, I want to prepare Ethan first. He doesn't know about you yet.'

'So who does he think his father is?' asked Adam, a sudden fiercely quizzical look in his eyes.

Sienna shrugged. 'He's not old enough to ask questions like that.' Actually, Ethan had more than once asked her why he didn't have a daddy but she'd always managed to avoid a definite answer, thankful that there were other single mothers at the nursery he attended. She believed that it would be best to tell him when he was older, when he could understand better.

'But he will have to know one day. So why not now?' Adam insisted.

'Because I need to prepare him,' she answered sharply. 'I can't suddenly introduce his father to him. I need to talk to him first, make sure he understands why you haven't been a part of his life.'

To her annoyance Adam's lips pulled into a brief, dry smile. 'And you will tell him—what? That his father's been busy making money? Actually, it should impress him. It does most people.'

'Most people don't know the agony it causes,' flared Sienna. 'It's no life living with someone who's rarely home.' She saw a pulse jerk in Adam's jaw and knew she had hit a raw nerve. Good! He deserved it. 'I'd be obliged if you'd phone for a taxi.'

Adam closed his eyes momentarily and Sienna knew that he was warring with himself as to whether to do as she asked or insist that he run her home himself. If only she hadn't broken her stupid heel. She did not want him anywhere near where she lived. She had been protecting herself as well when she'd said that she needed to prepare Ethan.

Just as she had begun to think that Adam was ignoring her request he reached out for the phone and barked a request.

'My driver is at your disposal.'

Sienna's brows rose though she said nothing, privately wondering whether there was anything this man could not organise at a moment's notice. Money spoke. And money ruined marriages! She compressed her lips and nodded her thanks.

'Before you leave I propose we arrange another meeting. We need to talk about our son and his future.'

Sienna felt her heart drop. It had been hard coming there, it would be even harder seeing him a second time. She had dropped a bombshell, which he would pick up and dissect and come back at her with suggestions that she would not like. Even though it was to be expected, even though she was the one who had started the ball rolling, she felt her whole body grow icy cold at the thought of seeing Adam again, of talking about Ethan, arranging for them to meet.

It was something she had shied away from for the past four years. She had known that Adam wouldn't want his life disrupted. But now she had done it, and she had to face the consequences. It was quite possible that he might insist she and Ethan move in with him. How disastrous would that be? On the other hand he might be happy to settle a sum of money on them. Wasn't money his god? Wasn't it all he wanted in life? His answer to everything?

Ethan would naturally be delighted to meet his father. He wouldn't know that Adam would remain a distant figure, seen only occasionally. So it would be up to her to stand her ground, declare that they were happy living as they were. She would allow him access, but as for anything else…

'What are you suggesting?' she asked stiffly. She was missing the extra three inches her shoes had afforded her. She needed to look up now into his face and it put her at a definite disadvantage. Nevertheless, she kept her chin high and her eyes cold.

'Dinner tomorrow night?'

'I thought you always worked late?' Her response came back with the speed of a bullet.

Even though Adam smiled, it did not reach his eyes. 'I'm prepared to make an exception.'

So miracles did happen! Or would it be a one-off? She'd like to bet that he would rarely make such exceptions. In the beginning maybe, but soon he would be back to his old lifestyle and poor Ethan would be left wondering what had happened to the father he had only just met.

'Very well,' she agreed reluctantly. 'I guess there are things we need to talk about.'

'I'll send a car for you.'

Sienna raised her brows. He would send a car! Not

he would pick her up. Oh, no, he didn't have time for that. He would send his driver. It would give him extra time at the office. Damn the man. She felt like slinging his suggestion back in his face, telling him that he didn't deserve to meet his son, he would be a failure as a father and she wished that she had never set eyes on him in the first place. But, of course, she said none of these things.

'Eight o'clock. You do have someone who can look after…Ethan?'

It was the way he said his son's name, the awkward way he said it, that made Sienna realise that the shock she had given Adam went far deeper than she had at first thought. It had shifted the earth from beneath his feet and he was having great difficulty in getting used to the idea.

Had she made a mistake? A big mistake? Nevertheless, she nodded. 'I have a friend who will look after him.'

'Good.' The word came out harshly. 'Till tomorrow, then.'

Within minutes Sienna was being driven away from the riverside development, sitting like royalty in the back of a gleaming black Bentley. In the rearview mirror she could see the driver's impassive face and knew he must be wondering who she was and what sort of a relationship she had with his employer. If only he knew!

Sienna lived in a rented two-bedroom ground-floor apartment in the north London suburbs and as Adam's driver pulled up outside she could imagine what he must be thinking. Nevertheless, she held her head high and her shoes in her hand.

Once indoors she flopped down on a chair in her living room. Tiny in comparison to Adam's oversized apartment, but comfortable. She had everything she needed here. Dropping her head back, she let out a deep sigh. It had taken a lot of courage facing Adam today and where had it got her? Precisely nowhere. OK, he now knew he had a son, and he wanted to talk about him, but he hadn't been exactly enamoured by the fact.

She went over their conversation in her mind and could see no part where Adam had shown enthusiasm or pleasure. Anger that she had kept him in ignorance, yes. But he had asked no immediate questions about Ethan, hadn't enquired whether she had photographs. She had to face him again to fill him in on the details he should have asked there and then. She guessed it was shock on his part, but even so…

And the outcome was that she would have to buy her friend a new pair of shoes. She glanced at her watch. Jo would be here any moment with Ethan. She had no children of her own and was always willing to look after him, even on a Sunday afternoon.

As if on cue, she heard the sound of their voices outside the door and jumped up to let them in. Ethan ran to her and wrapped his arms around her. Jo smiled. 'How did it go?'

Her friend lived in the flat above. They had both moved in at the same time and become firm friends. 'I broke your shoe,' Sienna said with a rueful grimace. 'It was a dumb idea, wearing them. I'm sorry.'

'What were you doing? Running away?' asked Jo with a laugh. 'And don't worry about it. They were stupid shoes. I could never walk in them.'

Ethan went to his room to play and Sienna grimaced. 'As a matter of fact, yes, I was running away. It was a waste of time going there. Adam didn't want to know.

He actually accused me of trying to get money out of him. He suggested Ethan wasn't his.'

Jo drew in a swift breath. 'He didn't! What did you say?'

'I suggested DNA.'

'And?'

'He backed down a bit.'

'And the outcome is?'

'I'm meeting him tomorrow night—for dinner.'

Jo raised her brows.

'He was in shock,' declared Sienna with a wry grimace. 'We didn't talk much, he needed time to get used to the idea. Can you babysit Ethan?'

'Of course.'

'You should see his place, Jo. It's out of this world. In fact, it's on top of the world. He lives in a penthouse suite overlooking the Thames. His driver brought me home—in a Bentley no less.'

'Then you should grab him with both hands,' said her friend with a wide grin. 'Why did you ever let him go?'

'It's a long story. Do you want a cup of tea?'

Sienna dressed carefully for her dinner date with Adam. She hadn't many good clothes; as a matter of fact, the trousers and top she had worn to face him were the best things she had, bought a few months ago to attend a wedding. But she couldn't wear them again or he would think she had nothing else to wear, so she matched a black strappy top—one she sometimes used to sunbathe in, but he wouldn't know that—with a black floaty skirt that was years old but nevertheless still looked good. She fastened a silver belt around her waist, added a silver necklace and slipped into black sandals. Her hair had been brushed until it shone, and with a slick of lipstick and a dusting of eye-shadow she pronounced herself ready.

Just in time. The car arrived. The impassive driver knocked on her door. Sienna slid into the back seat, inhaling appreciatively the rich smell of leather. And almost immediately wished that she was going any-where but to meet Adam again. It was going to be an uncomfortable encounter. There would be more recrimi-nations and almost certainly the suggestion that he wanted to meet Ethan.

But she wanted to feel comfortable with Adam first. She wanted Adam to feel at ease as well. Otherwise when father and son eventually met there would be an undercurrent and she didn't want that. It needed to be a happy meeting. She wanted Ethan to be ready, but even more than that she wanted Adam to treat his son in the way that a father should, with warmth and humour— neither of which were Adam's strong points.

She wished for the hundredth time that she hadn't gone to see him. It had been a huge mistake. One she might live to regret.

'Here we are, madam.' The driver jumped smartly out of the car and opened her door. Sienna felt almost like royalty. 'Mr Bannerman is waiting inside.'

Oh, he was, was he? Sienna felt like telling the driver to take her back home. Except just at that moment Adam appeared in the doorway of the restaurant. They were in Mayfair, in the heart of London's most exclusive district. Shopping, dining, living, all for the very rich.

Sienna felt distinctly out of place. Nevertheless, she

kept her head high and her eyes firmly on Adam's. He wore a grey suit and a white shirt with a grey and red tie and he looked the epitome of the successful business-man. While she felt like the poor relation!

'Sienna, you look good. I'm glad you made it.'

Liar! On both counts. She didn't look good, she didn't feel good. At least, not right now. She had when she had set out, but she hadn't expected to be wined and dined at one of London's most elite restaurants. She had thought, she had hoped, that it would be at one of the eating places she had seen near where he lived.

Nothing had prepared her for this.

However, she smiled her acknowledgement of his compliment and when he took her arm to lead her inside she felt a crazy awareness of the man she had once been so madly in love with.

It was insanity. They were here to talk about Ethan. Adam wanted to know more about him. She had brought photographs. But here she was experiencing a reincar-nation of the feelings that had once totally consumed her.

With an effort she dashed them away, relegated them to some safe place deep in her body. Hopefully they would never be restored. She was prepared to be civil with Adam, for their son's sake, but as for anything else—she would fight it every inch of the way. He had hurt her once, and she had no intention of letting him do so again.

CHAPTER THREE

ADAM had half expected Sienna not to turn up that evening. He had thought she would despatch his driver, telling him that she had changed her mind. Her revelation that he had a four-year-old son had stunned him, sent his whole world out of kilter, made a mockery of every thought he'd ever had about not wanting children to interfere with his lifestyle.

After a night lying awake, thinking about its implications, he had not even gone in to work today—which was unheard of. His PA had had the shock of her life when he'd phoned to tell her. Without a doubt his life was going to be disrupted, changed for ever, and it would take a hell of a lot of getting used to.

After Sienna had walked out on their marriage he had buried himself ever more deeply into his work. He had been fiercely angry that she couldn't accept his need to create a good life for them. In a fit of rage after she had left him, he'd taken out other women to try to get over her.

It hadn't worked.

Despite what he saw as her failings, and despite the reason he had married her in the first place, he had missed Sienna more than he had ever thought possible, and he'd eventually felt guilty because he'd known that he hadn't given her the attention that she deserved. In equal parts he had experienced relief. Nevertheless, it had allowed him the space and time to build up his business without Sienna constantly complaining that she never saw him.

Now, though, he found it hard to believe that she had kept something of such monumental importance from him. A son! It did not make sense. It was a nightmare. How could she have done that?

His fingers curled and he wanted to wring her pretty neck.

Being a father would make a marked difference to his life. In the years since Sienna had walked out his business affairs had grown beyond even his own wildest dreams. Success had come to him and he'd embraced it with open arms. He needed no one. He was master of his own universe.

Or at least he had been.

Looking at her now, seeing how nervous she was, he realised that it must have taken a lot of courage to approach him yesterday. He had not thought of that at the time, he'd been too intensely angry to feel anything else. In fact, he was still angry, but he knew that he must hide those feelings if he was to come to any sort of an agreement with her.

'Would you like a drink before dinner?' he asked. Sienna not only looked gorgeous in black, she smelled divine too, and Adam felt a swift surge of hunger. The skinny straps of her top revealed velvety smooth, lightly tanned shoulders and the rapidly beating pulse in the long line of her throat gave away the fact that she was incredibly nervous. The swell of her breasts peeping over the top of her camisole made his fingers itch to touch, to feel their weight in his palms, to tease her nipples into tight, hard buds. As hard as he was feeling!

The crazy thing was that she was still his wife. He would be perfectly within his rights making love to her, and yet he knew that she was forbidden fruit. The sweetest fruit, the most tempting fruit.

Damn! It had been a mistake inviting her here tonight. They should have met somewhere far more austere, like in a solicitor's office, and let a third party work out the best way forward.

'No, thank you.'

Adam had almost forgotten his question. Sienna's fragrance was exciting him, her nearness drugging him. He was in danger of making a fool of himself. Instantly he channelled his thoughts away from Sienna's appearance, reminding himself that she had done the unforgivable. She had wronged him big time and he would find it difficult to forgive her—if he ever did!

They were led to their table and Sienna sat on the very edge of her chair, her back ramrod straight, her eyes wary on his, as though she was expecting him to declare that he was going to take Ethan from her.

Menus were handed to them and for a few moments they both pretended to be studying them. Twice Adam caught Sienna looking at him, her eyes quickly averted each time, and he gave a grim smile. She too was clearly wishing that she was anywhere but there.

Their food and wine orders given, Adam sat back in his seat and looked at her. 'Are you ready to talk?'

'About Ethan?' Sienna knew that the huskiness in her

voice gave away her inner tension. All day long she had been dreading this meeting, and with good reason. The stern look in Adam's eyes, the mutinous set of his chin told her that he was still furiously angry with her.

Adam nodded. 'What did he say when you told him that you'd been to see his father? Is he anxious to meet me?'

Sienna swallowed hard. 'As a matter of fact, I haven't told him yet.' She had been waiting for the right moment but had begun to have her doubts that there ever would be one. Ethan wouldn't understand her predicament. He would want to meet his father, he would be ecstatically happy, he would expect them to all live together like one big loving family. And if he discovered that Adam was wealthy enough to buy him anything he wanted, he would instantly become his best friend.

Adam's reaction was exactly as she had known it would be. He roared with rage. His eyes grew even harder, shooting swift bullets of anger across the table, making a mockery of its fine linen tablecloth and elegant silver cutlery. 'You have not told him? Why not? Why did you come to see me if it was not to acquaint me with my son?'

Sienna closed her eyes. 'I made a mistake. I—'

'*No!* I will not let you change your mind. You cannot hide him away from me any longer. I have a right to see him.'

Adam's voice roared into her consciousness, overpowering her, stunning her. She snapped her lids open and stared straight into the harsh blue depths of cold-as-ice eyes. A shiver slid down her spine, reaching out icy tentacles to every part of her body.

'And so you shall,' she said, horrified to hear the

tremor in her voice. This was not the way to react. She needed to be strong. Drawing in a deep steadying breath, she stared at him unflinchingly. 'Once I have told him about you.'

'And when will that be?' came the caustic reply. 'Today? Tomorrow? Next week? Next month? It's not good enough, Sienna. You cannot drop a bolt from the blue like that and then expect me to sit back and wait patiently. I demand to see him. In fact, I don't see why we shouldn't walk out of here right now and—'

'No!' Sienna's voice rose. 'I *will* tell him, but in my own good time. And he'll need to get used to the idea that he has a father before I introduce you. It will be a big thing for him.'

'No bigger than it was for me.' Adam's face contorted into a scowl that scored deep lines on his forehead and narrowed his eyes until they were no more than two silvery-blue slits. 'I'm still finding it hard to believe that you waited so long to tell me. You shouldn't have had to go through Ethan's illness alone. For pity's sake, Sienna, I'm his father. I deserved to be told.'

He was right, of course. And she would have felt so much better during Ethan's illness if she'd had Adam to lean on. It had been a terrible time, not knowing whether her son was going to live or die. As she'd sat for hours beside Ethan's hospital bed she had longed for Adam's strength, had told herself constantly that he ought to be here, that she should have told him about Ethan. The burden had been almost too much to bear.

Yet still it had taken immense strength to seek him out—and now she almost wished that she hadn't. His anger was doing nothing to make her feel any easier about the situation.

She was given a tiny respite while her wine was poured. Adam as usual touched nothing stronger than water. Nevertheless, he tipped his glass towards hers. 'Here's to a promising future.'

Tension tingled in the air between them. His eyes locked with hers and Sienna felt her heart beating heavily in her chest. When she had sought Adam out yesterday she had never envisaged that she would be sitting here with him tonight, drinking expensive wine, experiencing shock waves of sensation because feelings she had thought long dead were making themselves felt.

It was actually impossible not to feel. Her love for him had once been so strong that she began to wonder now whether it had ever died. Or was it because he was dynamically sexier these days? Success sat on his shoulders like an invisible cloak. And a successful man was always irresistible. At least, to some women. She had never put herself in that category but looking at Adam now, seeing the man he had become, she could not contain a frisson of awareness. It ran through her veins like molten metal, hot and swift and consuming.

'It might take Ethan time to get used to the idea that he has a father,' she said quietly. And she needed time too. Their meeting, when it happened, would be an emotional one, there would be a big change in her life. Also in Ethan's.

She didn't allow herself to think of the effect it would have on Adam. He had been absent for so long that all she could think of at this moment was herself and her son.

Clearly she hadn't been thinking straight when she

had decided to seek Adam out, and she had not reckoned on the enormous personal trauma it would cause. If only she could turn back the clock. But, of course, that was impossible. She had started this, so now had to suffer the consequences.

Their first course arrived and for a few minutes there was silence between them, Sienna cautiously tasting her vinaigrette of white asparagus with truffles. It was, of course, superb. Adam would not have taken her to a restaurant where the food was not first class. He moved in completely different circles to her these days. It was a life she could have once had but had chosen not to. And she did not particularly want her son to be brought up in this exclusive society.

'Does Ethan look like me?'

Sienna drew in a deep breath and nodded. 'I have photographs.' She reached for her bag and passed Adam an envelope.

He was silent for a few minutes as he scrutinised each photo in turn and Sienna took the opportunity to study him. She could see so much of her son in Adam that it was frightening.

Her lovable little boy was going to grow up in the very image of his father. Tall, devastatingly handsome, a real ladies' man. And she would worry herself sick over the years, wondering what sort of a life he would carve out for himself. Would he be as driven as his father? Would he put success and riches before everything else? Before human relationships? Human emotions?

There had been times when she felt that Adam had never loved her, when she had wondered why he had asked her to marry him in the first place. His goal hadn't been a happy marriage and children and she couldn't help wondering now whether his relationship with Ethan would suffer as a result.

'May I keep these?'

Sienna nodded.

'There's no mistaking that he is my son.'

The words were said calmly and with no malicious intent, but Sienna couldn't help flaring. 'If you thought that I would lie to you, you don't know me very well at all.'

'But you can surely understand? All these years and not a word.'

Their eyes met and held and Sienna was the first to look away.

'I'm going to enjoy getting to know him. I'll take him along the Thames on my cruiser, we'll fly over to Paris to see my place there and—'

'Adam Bannerman, don't you dare!' Sienna felt herself exploding. She felt sparks of white hot anger sizzling inside her head. If he thought money was the way to impress his son, he was sadly mistaken. 'A walk along the river, feeding the ducks, a ride on some swings is all Ethan needs. Even just sitting down and talking to you, finding out he has a daddy, will be the most exciting thing that has ever happened to him. You can't buy his love, Adam. Kids need companionship and love and caring. Doing little things together. And if you can't get your head round that then it might be better if he never finds out about you.'

'It's too late for that.' Adam's eyes glittered into hers. Hard eyes, cold eyes, that told her she couldn't back out now. That he would demand access to his son whether she liked it or not.

'Nevertheless, we need to set out some ground rules,' she declared sharply. 'I don't want you trying to impress him with your wealth. He needs to get to know you properly first.'

'I agree,' he answered with surprising quietness, 'and the sooner the better.'

The subject of their son drew them closer by an invisible thread. Adam's eyes had never seemed bluer. Or more fierce. Or more direct. They burned through into the very heart of her, making her wriggle uncomfortably on her seat.

'Do I have to come knocking on the door and announce myself? I could do that, you know.'

And he would, thought Sienna. He would turn up without warning and she would be left quivering with apprehension. What if the two of them didn't get on? Adam clearly knew nothing about children and their needs. He would overwhelm his son, maybe even frighten him.

'I'll tell him tomorrow,' she promised. 'But he'll need a few days to get used to the idea. I'll ring you.'

Adam threw her a look of disbelief. 'And how long will I have to wait? Maybe I should come back with you tonight and—'

'No!' yelped Sienna, then looked around swiftly to see if anyone had heard her panicked cry. Fortunately not. 'He'll be in bed, for one thing. I'll tell him tomorrow, I promise, and then I'll leave it up to Ethan.'

'What if he doesn't want to meet me?'

Sienna shrugged. 'That's something you'll have to deal with.' Though she couldn't see it happening. Ethan would be so excited he'd want to see his daddy immediately.

'If you think that I'm going to ignore my son now that you've told me about him, you're wrong.' Hard eyes met hers. 'Very wrong. But I appreciate that he'll need a little time. I'll give you two days then if I haven't heard from you I shall turn up on your doorstep.' He whisked a card out of his pocket. 'Here's my personal phone number. Use it.'

The rest of the evening passed in relative harmony. They had both chosen turbot for their main course, which was cooked to perfection, as were the accompanying vegetables. Sienna had never eaten such delicious food and she felt slightly sad that she didn't have room for dessert.

By the time Adam suggested they leave Sienna felt more relaxed than she had expected. He had regaled her with stories about his work life, some amusing, some deadly serious, and she had finished the whole bottle of wine.

Consequently she felt mellow and sleepy and when they left the restaurant she didn't even flinch when he put his arm about her waist.

'Have I told you how stunning you look tonight, Sienna?'

His voice rumbled from somewhere low in his throat, vibrating along her nerves, making her pull suddenly out of his embrace. What had she been thinking, letting him touch her like this?

Without warning his head bent down towards hers and eyes that were the colour of a sun-kissed ocean took her prisoner. And lips that she had sworn would never touch hers again captured her mouth in a kiss that revealed with devastating thoroughness that none of her feelings had gone away.

They had simply lain dormant, waiting like Sleeping Beauty for her prince to kiss her and bring her back to life. Her body felt on fire, electric sensations fizzing through veins and arteries. Emotions she had thought dead rose up and embraced the kiss, responded to it, filling her body with a hunger she had not felt for a very long time.

But it was madness. Allowing these feelings to surface was sheer madness. Adam would gain the impression that she was willing to enter into a sexual relationship and that was most definitely not the case. He had caught her unawares; it was not going to happen again. Not ever! That part of their life was over. They would be civil with each other for their son's sake, but that was all. She was not going to share his life or his bed ever again.

She jerked away, her eyes wide and fiercely angry. 'What did you do that for?'

Adam's smile was smug. 'How could I help myself? You're more beautiful than ever, Sienna. How could any man resist you? I bet they queue at your door. Is there someone special in your life at the moment?'

Sienna thought about lying and saying that there was. Except this was Adam, and no matter what had happened between them she found it impossible to lie to him. 'There is no one,' she said quietly.

'Has there been?'

'I hardly think it's any of your business. We've both been free agents these last few years.'

'We are still married,' he reminded her.

'And has that stopped you going out with other women?' she riposted, her blue eyes hard and challenging.

'Touché,' came the unblinking answer.

'So I suggest we stop asking each other invasive questions and go home.' Actually, she would have liked to know how many other women there had been in his life but since she didn't want him questioning her about her own love life, finding out that it had been non-existent, it was best they kept quiet on the subject.

'And home is?'

'If you're thinking it's back to your place, you'd better think again.'

'So I'm coming back to yours, is that it?'

Sienna shook her head, her eyes very blue and wide with horror. 'You know that's not going to happen. Where's your driver? He can take me.'

Adam grinned. 'I've given him the rest of the night off. I'll be driving you home myself.'

Sienna closed her eyes and gave an inward groan. 'That will not be necessary. I don't want you turning up at my house until I've told Ethan about you.' The very thought sent a chill through her veins. It was her worst nightmare come true. She could just imagine what would happen if Adam followed her in.

He would insist on seeing his son. And even though Ethan would probably be able to cope with finding out that he had a father after all these years, she certainly would not.

'I won't come in if you don't want me to.'

Sienna glared at Adam as he led the way towards his waiting car. Not the one she had been chauffeured in. Something small and snazzy, intimate. Not her idea of an easy ride. She would be sitting close and personal and her heart would inevitably play a tune of its own, maybe even loud enough for Adam to hear, make him aware of her plight.

When he opened the door for her and stood back, she slid silently and reluctantly into the seat. The fact that he was smiling made her even angrier, which in turn made his smile wider. It became a self-satisfied grin and she wanted to slap his face. Only good manners prevented her.

He leaned too close for comfort before he closed the door. 'Have you any idea how beautiful you look when you're angry? It makes me want to kiss you again, Sienna, feel some of that fire.'

'I don't think so,' she slammed back. 'The fire I feel is of a very different kind to how it used to be.'

'Really?' His brows lifted and he made no attempt to move out of her space. In fact, he was so close that Sienna could clearly see the outer dark ring around the incredible blue of his eyes, feel the heat emanating from him, but more poignant still was the citrus scent of his cologne, the musk of his skin. It wafted over her like a drug and she knew that if he did not move soon she would weaken.

'You know what I mean. I'm angry with you, Adam. You engineered this whole evening so that you could take me home and hopefully meet Ethan. Well, you're not going to set foot inside my house. Ethan will be in bed and I refuse to disturb him.'

'Sienna, you might be angry with me right now, but I won't go back on my word.'

Still the smile remained in place and Sienna was sorely tempted. But somehow she controlled her impulse. 'I'm glad to hear it. Let's go.'

It was with excruciating slowness that he lifted himself away from her and closed the door. For a few seconds she was allowed breathing space until he slid in beside her and the whole car was filled with his essence even more powerfully than before. Sienna closed her eyes, asking herself for the thousandth time whether she had made the biggest mistake of her life in seeking Adam out.

Never in her wildest dreams had she envisaged that she would still be attracted to him. She had thought only that he needed to know about Ethan. It had blinded her to everything else, in the same way that her love had blinded her all those years ago. But now, with her blinkers lifted, she was in grave danger. Adam still had the power to stir her innermost emotions. How cruel was destiny to inflict this on her?

The journey was accomplished in total silence, Adam seeming to know instinctively where she lived. She guessed that his chauffeur must have told him but it didn't please her. The contrast between his sumptuous penthouse suite and her modest little flat could not be ignored.

She held her breath as he pulled up outside, waiting for his comment, but none was forthcoming. Instead, he looked at her long and hard, giving nothing away now of the raw feelings she had seen earlier. 'Two days, Sienna. That is all you have. Two days. And if I do not hear from you I shall come to take my boy away.'

CHAPTER FOUR

ADAM knew that it had been the wrong thing to say. He had seen the flash in Sienna's eyes, that over-my-dead-body look. And she had every right. If he was honest with himself, he would not be able to cope with a lively four-year-old on his own. It would mean employing a nanny, which would be stupid when Ethan already had a mother who doted on him and looked after his every need.

He could, though, give him a much better lifestyle. He had been horrified when he had seen where Sienna lived and he wanted to move both her and Ethan into his own place straight away. But he knew that she would need time to get used to the idea; she wouldn't just up sticks and come. Persuasion had to be the name of the game. Persuasion and the promise of a better lifestyle.

He wondered how she had coped when Ethan had been in hospital. He couldn't bear the thought of her coming back to her miserable little flat every day after visiting him. It didn't even look a particularly safe area and it was certainly not somewhere where he wanted his son to be brought up.

Why the hell Sienna had chosen not to tell him about Ethan he did not know. What if she had never told him? What if he had never found out? It didn't bear thinking about.

He would have to make some pretty dramatic changes to his lifestyle once he had convinced her to move in with him, but he could do that. All men with families had to adjust—except they did it more gradually! They didn't have active four-year-olds suddenly thrust on them.

And he was taking things for granted! What if Sienna flatly refused to move? What would he do then? He could imagine the stubborn look on her face, the way her lovely lips would compress and her blue eyes narrow.

'Over my dead body.' He could hear her words in his head now.

Sienna was a force to be reckoned with. There was no way on this earth he could make her move in with him if she did not want to. He would have access to Ethan, she would not deny him his parental rights, but he wanted more. He wanted his son—and he wanted Sienna!

Both of them!

It hadn't struck him until this moment how much he wanted Sienna. Those few hours they had spent together this evening had made him realise exactly how much he had missed having her in his life. She had always been hot in bed, no other woman had matched up to her. But he hadn't analysed their love life until now, he'd always been too taken up with his work to think whether anyone else was a better lover.

His whole body began to ache for her. And Ethan was the one who could bring them back together! What he needed to do was tread carefully, not push her but let her think that she was doing what she wanted to do.

Adam went to bed that night and dreamt that Sienna was beside him, that they were making love, that he had never felt so physically aroused, so dynamically charged, so completely satisfied. It was hellishly disappointing, therefore, when he awoke to find the space beside him empty.

'I'm going to meet my daddy?' Ethan's eyes were as wide as saucers. 'Where is he? Did he come looking for me?'

Sienna had just fetched him from nursery and he jigged up and down with excitement. 'Not exactly, sweetheart. I went to see him. I thought it was about time you two met.'

She needed to be honest with Ethan, even if she didn't fill him in on all the details.

Adam had scared her when he had threatened to take Ethan away. She had lain awake all night thinking about it, and during the morning while Ethan was at school she ran the scenario through her head so many times that she felt dizzy.

Now there was no going back. She had set the ball rolling. Ethan was beside himself, he couldn't keep a limb still. He wanted to go and see his father now, this very minute.

Every pulse in her body throbbed, her heart beat so loudly she could almost hear it. All she had to do was arrange a meeting but what if Ethan didn't like Adam? What if Adam didn't like Ethan? What if they didn't get on? Had it been wrong of her to tell Adam after all these years? Ought she to have left things as they were?

'Can we go and see Daddy now?'

Sienna winced as she heard the easy way Ethan referred

to his father. He was so matter-of-fact about it. Almost as though he had known it would take place one day. On the odd occasions she had thought about them meeting she had expected Ethan to be shy and slow to accept.

It clearly didn't look as though that was going to happen.

She could almost picture Ethan running towards Adam and throwing himself into his arms. Of course it wouldn't be like that. They would stand off and size each other up first. Their coming together would be slow and calculated.

'Mummy! Can we?'

Ethan tugged her hand and looked up imploringly, his dark blue eyes so very much like his father's that her heart missed a beat.

'Your daddy's at work. I'll ring him tonight and arrange something. Don't forget he's a very busy man.'

But when she phoned Adam later and told him that Ethan was ready to see him, she was shocked when he suggested they come straight away.

'You're not at work?' Not for one second had she thought that he would be home.

'I finished early,' he announced abruptly. 'Just in case. How did Ethan take it?'

Sienna drew in a deep unsteady breath and was glad Adam couldn't see the pained expression on her face. 'He's excited. But I didn't mean tonight. It's still too soon.'

'Sienna,' he growled, 'if my son is ready to meet me, let's do it straight away. I'll send a car.'

'No!' Sienna winced when she heard the screech in her voice. 'I mean, I'd prefer it if you came here. I don't want Ethan being overwhelmed. Meeting you is a big enough deal without him seeing how rich you are.'

'You find my wealth obscene?'

His words were sharp and she could imagine the fire in his eyes. 'Since you put it into so many words, yes. Ethan's world is very different, and I want him to be impressed by you, not your money. You'd be his hero if he knew you could buy him anything in the world that he wanted. We have to count our pennies, Adam. I want him to grow up knowing that money has to be earned. Do you understand?'

'And you think that I haven't had to earn my money? Dammit, Sienna, I've had to work very hard to get where I am today. Nothing came easily. I admire your principles, you're clearly instilling into Ethan the value of money and that is good, but—'

Sienna did not wait for him to finish. 'Actually, I think it would be best if—'

'I'll be there in half an hour.'

The line went dead before she could protest further and Sienna suddenly realised that her son had crept up behind her.

'Does Daddy have lots of money?'

'Ethan, you should not have been listening.'

'But does he, Mummy?'

'It's not important.'

'Is he coming to see me?'

Slowly she nodded and wrapped her arms about her son. 'But he won't be staying long because it's almost time for bed. Do you understand?'

Ethan nodded, sucking his thumb, something he'd done as a baby but Sienna had thought he'd got out of it. Although he had claimed to want to meet his father, he was clearly as nervous as she was.

Ethan was looking through the window when Adam's car pulled up outside. 'Wow!' he exclaimed. 'Is this him, Mummy? Look at his car!'

It was the same black sports car that Adam had brought her home in last night and Sienna sighed. So much for her telling him not to show off. The whole street would be out looking at it in a few minutes. And she wasn't wrong. Even before he had reached her door a band of youths appeared.

She saw Adam say something to them and then hand over a note. It reminded her of a film she had seen. Pay them well and they would look after his car. This wasn't the impression she had wanted to create. Maybe it would have been better to go to Adam's place after all.

But too late now. The bell rang and she hurried to open the door, and even though she knew that all Adam was interested in was his son, she could not stop her heart from racing when they came face to face.

He wore a casual cotton sweater and jeans, and she appreciated that he'd dressed down for his first meeting with Ethan. He'd clearly thought everything through and did not want to overwhelm his son in a Savile Row suit and tie, but had he realised how much it would impact on her own senses?

It was all she could do to drag her eyes away from him. A whole range of feelings danced through her limbs as she moved back stiffly for him to enter. Why did he have to be the sexiest man on earth? Why hadn't she got over him? All these years she had thought her feelings dead and yet all it had taken was a steady look from those deep blue eyes to bring everything back to life.

Of course she must deny it, even to herself. She was

doing this for Ethan's sake. Her own feelings didn't enter into it.

'You'd best come in. You're causing quite a stir.' She stood back for him to enter. The door led straight into her living room and Ethan had disappeared. For all his excitement he was suddenly shy.

Adam brushed past her and the clean smell of him, the same musky aftershave that had aroused her senses last night, infiltrated her nostrils. Behind her back she clenched her fists.

'You are all right with this?' he enquired, pausing to look intently at her.

Would it make any difference if I wasn't? she asked beneath her breath. She hardly thought so. Adam was on a mission and nothing was stopping him.

She nodded.

'And Ethan?'

'He's anxious to meet you. I'm doing this for his sake, Adam, you do realise that?'

The look in his eyes told her that he was very well aware of the fact that she had agreed to them meeting only because she thought it was right for their son. That if it had been left to her, she would not want anything to do with him ever again.

'Where is he?'

He looked around the room and Sienna could almost imagine him comparing it to his own sleek apartment. Too tiny, too cramped, the furniture too old. She jutted her chin without realising it, already on the defensive.

Before she could answer Ethan's head appeared around the door from his bedroom, and with excruciating slowness he walked into the room, his eyes never leaving Adam's face. 'Are you really my dad?' he asked, a whole host of wonderment in his voice.

'I surely am.' Adam squatted so that his eyes were on a level with his son's, and Sienna drew in a swift painful breath. They were so much alike it was unreal. Her little man would grow up to look exactly like Adam. He would have girls flocking around him like birds after crumbs.

As she stood and watched Ethan edge slowly towards his father Sienna felt her throat close. It had been wrong not to confess to Adam that she was pregnant. He had missed all those precious first years of his son's life.

She was filled with dreadful guilt as she watched Ethan's serious face suddenly break into a wide smile.

'I always wondered what my dad looked like.'

'And do you approve?' asked Adam.

Ethan nodded, suddenly losing his voice again—until suddenly a thought struck him. 'Do you have lots of money?'

Adam glanced at Sienna and she frowned fiercely, wishing that Ethan had not overheard their conversation.

'I'm all the richer for knowing you, Ethan.' And he held out his arms.

With only a moment's hesitation Ethan walked into them, taking Adam at face value and clearly liking what he saw. Sienna guessed that whoever his father had been he would have approved.

All she could hope and pray for now was that Adam wouldn't let Ethan down. That he wouldn't disappoint his son by carrying on his exhaustive work lifestyle, leaving no time at all to spend time with him. That he wouldn't believe buying his son's love with expensive gifts would compensate for his absence.

'Mummy, can we?'

Sienna realised that while she had been deep in thought Adam and Ethan had been having a conversation. 'Can we what, sweetheart?'

'Can we go and see Daddy's house?'

'I didn't mean tonight,' said Adam quickly as he saw Sienna's swift frown. 'But perhaps the weekend?'

'It's too soon,' she retorted swiftly. 'Getting to know each other is far more important. You can visit here, or we'll go for walks, the three of us.'

Adam's frown gave away the fact that he thought she was being deliberately awkward. But Sienna stood her ground. 'You need to get to know your son before you impress him with your living standards.'

'But he's only a child, he would not understand the difference.'

Sienna's brows shot upwards. 'Really? I think it might be best if we talked about this some other time.'

He finally got the message and for the next half-hour Adam played with Ethan, who dragged him into his bedroom to show him his toys. Sienna was actually surprised by how good Adam was with his son. She had expected awkwardness, an inability to come down to Ethan's level, and yet he lay sprawled on the floor, letting his son climb all over him. They played battles, and had races with his cars, until Sienna decided enough was enough.

'Much as I hate to interrupt your fun, it's past Ethan's bedtime.' She stood in the doorway, her arms folded, but she was not feeling as tense as she had earlier. Her fears that Adam would let his son down had been unfounded, although she knew that there was still a long way to go.

Adam ruffled Ethan's hair. 'Time for bed, I guess. It's been fun, Ethan. We'll do it again.'

'Can't you stay and put me to bed?' he asked plaintively.

Adam looked at Sienna and saw the mutinous set of her face. It looked as though he had already outstayed his welcome. 'Not tonight, but another time perhaps.'

'Will you come again tomorrow?'

This time Adam did not look at Sienna but he sensed her objection. It was telling him loud and clear not to overstep the mark. 'Maybe, if Mummy agrees, we could go out somewhere at the weekend?'

'Yes, please,' said Ethan immediately. 'We could go to the park. You can push me on the swings.'

'We'll see,' declared Sienna. 'Now, tidy your room before bed.'

'Can Daddy help?'

'Daddy is leaving,' she said pointedly.

'But I'll be back,' Adam called. 'Goodnight, son.'

'Night-night, Daddy.' Ethan darted across the room and wrapped his arms around his father's legs, and Adam felt a curious sensation that he had never felt before. Pride and love. It welled in his throat and threatened to choke him, and at the same time he felt a resurgence of anger towards Sienna for keeping him in ignorance of his son for all these years.

When Ethan was safely back in his room with the door closed, Adam turned to Sienna. 'I've missed out on so much. I have a lot of making up to do.' He did not tell her that when he had first seen his son, when he had seen the strong family likeness, he had felt a pang of guilt for thinking that Sienna had been lying.

It had been wrong to doubt her. He should have known that Sienna was too honest and decent to do anything like that.

'Which you can't do all at once,' she said softly. 'No matter what you're thinking, you need to take things slowly. You can't overwhelm him.'

Adam frowned. 'He didn't seem overwhelmed. He accepted me instantly.' What was Sienna trying to say? That she was going to regulate his visits? Once a week only? Once a month perhaps? This was his son they were talking about, his own flesh and blood. He would see him whenever he wanted to.

Sienna looked totally gorgeous with her face aflame and her eyes shooting sparks. He was so angry with her and yet at the same time he wanted to kiss her. He marched across the room and the intent in his eyes must have been clear because she moved away, heading for the door instead, her hand on the handle.

'Dammit, Sienna, I'm not going yet. We need to talk.'

'And I need to put Ethan to bed.' Her eyes flashed beautiful outrage.

'He's a fine boy, Sienna. You've done well. But he needs a man in his life.

'I think you should both move in with me, as soon as it can be arranged.' It was the best solution. He hated the thought of them living here. He wanted to take them away, give them a lifestyle more suited to his wife and child.

Sienna's eyes widened into enormous orbs of disbelief. 'If we did that, Adam, I'm afraid Ethan would be disappointed by the amount of time you spend at work.'

'I would change.'

Sienna sniffed her disbelief. 'With your track record?

Don't forget I had a father like you. He was always at work, I rarely saw him as I was growing up. It's why my mother divorced him. I don't want that for Ethan. I'd rather he had no father than one who neglected him.'

Adam felt Sienna's anger. It shot over him in hot waves and he had never seen her look more beautiful. He wanted to pull her into his arms and kiss her senseless. Dared he try it? Would it work? Or would it make things worse? He guessed the latter.

'I could learn to delegate.'

'And I'm expected to believe that?' Sienna's beautifully shaped eyebrows rose dismissively. 'You never took time off for me, no matter how I begged or complained. Why should I believe that you'd do it for Ethan?'

'Because circumstances are different now.' He drew in a steadying breath. He wanted to fight anger with anger but knew that it would get him nowhere, so forced himself to remain calm. 'I'm established now, I can afford to take time off.'

Sienna tossed her head, her blue eyes flashing. 'You didn't think it important enough to save our marriage. And yet you'd do it for Ethan. Have you any idea how that makes me feel, Adam?'

Adam kept his temper—just, but his fingers curled into fists. 'Sienna, Ethan is a great boy and I want to get to know him better, but I want you to be a part of my life as well.'

A flash of blue was Sienna's response. He had hoped she would say yes, he had hoped she would realise that it would benefit both of them. But her answer was clearly negative. She was telling him that he didn't stand a chance. Well, he would see about that. There were always ways and means.

'Goodnight, Adam.'

It was the definite way she said it that made him kiss her. He hadn't meant to act so soon but how dared she dismiss him just like that? And once he had the taste of her on his lips, once he felt the soft warmth of her body, he could not contain himself.

He tightened his arms around her and deepened the kiss, feeling a surge of raw hunger. Sienna was all and more than he remembered. She smelled divine, like a breath of spring, and his heart began a manic beat.

Sienna felt as though every atom of air had been drawn out of her body. What was she doing, allowing Adam to kiss her when she was so angry? Why hadn't she opened the door and pushed him out? Now she was in danger of responding, and what a fatal mistake that would be.

But could she help herself? Heck, no. Her body had a mind of its own and her lips parted beneath his. Memories returned of kisses in the honeymoon stage of their marriage, deep passionate kisses that had led to hectic love-making.

Whoa! She forced herself to stop there. Would allowing this kiss lead back to the same place? She dared not let it. It was too dangerous. She did not want a repeat of the unhappiness she had felt when Adam had been absent. And she did not want Ethan to experience it either.

At this very moment his father was his new idol, but if Adam let him down then there would be tears and arguments, and it would be the same old thing all over again.

With a strength born of desperation, she pushed Adam away. 'This isn't part of the deal.'

'You can deny yourself what you so clearly want?' he questioned softly, though she saw something hard in his eyes, something that scared the hell out of her.

'I don't want it,' she claimed loudly. 'I want only my son to get to know his father. I want nothing for myself.'

Adam's brows rose slowly, sceptically. 'Doesn't Ethan's happiness coincide with your own? Don't the two come together?'

'That was not my intention when I sought you out.' But heaven help her, something was going on inside her body over which she had no control.

When she had first met and fallen in love with Adam she had found herself thrown into a kaleidoscope of feelings from which there had been no escape. Even when she had walked out on him, it had been tough love. And it had taken almost all of the time they'd been apart for her to reach the decision that she was no longer in love with him.

And now this! The heat in her body was overwhelming. Adam's kisses had re-ignited the flame that had once burned so brightly that it hurt, and it was going to take every ounce of her willpower not to give herself to him again.

'Then it remains to be seen.' There was a glint in Adam's eye as he spoke, as he opened the door and headed outside.

Sienna closed it quickly, holding a hand over her thudding heart, but she could not help a covert glance through the window.

Adam was laughing and joking with the youths who had guarded his car. He handed them another note.

Sienna shook her head. He earned big money but it

meant nothing to him. It had definitely been a wrong move going to see him. Her own life and Ethan's would never be the same again.

CHAPTER FIVE

SIENNA'S dream was disturbed by Ethan jumping on her bed. 'Wake up, Mummy, wake up.'

She opened her eyes sleepily. She had been dreaming about Adam, about the row they'd had that had ended their marriage. It was so vivid in her mind that she could recall it word for word...

'It's absurd the hours you put in at work.' Sienna had been virtually dancing on the balls of her feet. 'I've had enough. You never listen to what I say. If you don't change I'm going to leave you, it's as simple as that.'

Adam's anger had risen as quickly as hers. 'Don't you dare criticise me when I'm only doing it because of you.'

'Because of me?' Sienna had echoed, her eyes widening. 'Adam, I couldn't care less if we didn't have a penny. It's a simple excuse but it doesn't work. You're doing it for yourself and no one else.' Her body had been stiff with rage, her eyes almost spitting bursts of fire. They'd had this same argument over and over and it hadn't made one iota of difference.

'It doesn't become you, Sienna, screaming at me like this.'

'And neglecting me doesn't become you either,'

she'd snapped. 'Anyone would think you didn't love me any more.'

When he hadn't answered, when he hadn't even looked at her, Sienna had turned and stormed out of the room. And the next morning she had packed her bags.

'Ethan, Mummy's tired. Go back to bed.' She had been disturbed by her dream and wanted a few moments to herself. Their marriage had indeed been stormy and she had congratulated herself on getting out of it.

But now Adam was back in her life, threatening to turn it upside down again. And unhappily she had brought it all on herself.

What if Adam was an absentee father, the same as he'd been an absentee husband? The thought stayed with Sienna and she was not surprised when a few days went by and she heard nothing more from him.

Ethan kept asking where he was. 'Your father's a very busy man,' she told him. 'He has a big business to run.'

'But I want to see him again.'

'And you shall, but we must wait for him to find the time.' What a thing to have to tell her son, but it was true. This was typical Adam. He couldn't even spare a few minutes to pick up the phone.

It was totally unexpected, therefore, when he turned up on Friday evening and invited them to spend the weekend with him. Sienna was furious. Hadn't she already told him that it was far too soon for anything like that?

'I don't think so,' she said. 'We can go out tomorrow if you like, just for the day, for a walk somewhere, a picnic perhaps, but—'

'Oh, Mummy. I want to see Daddy's house.'

Sienna hadn't realised that Ethan was behind her, she had thought he was playing in his room, and although every instinct told her to refuse, she took one look at her son's face and knew that she could not disappoint him.

If Adam had phoned first she could have told him that it was a no-starter, but, no, he had to come in person, knowing that she would be unable to let Ethan down when they were standing face to face.

'I would have appreciated some warning.' Anger flared in her eyes and she felt like pushing him out and slamming the door on him. Instead, for Ethan's sake, she tried to keep some semblance of sanity.

'There was always the chance that you'd say no.'

'Exactly.'

'But now the matter's settled, I suggest you pack a few things and we'll be on our way.'

Again her eyes flashed, especially when he was looking so smug and satisfied. Without another word she marched through to her bedroom, throwing clothes into a holdall, doing the same for Ethan, then returning to stand in front of Adam.

Her eyes were filled with resentment and anger but he chose not to notice, smiling broadly instead. Ethan, too, was jigging up and down with excitement.

Adam's Bentley was waiting outside, his chauffeur standing beside it. Ethan's jaw dropped but he said nothing. It was so unusual for him to be at a loss for words that Sienna knew he was overwhelmed, and sitting between them his eyes were everywhere.

She was actually glad that Ethan shielded her from Adam. Despite her anger, she was very much aware of him. There was some infinitesimal spark inside her that refused to die out. She had sworn to herself after her dream, the dream that had reminded her of all that had happened, all the bad times, that she would not let herself get aroused by him again.

But how impossible was that?

He was still incredibly handsome and sexy. The first moment she had ever clapped eyes on him she had known that this was the man she had wanted to marry.

And she had never fallen out of love with him!

Oh, God, was that really true? Was she still in love with him? The answer was a miserable yes, though she would never admit it to Adam. It scared her to admit it to herself. He would never change. He might try, he might even succeed for a few weeks, but he would inevitably go back to his old ways and where would that leave her and Ethan?

He would strive to persuade them to move in with him, and it really would be tempting. But wise? She did not think so. All he wanted was his son. And if she was a means to an end then...

She must keep a level head on her shoulders, not let Ethan's enthusiasm or Adam's sweet-talking change her mind.

Watching her son's reaction as they approached Adam's home, seeing the way his eyes widened as they passed through the gates, watching the expression on his face as they were whisked smoothly up in the high-speed lift, she knew that these first impressions were what she had feared.

But Adam was heedless of the long-term effect this might have on his son. He smiled each time he saw Ethan's changing expression and over the top of his head he smiled even more complacently at Sienna.

And Sienna was yet further dismayed when she saw the toys that were piled up for Ethan in one of the bedrooms. It looked as if Adam had bought the entire shop.

'What are you doing, Adam?' she asked fiercely when Ethan was out of earshot. 'Are you trying to buy his love? You could have given him a drum or a football and he'd have been just as happy.'

'I have a lot of making up to do.'

'If you think spending money on him is the answer, think again. It's stupid. He wants you, not your money. Haven't we already discussed this?' She had been afraid that he would splash his money around to impress his son and she'd been right.

'You're incredibly sexy when you're angry, do you know that, Sienna?'

Her eyes flashed her displeasure, her whole body stiffening and rejecting him. 'This isn't about you and me.'

It was like water off a duck's back. Adam smiled, completely unperturbed by her words. 'You have the most amazing eyes. They tell me what your voice doesn't, do you know that? And at this moment they're telling me that you're wondering whether I'm going to kiss you again.'

Sienna shot him a blast of anger. 'Trying to butter me up will not change my mind about how I think your relationship with Ethan should go. I want you to stop believing that you can buy his love. It has to be earned. He wants a father. Not presents, not fancy cars, not houses that look as though no child would ever dare play in them, but a father's companionship. Can you give him that?'

By the time she had finished Sienna's breathing was all over the place but she didn't care.

But he either hadn't been listening or he chose to ignore what she was saying. He had edged closer without her even realising it, his eyes darkening and narrowing, and if she didn't move now all would be lost. For how could she not succumb to his kisses when her body was betraying her harsh thoughts? It knew only that this man could take her on an emotional roller-coaster ride, a ride that would tilt her into a world where nothing mattered except feeding her senses.

And what senses!

Even standing here, warring with him, every one of these senses was on red alert. It was as though the time they had spent apart had never happened. She actually wanted his kisses, her body called out for them, and yet the sane part of her mind warned her that to do so would be a huge mistake. One she might later regret.

But did she listen to the sane part of her mind? No! When Adam was so close that she could see each one of his incredibly long eyelashes individually, when she could, if she so desired, reach out and touch his jaw where already new growth was showing, when she could hear his breathing and see the sudden flare in his eyes, it was too late to back away.

A warm hand curved behind her neck and eyes that she'd once felt herself drowning in burned into hers, asking the question but not waiting for an answer.

Sienna's heart drummed an age-old rhythm. Each beat built up her senses, and when Adam's lips claimed hers she was totally ready. It was like much-needed rain after a dry summer. It was like finding water in the desert. It fed her inner needs and against her better judgement she returned his kiss.

It dived deep into the heart of her, arousing senses that had long lain dormant, sending thrill after thrill through her body so that she tingled and sizzled and did not want him to stop.

It was Ethan who put a stop to it, running into the room to show his father a toy boat. It did not faze him that they were kissing—he merely tugged at his father's sleeve. 'Daddy, I have a boat just like this at home.'

With her cheeks flaming, Sienna was thankful that her son saw nothing wrong. She guessed he thought it was what all mummies and daddies did. But it brought her to her senses, made her realise that spending any length of time with Adam was dangerous.

'Then you're a very lucky boy to have two boats,' said Adam. He too appeared untroubled by the interruption, though he did look darkly at Sienna, as if to say that they would carry the kiss on at another time. 'And guess what, Ethan? I have the real thing.'

'You do?' Ethan's eyes widened into two enormous orbs. 'A real boat?'

'A real boat.'

'Can I see it? Can I go on it? Where is it? Can we go now?'

'*Ethan!*' Sienna was appalled by Ethan's questions. 'You cannot go on your father's boat. I will not allow it. You're too young.'

'I can swim, Mummy, if you're frightened I'll fall into the water.'

'Of course you can, but it's different in the river from the swimming baths. Go back and play.'

Ethan looked crestfallen but did as he was told and as soon as he was out of earshot Sienna turned on Adam. 'You shouldn't have told him. Haven't I told you not to flash your wealth in front of him? You'll make him impossible to handle.'

'And why would that be?' Adam's thick dark brows drew together over eyes that were suddenly fierce. 'He'll find out one day, why not now?'

'Because it's too much too soon. He's only four, Adam. He doesn't really understand.'

'Exactly. Therefore I don't see what you're worrying about. Now, what were we doing before we were interrupted?' A faint smile twisted the corners of his lips as he moved in on her again, but Sienna was too quick for him.

If he thought she was going to slip back into a relationship with him because of Ethan, he was sorely mistaken. She might still fancy him like mad but she could get over that. She'd done it once, why not again?

Except that now, because of Ethan, he was a permanent part of her life. She could not introduce Ethan to his father and then never let him see him again. Somehow she had to ignore the emotions that flowed through her like a raging river. She had to pretend they did not exist. Adam was Ethan's father. Full stop. Not her lover any more. Just Ethan's father.

'It's time for Ethan to have a bath and go to bed,' she declared, hoping her voice sounded normal.

Earlier Adam had shown her the bedrooms. One room with twin beds that he thought Ethan could use, a room with a double bed, both rooms having their own bathroom, and his own impressive suite with its king-size bed and not one but two bathrooms and an inter-connecting dressing room.

Talk about excess, she had thought, though she had wisely kept her words to herself.

Ethan was totally impressed that he had his very own bathroom and Sienna thought that she might have problems getting him to sleep in a strange bed. But, no, he dropped off straight away, after persuading his father to read him a bedtime story.

Adam appeared a little awkward at first but soon his voice relaxed and he even managed to put on different voices for each character.

'Thank you,' she said. 'Ethan loves being read to.'

'He's a good child. You've brought him up well, Sienna.'

His voice dropped to a low husky growl and alarm bells went off in Sienna's head. Things were moving a lot faster than she had intended. It felt like only yester-day that she had faced him and told him that he had a son. Now they were staying with him and she was afraid that a weekend would lead to something more.

'I only wish that I'd known about him from the be-ginning.'

Then you shouldn't have ignored me and spent all your hours at work, thought Sienna. He had no one to blame but himself.

'But I intend to make up.'

Her eyes flashed a warning. 'All he wants is your love.'

'And how about you, Sienna? What do you want?'

The steady look in his eyes, the husky tone of his voice, warned her that she needed to be careful. 'I want

Ethan to be happy. I don't want him to get too close to you and then you let him down.'

'You think I'd do that?' Blue eyes darkened and narrowed, his chin lifted with familiar arrogance.

'You let me down and it destroyed our marriage.'

'Only because you didn't understand. You never made allowances. There was a reason I—'

Sienna's eyes flashed as fiercely as his. 'The fact was you neglected me. And if you dare do that to Ethan, I'll make sure you regret it to the end of your days.'

'There is one way you can ensure I don't neglect him.'

Sienna's heart drummed a little more quickly. 'And that is?' She knew what he was going to say and she had her answer ready.

'You can move in with me.'

'Not in a million years.' The words came out as quick as a flash. 'I've had one dose of living with you, Adam. It didn't work then and it wouldn't work now. Besides you can't cage Ethan in an apartment. It wouldn't be fair.'

'Then I'll buy a house with a garden. Problem solved.' He folded his arms and looked at her down the length of his nose.

If only it were that easy! Adam really had no idea what this was all about. It wasn't about them moving in with him. Despite what Sienna had said, she now knew that this wasn't about Ethan any more. It was about the two of them.

Their relationship.

Adam was as sexy as hell and there was clearly still an incredibly strong attraction between them. They would be spending more and more time together because of Ethan, and if things continued the way they were, Sienna knew, deep in her heart, that it wouldn't be long before she was sharing his bed again. But there was more to life than making love. Adam could declare as many times as he liked that he would change his working habits but she knew differently. Words were easy. Doing it was another matter.

He enjoyed the cut and thrust of business, it was his whole life, it meant more to him than a wife, and it would inevitably mean more to him than a child. Even though he would say he was doing it for Ethan. To provide for his future.

Heavens, he was wealthy enough never to work again. But work was his first love and his last love. She and Ethan would always come a poor second.

'I suggest we take things one step at a time, Adam,' she said carefully. 'Let's see how we get on. This is all very new for Ethan. He's excited now but—'

'But you're still afraid I'll let him down? Maybe not today or tomorrow, not even next week or next month, but in a year's time you're wondering what sort of a father I'll be?'

There was steel in his voice, which made her shiver. Nevertheless, she kept her tone firm and her eyes hard. 'You're forgetting I know your track record.'

'We also had a track record in love-making.' His voice changed, softened, and he took a step towards her.

Sienna held her breath. It would be so easy to melt into his arms, to let him kiss her senseless and carry her off to bed. That huge bed with its tempting gold and cream quilt. Not a man's colour, though it creatively relieved the brown carpet and curtains.

It was a sumptuous bedroom and everything inside

her quivered at the thought of sharing it with him. Their earlier kiss, brief though it had been, had rolled back the years, made her aware of the power Adam had once wielded over her. And when he looked at her from beneath those thick dark brows, the sort of look that would turn any woman's bones to jelly, she knew that that power had not waned.

It felt like a trickle of electricity running through her body, sparking and tingling and making her want to feed from his kisses. Which was crazy, considering their circumstances. But if he touched her now, if he attempted to kiss her, she would not be able to stop him. Instead, she would go up in flames.

'That was then, Adam. Things are very different now.' Somehow she kept her voice steady and indifferent.

Adam's lips quirked. 'A pity. It's been a long time since anyone shared my bed.'

Sienna let her brows rise upwards in a searching question.

'You think I've had a stream of women in your wake? Not so, Sienna. I've dated, yes, but I've brought no one here. This is my sole preserve—though I'm willing to share it with you.'

'It's a pity, then, that I don't want to.' Sienna kept her eyes steady on his.

'Maybe I could persuade you?'

Another step and he was so close that she could feel the warmth of him, see the intent in his sensational blue eyes, smell the rich male scent of him. It was a heady cocktail. A dangerous one.

She closed her eyes in self-defence, not wanting to see him, not wanting to feel. And was totally shocked when his arms slid behind her back and his mouth claimed hers all in one swift, devastating movement.

Unable to move or speak, unable to stem the tide of hunger that shot through her, Sienna kept her eyes tightly closed and allowed herself the luxury of feeling Adam's power, of experiencing a sensational explosion of feelings so strong that they stunned her.

Crazily she did not want him to let her go, she wanted to spend the night in his arms and in his bed, making amazing love. Adam had always been an innovative lover but she imagined that he would have improved, that he would take her to places she had never been before.

And her body cried out for fulfilment.

'So what is your answer, Sienna?' Adam lifted his mouth from hers and Sienna immediately felt that he had deserted her.

She shot her eyes wide. His kiss had disturbed her senses, made her forget everything except the thrill of the moment.

If he was going to carry on kissing her like this, turning her body into a mass of sensation that could only be relieved by making love, her answer had to be yes.

But if his intention was to win her over solely so that he could have access to his son, she would be foolish. There was no way on this earth that she was going to let Adam use her.

She pulled swiftly away from him, darts of sudden hostility shooting from her eyes. 'I need my head examined.' She needed more than that, she needed brain surgery. How could she have let him kiss her?

There were dark, dangerous thoughts going through

his head and if she wasn't careful she would play straight into his hands.

To her amazement Adam laughed, a cruel laugh that sliced into her heart, and his face was inscrutable as he moved away. 'Drinks on the terrace?'

Sienna wanted to be anywhere but with Adam. He had tested her and humiliated her, and unfortunately there was no escape. It might be a luxury apartment but there was no place to run. She was committed to spending the weekend with him, whether she liked it or not.

CHAPTER SIX

SIENNA chose to sleep in the same room as Ethan. Here she was safe. Here she could relax. Adam's continual assault on her senses spun her out of control. But also served as a timely warning.

It was total insanity letting him see that she was still painfully weak where he was concerned and she needed to be careful, to be on her guard at all times, to make sure that it did not happen again. Otherwise he would have her back in his bed. Not because he loved her, she knew that there was no chance of that, but because he wanted Ethan and he knew that they came as a pair. In effect he would have the best of both worlds.

After breakfast they walked along the river, they fed the ducks, they lunched at a riverside restaurant, and Ethan never stopped talking.

He was a welcome diversion. This was what the weekend was supposed to be about. Ethan and Adam getting to know one another.

To give him his due, he was very good with Ethan. They had long conversations and he didn't try to impress his son again by splashing his money around.

It was not until they got back to his apartment and

Ethan shot away to play with his new toys that she found herself once more alone with Adam.

He had discovered what a joy Ethan was. How good it felt to have a son, his own flesh and blood. A little companion. Sienna had denied him that pleasure and he made no attempt now to hide his resentment. 'I've enjoyed today with Ethan,' he said, 'more than I thought possible. But I'll never forgive you for keeping him a secret.'

'Perhaps I should have told you sooner, but do you remember what our marriage was like, Adam? What do you think you would have done if I'd told you I was pregnant?' Sienna's brows drew into a swift frown. 'Don't answer that, allow me to. You'd have been angry, furious, in fact. You'd have said it was all my fault. You weren't ready for children, or marriage for that matter.'

'Maybe I wasn't,' he agreed, ignoring the hint of guilt at the back of his mind. 'Nevertheless, you stole his first years from me, Sienna. I've missed out on seeing him learn to walk, to say his first words, all the cute little things that babies do.'

'Cute little things?' echoed Sienna, her eyes flaring. 'When have you been interested in cute? You had time for no one, Adam Bannerman. No one, not even me.'

'So how did we produce a baby if I had no time for you?'

She tossed him a scornful glance, one that could have frozen water. 'Because like all men there's one thing that you cannot do without. But rest assured, Adam, it will never happen again.'

Her demeanour, her whole attitude, fired him up and made him want to kiss her despite his anger. He knew that to do so would be fatal, but it did not stop him

thinking about it. Sienna had grown spectacularly beautiful over the years. She had an added confidence about
her now, a haughty look. He loved the way she tilted her
chin, the way she challenged him. She'd been lovely
before but the in-between years had turned her into one
very stunning woman.

Her rich chestnut hair seemed to have thickened and
he was sorely tempted to run his fingers through it.
Snatch her face close to his and kiss her fiercely. Her
blue eyes were clear and bright and they danced with
fire. Hell, he could feel himself hardening.

It had definitely been a mistake suggesting they
spend the whole weekend with him. He'd arranged it for
his son's sake, because he wanted to get to know Ethan,
but the power of Sienna was in danger of overriding it.

He had never expected to feel like this about her.
He'd been as angry as hell when she had told him about
Ethan, so angry he could have throttled her with his bare
hands, and, yes, he still was angry. But now that he'd
spent time again with Sienna he was beginning to realise
how stupid he had been to let her go.

And stupid also to think that there might be a future
for them, because she'd made it crystal clear that it was
not what she wanted.

Even though she responded to his kisses!

There was certainly more to Sienna than he had ever
thought. Not only had she improved in looks, she had
more guts, more of everything, in fact.

Sienna did not wait for Adam's answer but walked
away from him, out onto the terrace where she could look
out over the Thames, throwing over her shoulder as she
did so, 'Why don't you go and play with your son?'

She wished that her own body was as reassuringly calm as some of the boats making their way slowly towards their goal. Their earlier kiss still haunted her. It had been madness, letting it happen. On the other hand, it was a timely warning. One she must remember.

When Adam spoke softly in her ear she jumped because she had believed, had hoped, in fact, that he was safely with Ethan. She needed this breathing space to come to terms with what was happening. Had he deliberately trodden softly? Was he trying to home in on her thoughts?

She turned round swiftly—and found herself trapped between his arms. He was not touching her, not even a hair from his strong powerful forearms caressed her body. But she was his prisoner nevertheless, his hands either side of her on the safety rail. Judging by the way her body reacted, though, he may as well have been touching her.

The musky scent of his skin filled her nostrils and with her heartbeats accelerating to a million times a minute, a flood of heat gathering speed through her limbs, she stood in total shock, her eyes locked with his. 'What do you think you are doing? Ethan might—'

'He's asleep.'

'What?'

'I think his walk wore him out. He was lying on the floor with his toy boat in his hand. I've lifted him onto the bed.'

'I'd best go to him.' Sienna attempted to push past Adam but he was having none of it. He caught her arm and swung her to face him.

'He's fine, Sienna, you worry too much.'

She worried! What did he think mothers did? 'How

dare you tell me whether I worry or not, Adam, when you know nothing about children? When I've spent the last four years caring for Ethan, worrying about him. When I sat by his hospital bed for days and nights, not knowing whether he was going to live or die. They were the worst days of my life. If Ethan had died, I would have wanted to die too. So don't tell me not to worry.'

Adam's face became harshly angular, his skin stretched so tightly across his cheekbones that it looked as though it had been carved out of stone. And she had no idea what was going through his mind.

'You didn't have to be alone,' he said, his voice coldly damning now. 'You could have told me. I could have shared your fear. I would have been there beside you. Dammit! You should have contacted me.'

Words were easy, she thought. It would have taken an earthquake to drag Adam away from his business affairs. She certainly couldn't imagine him sitting for hours in hospital. His eyes, which were sometimes incandescently blue and dangerous, were now dark and accusing. His hand on her arm like a band of steel.

He didn't care about her, thought Sienna. It was only Ethan. She could walk out of here right now and he'd be perfectly happy—so long as she left her son behind. Fuming, she twisted herself free.

She went into Ethan's bedroom, pulling up short when she saw him safely curled in the middle of the bed. He looked such an angel when he was asleep, one hand outstretched on the pillow, his dark hair tousled. Adam had pulled a sheet over him and he hadn't stirred. Her little man! How she loved him.

'Are your fears allayed?' Adam's voice came softly

over her shoulder, all the harshness suddenly gone out of it.

Sienna spun around and almost cannoned into him. She nodded, not trusting her voice.

When she walked from the room Adam followed. 'We've created a unique little boy.'

'Yes.' It was all she could manage.

'But he needs both parents.'

Shock waves rippled through her. Her words rattled into the air between them when she spoke. 'We need to do this gradually, Adam. Ethan's all over you at the moment, but it's new. Wait until he finds you're always at work whenever he wants to tell you something or do something exciting with you. The novelty will wear off.'

'You're not even giving me a chance.' The disapproval in his voice did nothing to calm her down.

Sienna felt her hackles rise. 'If you think I'm going to repeat this weekend, think again, Adam. It's turning into a nightmare.'

'Not from my point of view.' There was still a hard glint in his eyes. And his lips pulled into a straight grim line, his whole demeanour one of superb confidence.

Sienna felt like taking a swipe at him. 'You should be where I'm standing.'

Cold eyes condemned her, telling her clearly that if he had to he would fight for Ethan, and Sienna felt ice trickle down her spine, spreading its fingers until her whole body was frozen. He did have rights, she was aware of that, but even so...

She was the first to turn away, to walk stiffly out of the room, to turn her back on this man who had broken her heart once and looked set to do it again.

If only there was somewhere to run! She was effec-tively his prisoner here in this chillingly perfect apartment. And she had another day to go before they went home.

Sunday followed a similar pattern. Sienna had slept in Ethan's room again and now they were on the London Eye. She pointed out St Paul's Cathedral to Ethan. Big Ben and the Houses of Parliament. But he was more interested in the Thames itself.

'Look, Daddy, boats!' he exclaimed excitedly, pointing into the distance. 'Which one is yours?'

'It's the furthest away,' answered Adam, winking at Sienna. 'Can you see it?'

'I think so,' said Ethan, screwing his eyes up and con-centrating hard.

Sienna knew that she was not going to hear the end of Adam's boat. Ethan would go on and on about it and wouldn't be satisfied until he had actually seen it close up and been on board. But it was not going to happen today. Once they had finished their ride and had had lunch, they were going home. She would insist on it.

But things did not work out the way she wanted. They had lunch at the riverside restaurant near Adam's apartment and afterwards he insisted on taking them both to see where he worked.

Actually, she was curious. Even when they had been together, she had never been to his offices. He had never invited her and she had never asked. So why he wanted her to see it now she had no idea. To impress, she guessed. Though Ethan was too young and she already knew that it would be state of the art.

She wasn't mistaken.

It was a different address from the one he had used

when they had first married. He had gone up in the world, of course. His offices were on the top floor—yet again—with views over London equally as impressive as those from the London Eye.

Everything was operated by the touch of a button and Ethan was in his element. Mirrors on the walls turned into screens for video conferencing. Monitors popped up out of desks. All the sort of stuff she had seen in futuristic movies.

'It's very nice,' she managed.

'Is that all you can say?'

Sienna shrugged. 'What do you want me to say? Your wealth doesn't impress me, Adam, and it never has. I wanted a man who cared for me, who thought more of me than he did his work. If you want my opinion, I think you're happier married to your work than you ever were to me.'

'So why didn't you divorce me?'

Sienna shrugged. It was a fair question, something she had occasionally asked herself. 'I didn't need a divorce. I had no other man in my life.'

Adam's brows rose. 'So if anyone asked where your husband was, what did you say?'

She would have liked to declare that she had told everyone she had walked out on him because he was more in love with his job than with her, but she didn't. She would have liked to say that she had told everyone that the love had gone out of their marriage, but she didn't. She would have even liked to say that she'd told everyone he was the lousiest husband in the world, but she didn't.

'I simply said that it didn't work out.'

A frown furrowed the space between his eyes, as if he had expected, wanted even, a better explanation than that.

'I don't believe in airing my dirty linen in public. What did you tell people? That I didn't understand you, that I didn't approve of your need to work so hard?'

'Something like that,' he agreed easily. *'Ethan!'*

They had both been so busy niggling at each other that they hadn't seen Ethan climb on a chair. They knew nothing until he fell over backwards and his head hit the floor.

Sienna screamed.

Adam bounded towards him.

She saw blood—and almost fainted herself.

It was during the next frantic few moments that Adam became her strength. She did not remember him phoning for an ambulance, she remembered nothing except cradling Ethan in her arms, trying to stem the flow of blood with the handkerchief Adam had swiftly pushed into her hand, soothing him when he cried that his head hurt.

In the ambulance he was sick, twice, and when they got to the hospital they were immediately taken into an examination room where he was sick again. She continued to hold the pad to Ethan's head and talked to him constantly because she was afraid of concussion. 'Where is everyone?' she kept asking, almost out of her mind with worry.

'They're very busy,' answered Adam, trying to look reassuring when she knew that he was as concerned as she was. In fact, he probably blamed himself for letting Ethan play on the chair, for even taking them to his office.

A nurse came to check on Ethan and confirmed that

they were doing the right thing in keeping him awake. 'A doctor will be with you shortly.'

'Can't you do anything?' Sienna asked Adam crossly when several more minutes went by and there was no sign of anyone.

'Relax, Sienna,' he answered calmly. 'He is in the best place and if they thought there was anything seriously wrong they'd be examining him by now. We just have to be patient.'

'Patient?' she cried. 'When my son's split his head open? I thought head injuries were always treated seriously.'

'I'm sure it's not as bad as it looks,' said Adam, trying to soothe her. 'I remember doing a similar thing when I was Ethan's age. Boys will be boys.'

But then a doctor appeared and after examining Ethan thoroughly he said that no serious damage had been done. 'He'll need stitches, of course, but you'll be able to take him home. Keep waking him every two hours throughout the night in case of concussion but otherwise you have very little to worry about.'

When they left hospital Adam's car was waiting outside. Sienna didn't bat an eyelid, she was too worried about Ethan to even think about how it had got there.

'We'll go back to my place,' he said decisively. 'I'm as worried about Ethan as you are. I feel totally responsible. And naturally you will stay until he is completely better. I'll take some time off to help you look after him.'

Was she really hearing this? wondered Sienna. Was this what it had taken to convince Adam that being a husband and parent was equally as important as earning a living? Wonders would never cease. But she wanted Ethan in his own bed.

'Thanks for the offer, I appreciate it, really, but I'd prefer to go home,' she told him firmly. 'It will be better for Ethan. He'll be more comfortable in familiar surroundings.'

Much to her surprise, Adam agreed. 'You're right, of course.'

But her comfort zone was shattered when they arrived at her flat and Adam calmly announced that he was going to stay the night. 'You don't think I'd leave you under the circumstances? I feel responsible, Sienna.'

Sienna began to panic. 'It wasn't your fault. We'll be all right. He's had cuts and bruises before.'

'But nothing like this, I'm sure. And he is my son. I want to be there for him.' The controlled look on Adam's face told her that there was no point in arguing.

Fear skittered down her spine. Adam would take over. His presence would fill her tiny rooms. But more worrying still was where would he sleep. The couch wasn't made for a six-foot-three hunk. And he certainly wasn't sharing her bed. She did have a sleeping bag, though. He'd have to make do with that, on the floor if necessary. And maybe he might find it so uncomfortable that he'd go home.

And pigs might fly. She knew Adam's gritty determination only too well. It entered into every facet of his life. It was what had made him the success he was. It was what would determine Ethan's future, and maybe even her own.

A scary thought. When she had announced that he had a son she had somehow believed that he would be a part-time father, seeing Ethan only when it suited him. Not for one second had she expected that he would want, demand even, that he play a big part in his son's life. And incidentally in her own.

Ethan was in his element, being the centre of attention, and he insisted that his father put him to bed. Sienna hovered and supervised and then sat by Ethan's side, holding his hand, while Adam read to him.

Adam had never, in the whole of his life, imagined himself taking part in such a cosy domestic scene. Seeing Ethan in bed in his own apartment was entirely different. This was Ethan's room, it was filled with well-loved toys, it had his own personality stamped on it.

And what a little personality he was. Already Adam was proud of his son and he'd been devastated when he'd fallen and cut his head. It had been the worst moment in his entire life. He felt totally responsible.

At the hospital it had reminded him of the occasion when he had been admitted with a suspected broken ankle—although it had turned out to be nothing more than a bad sprain. His anxious parents had never left his side, though, and he could now understand their extreme concern.

'The end.' He closed the book and looked at Ethan, but he was already asleep.

They crept out of the room and Sienna went in to the kitchen to make coffee. Adam wanted to follow but space in there was at a premium, and he also guessed his presence wouldn't be welcome. She still gave off very strong vibes that he wasn't wanted there.

He ended up sitting on the couch. A distinctly uncomfortable couch.

It had been a turning point in his life when he had found out about Ethan. And this was yet another one. Who would ever have thought that he'd be spending the night in a cramped little flat? He'd worked for years to lift himself above the ordinary. He'd reached the pinnacle of his career. And yet he felt happier here than he had for a long time.

It was the strangest feeling.

But it was only because of Sienna and Ethan. He could never allow them to continue living here. For one thing this place wasn't big enough, and he felt sure it wasn't safe. He'd been entirely serious when he'd said that he would buy a house with a garden. He had even phoned an estate agent friend of his and set the ball rolling.

Not that he had told Sienna. But if he presented her with a *fait accompli*, there was nothing she could do about it. She undoubtedly deserved better than this.

'You look tired,' he said, when she came in with their drinks, setting them down on a coffee table in front of him.

Sienna nodded. She *was* tired, tired of this game that Adam was playing. He was beginning to act as though they had never been apart, and Ethan was unwittingly drawing them closer together.

She sat in the chair and he watched every movement she made. The way she crossed her legs, the way she tossed her hair back from her face, the way she reached out and took her cup, holding it as though it was a barrier between them.

Adam didn't fit into this place. She had never for one moment thought that he would stay. And now there was no way she could get rid of him.

'Ethan's quite a little soldier, isn't he?'

Sienna nodded. 'He's always been a battler. He shrugs off wounds in the same way that we shake raindrops off our clothes.' And how she wished she could shrug Adam out of her life the same way.

In the confines of her living room the air had thickened until every breath she drew became painful. At least in his apartment there had been acres of breathing space. Here there was nothing. It was like being caught in a trap with him.

'I don't mind admitting that he scared the hell out of me when he fell. What if anything had happened to him, Sienna?'

She looked at him with wide, pain-filled eyes. 'It doesn't bear thinking about. Ethan's my whole life. I love him so much that it hurts.'

'You do know that if I'd known you were pregnant I would never have let you go?'

'Perhaps not,' answered Sienna. His words were soft and all the more plausible because of it. 'It happened, though, and we can't put back the clock.'

'You shouldn't have had to bring him up on your own. Every child deserves both of its parents. And you certainly shouldn't have had to cope with him being seriously ill. I wish you had told me, Sienna.'

Sienna wasn't sure that it would have helped matters, nevertheless she could see that Adam was seriously affected now by Ethan's accident. It had given him a taste of what it had been like for her when he had been seriously ill. It was something she never wanted to go through again.

'We've both grown up a lot since I left,' she said. 'I'm not sure bringing up a baby would have been a pleasure as far as you're concerned. We'd have probably had more rows than before.'

Adam groaned. He did not actually say that he agreed but she could see it in his eyes. 'And now I need to make up. You've suffered enough on your own, Sienna. In future I'm going to take the weight off your shoulders.'

Quite how it happened she didn't know, but her cup was taken from her and she was hauled to her feet and held in a powerful embrace. Unable to stop herself, Sienna buried her head in his chest, feeling the throb of his heart match her own. Tears filled her eyes, the events of the past few hours finally catching up with her.

When Adam lifted her chin to look into her eyes he gave a groan and held her even more tightly. 'It's all right, Sienna. It's all right to cry. You've been strong for Ethan but you can let go now.'

He stroked her hair back from her face and kissed her brow—just as she did Ethan's when he fell and bumped himself. Except that this didn't feel like a mother's kiss, or even a father's. It felt like a lover's...

And she had run out of strength. There was nothing that she could do to stop him. It actually felt good to be held against someone as strong as Adam. For the past five years she had had no one to support her. She had been the strong one, the capable one. Now, though, it felt as though all her trials had come together and she was unable to bear up any longer.

'I think I'd like to go to bed,' she said quietly, adding, when she realised exactly what she had said, 'By myself.' If she stayed in Adam's arms any longer, she would melt. She would give in to the urges that were already beginning to form. Dangerous urges that ought to have no place in her heart.

'If that is your wish.'

'You know it is, Adam.'

'And I am to sleep—where?'

'The couch, the floor, the choice is yours.' She struggled out of his arms. 'There are only two beds in this house. One is Ethan's, the other is mine. I have a sleeping bag somewhere you can use.'

'That should be fun!'

It was his tone of voice that made her smile. 'You knew the set-up before you invited yourself. You've no one else to blame.'

'Have you no heart, Sienna? Are you sure that I cannot persuade you to share your bed? After everything we've gone through today, can't you take pity on me?'

His expression reminded her of Ethan's when he was trying to wheedle something out of her. It made her laugh.

And Adam jumped in.

With one swift movement she was back in his arms and he was carrying her through to the bedroom. Their coffees sat congealing on the table. She thought of nothing except the heat of Adam's body next to hers.

CHAPTER SEVEN

'ADAM, we shouldn't be doing this,' insisted Sienna. 'Not while Ethan's so poorly.'

He merely grinned. 'You can't get out of it that easily, Sienna. And since we have to keep waking him, there's no point in us going to sleep. We have to fill in our time somehow.'

His kisses became more demanding, more urgent, as though he had been waiting all day for this very moment. Not that he could have expected they would end up here, and neither had she!

With a sigh she gave herself up to Adam's kisses, his magical, heart-stopping kisses. Kisses that had more fire in them than ever before.

Feelings that had been buried rose as swiftly as a bird in flight and when Adam began to remove her clothes she made no attempt to stop him. With each inch of flesh that was exposed Adam covered it with kisses, her arms and shoulders, his tongue finding the pulse at the base of her throat, resting on it, feeling its frantic beat.

In fact, every one of her pulses throbbed. Sienna felt as though her whole body had been taken over by this man. He was making it his own and there was nothing that she could do to stop him.

She felt uplifted. As though something had been missing from her life and now she had found it again.

And this was only the beginning!

When Adam turned his attention to her breasts, when he cupped them in his capable hands, when he took her nipples between his teeth, nipping gently at first but then biting and sucking each one in turn into his mouth, her whole body was in danger of igniting.

Unaware that tiny groans kept escaping the back of her throat, Sienna gripped Adam's shoulders. A smile softened his eyes but his mouth never left her nipple.

Sienna wanted to smile herself but was feeling too much going on inside her body to do anything other than grip Adam's shoulders and dig her nails deep into his firm flesh. She wanted more of this man who had once been her whole life, who could arouse her more magnificently than any other man she knew.

A trail of kisses to her belly button had her squirming and writhing, and when he flicked the button on her jeans and dragged them off in one swift economical movement, her tiny black lace briefs following suit, she felt freedom as never before.

She lay back and closed her eyes, her legs parting involuntarily. Adam's mouth continued its course, his fingers twirling and gently pulling the dark hairs that covered her femininity.

She heard the groan of satisfaction in his voice, a groan that continued as his tongue replaced his fingers, as it sought and reached the very part of her that was hot with need.

Involuntarily she lifted her hips, offering her now throbbing and parted core. It was her ultimate gift, born of desperation. Adam had reached deep into her emotions, he had brought them back to vigorous life, and she could not go on unless he made love to her.

At first it was his tongue and expert fingers that brought her to the edge, and it was almost more than she could bear. 'Don't do this to me, Adam,' she cried, her nails clawing his back. 'Don't torment me like this. Make love to me.'

She was hardly aware of uttering the words, she knew only that she would be the one taking the initiative if he didn't hurry up.

But in seconds he was out of his clothes, obeying her command, and Sienna's world exploded. Making love in the past had been good but never this magnificent. She had thought it was, she had been eminently satisfied, but time apart had taught her that Adam was even more knowledgeable now in what women wanted.

When they were both fully sated, when their bodies lay limp, he held her closely to him, stroking her hair, letting her know without words that he too had experienced something uplifting and wonderful.

It was not until their bodies cooled and her breathing returned to normal that Sienna began to have doubts about her sanity. Their love-making had been intense and fantastic, she could not deny that, but how could she have let this happen? What had got into her? They hadn't even used protection. And why was Adam a better lover now than he had been before?

Because of all the other women he had bedded in her absence!

It was a bitter pill to swallow.

Or had she been more receptive, forgetting the bad times, conscious only that Adam had the power to turn her into someone she hardly recognized?

Already she could feel her body springing back to life, ready for another assault on her senses. But it would be wrong to allow it. She had let herself down. It must never happen again, good though it had been. More than good actually. Remarkable, incredible, out of this world!

Adam's hold on her relaxed. He had fallen asleep! With a grunt of satisfaction he settled more comfortably. Was he dreaming about what had just happened? she wondered. Did he feel as fulfilled as she did, but without the self-recrimination?

Adam would never blame himself for anything he did, she knew that for a fact. His actions were always calculated and deliberate, whether he was making love or finalising a business deal.

It was herself she had let down. She had given in too easily. Without words she had told him that she was his for the taking whenever he felt like it.

Heat of a very different kind flooded her body now and she rolled away from him in disgust, giving a little huff as she curled her knees up to her chin, vowing never to let him touch her again.

'Sienna? What's wrong?'

So he was not asleep!

'This is wrong,' she hissed fiercely, pushing herself up. 'Me and you. After everything that has happened between us. You never loved me, did you, Adam?' At last she asked the question that had troubled her ever since she'd walked out.

Adam sat up too and looked at her for several long seconds, seeming to be reflecting on her words, wondering how to answer, and when he did it was not what she expected.

'It's true, I didn't love you.'

Shock waves rippled through her. Agonising waves! So she was right! It wasn't good hearing it but before she could respond he spoke again.

'I liked you, Sienna, a lot. I was very fond of you. But…' He fought for the right words. 'I don't know how to say this, but…I'm afraid to love. I made a promise to myself many years ago never to do so.'

His words made no sense and Sienna shot him a sharply suspicious glance. 'So why did you ask me to marry you? Why did you let me think our marriage was a love match? No wonder it fell apart. What's there to be afraid of?' The situation was getting more bizarre by the second.

Adam drew in a long, slow breath and let it out again even more slowly. Sienna began to think he was not going to answer until he finally said, 'My father loved my mother very much. So much that when she died he lost control of his life, couldn't focus. He became a broken man and went from being someone I respected to someone I could hardly recognise. He turned to drink and eventually that became his crutch, his reason for living.'

Sienna's fingers fluttered to her mouth, her eyes widening. She had met Adam's father and had known of his drinking problem, but had never thought about the cause of it until now. The news that it had followed the death if his wife shocked Sienna terribly and she understood now why Adam had never talked about the issues before.

'Is that why *you* never touch alcohol?'

Adam nodded, his eyes dull and sad, making her wish that she had not asked the question. 'I did not want the same thing to happen to me. If losing the person you love causes such pain that you lose control of your life, change beyond recognition and feel the need to blot it out with drink, then it is better to never love at all.'

So Adam had never loved her and never would! It was a sickening, saddening thought. He was a strong man and it was ironic that he could make such spectacular love, and yet not be *in* love with her. And more incredulous still was the fact that she still loved him.

And Adam would never let her go now because of Ethan!

'I'm sorry,' she whispered, her heart aching for him. 'Sorry for you and sorry for your father. I didn't know that that was why he drank.'

'And why would you?' he asked sharply, swinging his legs off the bed and standing up. 'It's not something I shout from the rooftops. My father became a liability. A sad, drunken old man. His death was a merciful release.'

'And your grandfather, how did he take it?' She knew that Adam and his grandfather weren't on the best of terms. She had heard them having a terrible row just before their wedding and Adam hadn't spoken his name again.

Adam's eyes grew icily remote. 'I'd really rather not talk about him.'

Sienna nodded, she could see how painful his memories were. 'Perhaps you'd like to go and wake Ethan? Check that he's OK?' She felt that he needed something to do to take his mind off their unfortunate conversation. She dearly wanted to check on her son herself, but Adam's need at this moment was greater than hers.

Immediately his face softened into a ghost of a smile and he pulled on his pants before swiftly disappearing from the room.

Sienna struggled with the information Adam had given her about his father. She had only met him a couple of times and his drink problem had been strongly evident then. She had often wondered why Adam had not persuaded him to seek help but had never dared ask, as it had seemed such a touchy subject. Now she realised that he must have tried, he'd probably been in despair, but his parent had been beyond help.

And all because of love!

In an odd sort of way she could understand Adam's reasoning about not wanting to fall in love. Understand it, yes. But not agree with it.

'Mummy.' Ethan seemed none the worse for wear as Adam carried him into her room. In fact, he seemed proud of his injury. 'Daddy says I'm a brave little soldier.'

'And so you are, sweetheart,' she said, smiling. 'And so you are.'

'And Daddy says we can go on his boat tomorrow.'

Sienna frowned and looked at Adam, who simply shrugged and tried to look innocent. 'Oh, Daddy did, did he?' she asked. 'And what about school?'

Adam answered for him. 'I thought Ethan deserved a treat for being so brave.'

It sounded as though she had no say in the matter and although she was cross and intended telling Adam when they were alone, Sienna nodded briefly. 'I wasn't going to send him anyway, so perhaps yes. I'm sure Ethan will enjoy it. So long as he's careful.'

'And how about his mother? Will she enjoy it too?'

Sienna did not know how to answer. Travelling the Thames on a private cruiser had never been within her range. She had done the occasional river cruise but always with dozens of other passengers. This would be a totally new experience. And if Ethan hadn't hurt himself she would not have agreed to it, at least not this early in Adam's relationship with his son.

'Won't you be going to work?'

Adam shrugged. 'I can afford to take a few more days off.'

Which he had never done for her!

Because he didn't love her!

So why had he married her in the first place? Why had he needed a wife? Sienna wanted to ask him but now didn't seem the right time. 'I think Ethan should go back to bed. In fact, we should all try to get some sleep.'

'I want to sleep with you and Daddy, Mummy.'

Sienna hadn't the heart to say no and actually it would be easier as they had to wake him frequently. So Ethan snuggled down between them, a smile on his face, and although Sienna had thought she would not sleep, not after what had happened between her and Adam, and certainly not with Ethan sharing their bed, she somehow managed it, and when she awoke she had the bed to herself.

She had dreamt that they were making love again, desperate, uninhibited love. Her heart was still racing, her body bathed in sweat. She was a fool. She was setting her own fate by letting Adam get close. It was giving out the wrong impression.

Ethan deserved to get to know his father, yes, he deserved to spend time with him, but she knew that Adam wanted them to live together and she didn't see how that scenario could ever work—not again. Her mind would constantly dwell on the fact that it was a loveless marriage. Always had been and always would be.

Hearing Adam and Ethan talking in the kitchen, she silently slipped through to the bathroom. After showering, she dragged on clean jeans and a white T-shirt with a broken red heart on it. There were no words but she guessed that Adam would get the message.

When she joined them in the kitchen, though, Sienna couldn't help smiling. Ethan was busy laying the table while Adam whisked eggs. It was a perfect domestic scene. When had he become a dab hand at cooking? she asked herself when he presented her with perfectly cooked scrambled eggs on toast. It was not something she could ever imagine him doing. His eyes rested on the message on her T-shirt, and he looked at her questioningly but said nothing.

After breakfast she washed up while Adam took his shower, and after she had got an excited Ethan ready, Adam's driver appeared as if by magic. When they arrived at where his boat was moored Ethan jumped up and down with glee.

Sienna was a little concerned that his over-excitement might have a detrimental effect. The stitches didn't seem to be worrying him, though. He never even mentioned them.

She did her best to keep him calm while silently admiring the cruiser's sleek lines. There was nothing modest about it and she had expected no less.

Adam was very much the man of the moment, taking charge with smooth efficiency, letting Ethan sit between his legs and pretend to steer.

But he never ignored Sienna. He included her in their conversation, looked across at her constantly with promise in his beautiful blue eyes, managing to keep her in a constant state of arousal—much to her annoyance.

She didn't want to feel. She didn't want this man back in her life, not like this, not when he was behaving as though it was a foregone conclusion that they would become one happy family.

He was undoubtedly doing his best to achieve that status but it was not so simple. Adam was hard to resist, as last night's love-making had proved. Nevertheless, his confession that he had never loved her really had knocked the ground from beneath her feet.

As far as he was concerned, though, nothing had changed. And the stakes were high.

Adam wanted Ethan. And if Ethan came with his mother then so be it. She was good in bed and that was enough.

It was all he had ever wanted her for! It was a disheartening thought. And the more she thought about it, the truer she knew it was.

They stopped for lunch at a riverside café but as they made their way back afterwards Ethan began to complain of a headache.

'I knew it would be too much for him.' Sienna's eyes flared as she faced Adam.

'Sienna, he'll be all right.' Adam kept his tone calm, his whole demeanour suggesting that she was worrying for nothing.

'I'll take him into the cabin and see if he'll go to sleep,' she announced, her eyes flaring a magnificent blue. 'He's over-excited. Didn't the doctor say he should be kept quiet?'

She did not wait for Adam's answer, holding her son's hand as they descended into the cabin. Here she laid Ethan down on one of the couches and sat beside him, smoothing his brow and singing softly.

Within a few minutes he was fast asleep.

'I didn't realise you could sing. You have an amazing voice, Sienna.'

With a start she realised that Adam was standing at the top of the steps, looking at her. And she realised also that the boat was no longer moving. 'Why have we stopped? I want to get Ethan home.'

'I thought I'd check that he was all right.' He came slowly down the steps, his eyes never leaving her face. 'But now I'd like you to sing for me.'

'I don't think so.' Sienna looked defiantly into his eyes. 'Let's go, Adam. It was kind of you to suggest this boat trip but I was crazy to agree. Ethan's clearly not up to it after his accident. '

'I guess the little guy's just tired after his disturbed night.'

He was probably right but she didn't need him telling her what was wrong with Ethan. 'I want to get him home.'

'Have you any idea how fantastic you look when you're angry, Sienna?'

If he thought flattery would get him anywhere he was grossly mistaken. 'You never used to think that. You always said I made myself ugly when I shouted.'

'I said many things I shouldn't have said,' he

admitted with a rueful grimace, his eyes shadowed for a brief moment. 'But I've grown up too, Sienna. We're two different people now.'

Maybe they were, but it didn't mean that they were going to get back together.

Almost as though he had read her mind, Adam said softly, 'I meant what I said last night, I can't change that, but for Ethan's sake I think we should give our marriage another try. He deserves both parents.'

'You mean you're going to *try* to fall in love with me?'

Anger flared from his eyes then, fierce blue sparks that spelled trouble. 'I didn't say that. You know my feelings on the matter. But we make a good pair, Sienna.'

'You mean in bed?' she tossed hotly. 'And that's all you really want me for, isn't it? Go to hell, Adam.'

'Mummy, why are you shouting?'

Sienna groaned. She flayed Adam with her eyes and turned to her son. 'I'm sorry, my darling. How are you feeling?'

'My head still hurts.'

Again Sienna turned a recriminating stare on Adam. 'We need to go home.'

Another glare and he had gone.

Adam had thought that for Ethan's sake Sienna would jump at the chance of reviving their marriage. Last night in bed she had proved that the spark between them had never died. It had ignited into glorious passion and he wouldn't be human if he didn't want more of the same.

God, she excited him. It was a different Sienna who had embraced their love-making with open arms. Either that or he'd never realised her full potential. Maybe he shouldn't have admitted his inability to fall in love. Was it this that was holding her back now? Would she never walk into his arms again? Never share his home?

And how he wanted her!

Every time he thought about last night a treacherous hunger filled his body. In fact, he had only to look at Sienna, to catch her eye, and he was ready.

He wanted her back in his home and in his bed. Tonight preferably.

Today had started with such promise that he felt cheated when they arrived back and Sienna barely spoke to him as he tied up the boat, and when he suggested that they go back to his apartment as it was nearer she flatly refused.

'Ethan needs his own bed,' she declared emphatically.

It was always Ethan, thought Adam, and he couldn't help wondering whether she was using their son as a barrier to hide her own feelings. He smiled inwardly. If it was her feelings she was afraid of, it was all to the good. Time would tell. All he needed was patience.

The trouble was patience wasn't one of his strong points. When he wanted something he usually went all out to get it.

When they reached Sienna's flat and he made to follow her indoors she turned to him. 'I want you to go home, Adam. I want peace and quiet for Ethan—he's had quite a day.'

Even though she wanted him out of the way he was determined not to go. He could see no reason why he should not stay a while.

And in the end Sienna gave in. She decided that here was no sense in arguing in front of Ethan, who by this time looked very pale and tired. But she ignored Adam as she gave Ethan some medicine for his headache then undressed him and put him to bed.

Adam waited patiently, putting on the kettle and making tea because Sienna looked as though she needed it.

'It was too much for him today,' she said quietly.

'It was my fault.'

She said nothing, she did not want to start another argument. Instead, she sipped her hot, strong tea, which was just as she liked it, and slowly began to relax.

After they had finished and put their cups down on the table, Adam took her into his arms and fool that she was she let him. She needed comfort, she needed reassurance. Last night and today had taken their toll.

Adam stroked her hair back from her face with warm, gentle fingers, and his closeness began working its magic. Already she could feel herself relaxing, feel the heat of him warming her, the clean male smell that was essentially Adam filling her nostrils.

But then amazingly, surprisingly, he announced that he was leaving. 'You need your rest too, Sienna. You look tired.'

He was right, she was tired. Contrarily, though, she could think of nothing better than Adam joining her in bed tonight.

He smiled, as though he had read her thoughts. 'Goodnight, Sienna. I'll be in touch.'

CHAPTER EIGHT

IT WAS almost mid-morning and Sienna was keeping Ethan home again. He had looked pale when he had woken up and she didn't think it fair to send him to school. They had just finished breakfast when the doorbell rang.

'Don't tell me you're taking another day off?' were her first words when she discovered Adam on the doorstep. If one small boy had made this much difference to his life then maybe they should have started a family straight away when they had first married. And maybe their lives would never have changed. She would not have walked out on him.

Maybe!

'How's Ethan?'

Sienna appreciated his concern but she couldn't help wondering whether Adam had an ulterior motive in turning up here today. He had made it clear that he wanted them to give their marriage another go and that he wanted them all to live together as one big happy family.

Which was not what she wanted. Even though she had longed for him in bed last night. Even though she had imagined him at her side, and replayed in her mind the amazing way he made love.

It had been a frustrating exercise. It had made sleep impossible and left her feeling tired and out of sorts this morning.

And now he had turned up again!

'You could have phoned to ask that.' She didn't want Adam calling on them at any odd time. It was disrupting for her and had to be the same for Ethan.

Not that Ethan minded. He heard his father's voice and came running. Adam scooped him up in his arms with a big grin on his face. 'How's my injured soldier this morning?'

'I'm good, Daddy. Have you come to take us out again?'

'No!' It was Sienna who spoke. 'You need a quiet, relaxing day, Ethan. And I'm sure your father has much better things to do. Shouldn't you be at work?' she asked Adam pointedly.

He wore a blue short-sleeved shirt that matched his eyes and did nothing to hide his muscular chest, and a pair of navy linen trousers that sat low on his narrow hips. There was a raw sexiness about him that triggered an unfortunate response.

Sienna dashed it away. 'Adam?'

'I'm going in later,' he told her, his lips curved in a mysterious smile. 'There's something I want to show you first. Both of you.'

'Then I suppose you'd better come in.' She turned back into the room, hating herself for feeling anything other than animosity towards Adam. 'What is it?'

Another secret smile as he put Ethan down. 'We need to go and take a look.'

Ethan looked at his father. 'Where are we going?'

'It's a surprise.'

'I like surprises. Will I like it?'

'I jolly well hope so.'

'Come on, then, let's go.' And he tugged at his father's hand.

Sienna was less eager. There was something about Adam that worried her. He had an air of the cat who had stolen the cream. He was planning something and she couldn't help feeling that she was not going to like it.

'So where is this surprise taking us?' she asked, attempting to keep her tone light, aware that she failed miserably.

Adam grinned again, one of those grins that seriously creased his eyes and made him look as sexy as hell.

Sienna felt like hitting him.

'You'll have to wait and see.'

'You're worrying me, Adam, do you know that?' she asked as soon as they were alone, whilst Ethan went to grab his things. 'Are you the same man who would never take a day off?'

'The very same,' he agreed. 'But I have a family to look after now.'

'To look after?' Her eyes widened. 'We don't need looking after, Adam. I only told you about your son because—'

'Because he almost died and your conscience was bothering you,' he cut in swiftly and harshly, his smile fading. 'But the fact is that now I know about him I intend behaving like a responsible parent. You cannot take that away from me. I will not let you.'

He would not let her! Sienna felt like telling him he

couldn't stop her, but at that moment Ethan came running back. 'I'm ready, Mummy. Can we go now?'

With reluctance she nodded, trailing them out of the house. Little though he was, Ethan had the same walk as Adam, even his shoulders squared in the same manner, and she couldn't help feeling proud of him.

Adam had driven himself here today and Sienna lifted her eyebrows when she saw that a child booster seat had been fitted into the back of a silver limousine. She was impressed but not for the life of her would she admit it.

He drove no more than a few miles before pulling up outside a house in a leafy cul-de-sac where houses had walled gardens and electronically controlled gates.

Ethan's jaw fell when the gates opened all by themselves and Sienna wondered what they were doing here, who it might be that he was taking them to see.

It was with great astonishment, therefore, when they walked up to the front door of an imposing red brick house and he presented her with a key. 'Take a look at your new home.'

'*My* new home?' It was all she could manage. Her thoughts were racing at a mile a minute and her heartbeat was erratic. What the devil was he talking about? She knew he didn't like her living where she did—but he wouldn't really buy her a new house, would he?

A host of questions flitted through her mind, each one tumbling over the other in their haste to be heard. She turned on Adam with a questioning stare. 'You'd better explain.'

'I've bought it.'

It was a plain statement of fact. But all the more devastating because of it. 'Why?'

'I've bought it for us.'

Us!

It was the one word that registered in her mind. Us! Adam, Ethan and herself. The three of them. Living together. Here. Permanently.

'You're out of your mind.' They were the first words she could think of. 'I have no intention of living with you.' Was he crazy or what? Did he really think she would agree to move in with him? Had he no real idea how she felt?

'Not even for Ethan's sake?' His eyes locked with hers. Serious eyes, a serious face. 'He needs both of us. And I need to get to know him better.'

'Which you can do, gradually. It doesn't mean we have to move house. You cannot manipulate me like this, Adam.'

'It's not manipulation, Sienna. It's logic. It makes perfect sense.'

Sienna closed her eyes, praying she was dreaming, that the house and the situation were not real. Adam was being so reasonable that she wanted to scream. But she knew it would get her nowhere. She needed to meet calm with calm, especially with Ethan hopping excitedly from foot to foot.

'Is this where we're going to live?' he asked excitedly.

Sienna put her hand on his shoulder. 'I don't know yet, sweetheart.'

'Can we go in?'

Sienna realised she still had the key in her hand. Reluctantly she inserted it into the lock and pushed open the door. Ethan raced inside. She stepped over the threshold more slowly. The entrance hall was huge, lofty and beautiful. Much as she was determined not to like this house, the immediate effect was one of awe.

The floor was tiled, the walls pale, and there was a profusion of pot plants. A staircase curved upwards from one side and several doors opened out on the other. There was a dark green leather settee and a table with a telephone and a lamp on it.

It was picture perfect and she guessed that the whole house would be the same.

'What have you done, Adam? How could you buy this without consulting me?' Ethan had skipped off to explore so she didn't fear that he would overhear their conversation.

'I don't like where you are living.'

'And you think that gives you the right to—to do this?' Her throat felt tight and panic began to set in. 'It's very generous of you but—'

'Generosity doesn't come into it,' interrupted Adam. 'I will not have Ethan living in that lousy flat of yours.'

'Lousy? We have managed fine there up until now, thank you very much,' Sienna said, and glared into Adam's eyes, which were almost navy and dangerously fierce. But deep down she knew that a part of what he said was true. Her flat was small and cramped and the area certainly left a lot to be desired. A number of times recently she had worried at how safe it really was for her and Ethan, but she couldn't allow Adam to railroad her like this.

How she wished again that she had never gone to his damned too-grand penthouse that day. Adam had gone up in the world whereas she had gone down, but at least she'd been happy. Now he was taking that happiness away from her. He was making it his business to organise their lives.

'Look, you've done a fantastic job with Ethan,' he answered, his voice surprisingly calm. 'But sometimes you need to accept help when it is offered. It isn't always easy to see what's best for us.'

'And you're saying that you know best?' she asked, finding it difficult to keep her tone down. She did not want Ethan to hear them arguing, but on the other hand how impossible was it not to get irate?

Adam lifted his wide shoulders and spread his hands wide. He did not speak.

Sienna pushed herself to her feet. 'I suppose I'd better take a look round while I'm here.' She needed to put distance between them and to her relief Adam let her go. He did not even follow. She explored each room— the fantastic kitchen, the three separate living areas, a massive conservatory overlooking a garden with a swimming pool and a tennis court, and that was only what she could see! Upstairs there were six bedrooms and the same number of bathrooms, all furnished to a very high specification.

And he had bought it! He'd clicked his fingers and it was a done deal. What did it feel like to have power like that? Money like that? And did she want to be a part of it? As far as she was concerned, money did not buy happiness.

She and Ethan had been very happy until Adam had appeared in their lives, and they had had nothing. Happiness was a state of mind, not how much money you had to spend.

'Mummy, are we going to live here? *Mummy?*' Ethan had trailed after her, running in and out of rooms, jumping on beds, so excited that she feared he might fall and hurt his head again. At the very least she feared his headache would come back.

'Mummy's thinking about it.'

'We'll have to persuade her to say yes.' Adam's voice came from very close behind, a rough, deep growl. His persuasive voice. One that had once turned her limbs to jelly.

It seemed a long time ago now. When they had first married. She had thought he was the sexiest man on earth.

Actually, he still was sexy, but he was also aggravating and so damned sure of himself that she wanted to scream. If this was what money did, if it empowered him to such an extent that he thought he could do whatever he liked, have whomever he liked—which in this instance meant her—then she wished he was a pauper.

The man she had fallen in love with had had very little money. It had only been when making it had become his obsession that their marriage had failed.

Ethan ran away to explore some more and Adam turned her to face him. 'Ethan loves it already.'

Sienna nodded. That was one thing she could not dispute.

'So here's the deal.' He took her hands and although she would have dearly loved to snatch away Sienna remained still and silent, listening to her heart beat with sudden frantic haste. She wasn't sure whether it was because of his nearness, his touch, or the thought of what he was going to say. Or maybe a combination of all three!

'You and Ethan move in here and I pay all the bills.'

So he wasn't moving in with them. It was as if a whole weight had lifted from her shoulders.

But her pleasure was short-lived.

'In exchange we give our marriage another try.'

Sienna's heart stopped beating. Her eyes fixed themselves on Adam's face. He looked very pleased with himself, as well he might, but if he thought she was going to agree, he was seriously out of his mind.

'You really think I'd do that?' she asked, her eyes suddenly hostile. 'It's an impossible proposition. I'm wasting my time here, and I'm afraid you've wasted your money.' There was the gravest danger that she would lose her heart to him again, only to have it once more broken when he went back to his old ways. It was something she dared not contemplate.

She loved the house and the area, it was such a far cry from where she lived now, and she would have no more financial worries. But as well as worrying about her heart she had Ethan's emotional well-being to take into consideration. If it didn't work out between her and Adam, she would be the one left picking up the pieces. She couldn't do that to her son. She simply couldn't.

She turned and was about to call Ethan to tell him that they were leaving when Adam spoke. 'You're making a mistake, Sienna.'

'Am I?' She drew herself up to her full height, which was still a few miserable inches shorter than he was. How she wished for high heels. But she met his eyes bravely, telling him without words that she did not agree.

'You're not thinking about Ethan.'

'Oh, yes, I am,' she declared firmly. 'I'm only thinking about him.'

'In which case you'll realise that he'll be far better off here.' Adam's eyes bored into hers. It was almost as if he was trying to hypnotise her into saying yes.

'Not with an absentee father,' she retorted, hearing

the sharpness in her tone but not caring. Adam was being impossible. How could she live here happily? 'He's already beginning to idolise you, Adam. You'd break his heart if you let him down.'

Adam's eyes flickered a savage warning. 'I have no intention of doing that.'

'Easy words. You don't know what you're doing half the time. You think that putting food and money on the table is the be all and end all. You have no idea that it's relationships that count.'

'So you'd rather our son be bought up in a slum than—'

'My flat is not a slum,' cried Sienna, aghast that he should think that and deeply offended. And yet she could see why his thoughts went along those lines, living the way he did.

'No, it isn't, Sienna. You keep it beautifully. It's the area you live in that worries me.' His voice dropped to a low growl. 'You could keep this house beautiful. Doesn't it appeal? Would you like me to—?'

'Of course it appeals,' she cut in speedily. 'It's lovely. It's the nicest house I've ever seen. But I…' Sienna stopped her thoughts. She was looking a gift horse in the mouth. She really would be crazy to turn him down flat. Maybe they could make it work.

But on her terms!

'But what, Sienna?' prompted Adam, a faint smile flickering at the corners of his mouth.

She met his eyes with her head high and a similar smile on her own lips. 'Actually, I've changed my mind. I *will* move in with you.'

She saw the triumph on his face and took pleasure in

knowing that it would be immediately wiped off when he learned what her conditions were. 'I'm willing to give our marriage another go.'

'I knew you'd see sense, Sienna.' Her made a move towards her but Sienna backed away.

'Provided that you take our marriage and your role as a father seriously.'

He nodded. 'You have my word on that.'

Sienna seriously doubted it. Words were easy. Actions were harder. 'In return, I shall expect you to leave your office at five o'clock every night. No working late. And every weekend we'll spend together as a family.' She watched his smile fade, though it didn't go altogether. Perhaps he thought she wasn't deadly serious. Perhaps her next request would tell him exactly how determined she was.

'And if you break your promise just once—I shall leave and take Ethan with me.'

The pause that followed told her that she had read him correctly. He would never agree to this. He could not possibly give up so many of his working hours. She may as well call Ethan and leave now. It was a nice dream, thinking they might live here, but it would never happen.

Goodness knows what Adam would do with the house. Sell it again? Move in himself and get rid of—

'I'll do it.'

Sienna stopped breathing.

Adam smiled.

Her heart thudded. Had she heard him correctly? Never in her wildest imaginings had she thought to hear those words.

'Have you nothing to say?' he prompted now, still with an irritating smile on his lips.

'I…' Sienna swallowed hard. 'I wasn't sure that—'

'That I would agree?'

She nodded.

'I'll do anything to keep my family together.'

The proprietorial way he said 'my family' stunned Sienna. He sounded like a proper family man and yet…

'It will be much safer for Ethan, for one thing,' he continued, cutting into her thoughts. 'But it also means I'll have my wife back. And I won't let you down this time.'

Sienna struggled to come to terms with the fact that she was now going to be trapped in a house with a man who did not love her. He might say he wouldn't let her down but that wasn't the point. He had already done that. He had already proved that she didn't really mean anything to him. It was Ethan he wanted now, and since they came as a package…

Fate was cruel. She had thought that she was doing the right thing on the day when she told Adam he had a son. And now she was going to be locked back into a loveless marriage simply so that he could have access to him. She had somehow walked right into his trap.

Half expecting Adam to take her into his arms, Sienna was relieved when he did nothing more than smile complacently, as though he had known all along that she would agree to move in. It would have made him look pretty silly if she hadn't.

In truth, she was grateful to him, not that she would ever admit it. There had been times when she was a little bit scared living where she did. This was going to be an exciting new future for both her and Ethan.

* * *

The speed with which Adam moved her out of her flat and into the house left her breathless. She took few possessions with her—clothes, photographs, Ethan's favourite toys. Nothing else was of any value. The only person she told that she was moving out was Jo upstairs, who wished her the best of luck and said she had known, from the second she had seen Adam, that it would happen.

Adam did not know why he wasn't feeling as happy as he should that Sienna had left her dreadful flat and moved into the house he had bought for her. Was it because she wasn't as thrilled as he'd hoped? Had she thought that he wouldn't agree to her request that he make time for them? Or was it because he had a sneaky feeling at the back of his mind that he had somehow bullied her into it?

Their love-making had always been amazing. Even when he had been tired and brain-dead from a hard day at work she had always managed to entice his libido into life. And he was looking forward to a future with her back in his bed every night.

She had crept beneath his skin in a way he had not expected. He was still damned angry that she hadn't told him about his son, but Sienna herself was sexier than ever, even in those dreadful jeans she insisted on wearing. He wanted to see her in something more feminine, something alluring. He wanted to take her shopping and buy her rich splendid clothes that showed off to perfection her spectacular figure.

And what had that damned T-shirt with the broken heart on it meant? Was she trying to tell him that her heart would never mend? That she would never truly be his again?

The thought crossed his mind that now she had found

out that he didn't have it in him to love someone unconditionally, she might try to back off. She might not keep her promise to share his bed.

It had taken a great deal of courage to admit the truth to her, but he had felt that if she was to become a major part of his life again then she deserved to know. Otherwise she would expect more from him, she would expect declarations of love, and that was never going to happen.

After his mother had died he had been grief-stricken. They had had a very close bond and having to put up with his father's anguish as well as his own had shown him how dangerous it was to love someone so completely that they became your whole life. That you could not function without them.

Neither did it sit easily on his shoulders that he had shown his vulnerability to Sienna. He had thought it would help, but actually it looked as though the whole thing had spectacularly backfired.

She knew now that he had never loved her, that he *couldn't* love her!

Sienna had been shocked by his confession but there had been no time for questions. Ethan had interrupted their conversation and he had actually felt relief. It had been a hard enough thing for him to do without an inquisition following.

He felt fortunate now that Sienna had agreed to move into the house even with her conditions. For a while he had thought she was going to refuse altogether.

'Do you have everything you need?'

Sienna nodded. 'You've been very kind. I cannot believe you've done all this for me.'

'And Ethan,' he added curtly.

Of course! Sienna's thoughts were suddenly bitter. It was for his son, not her, that he had provided this magnificent house. He would have left her to rot in her flat if she hadn't borne his child. In point of fact they would never have met again because she certainly would not have gone to see him. They might even have been divorced by now.

'Then I'll leave you to settle in. I need to call in at the office as well as packing a few things for myself.' He gave Ethan a hug and a kiss. Seemed to contemplate doing the same to her, but changed his mind, striding to the door instead. The next moment he had gone.

'So, Ethan, what do we do now?' It was more a rhetorical question than anything else because there was nothing to actually do. The house was beautifully furnished, the fridge and freezer well stocked. She was going to rattle round in it like a dried pea in a pod, and more especially when Ethan went back to school.

'I'm going to ride the rocking horse,' he declared loudly. One of the rooms had clearly been a children's room and a huge rocking horse had been left behind— unless, of course, Adam had bought it! That was something she hadn't thought of. Nevertheless, Ethan was totally impressed and happy to sit and rock.

Suddenly the front door opened and Adam appeared again. 'I meant to give you this.'

It was a store card. A major, expensive department store. Sienna's eyes widened. 'Why? What for?'

His brows rose as if it was a stupid question. 'For whatever you need. Clothes, toys, anything you like. Go shopping, Sienna. Have fun.'

She hadn't even thought about clothes but clearly

Adam had. She was his wife and he would want to show her off. Trying to bring Ethan up on a shoestring had left little or no money to spend on herself.

Living here, she would seriously need to update her image—was that what he was saying? He wanted a wife to be proud of, not someone who walked around in jeans and T-shirts.

'You don't approve?' His voice cut into her thoughts, his tone hardening. 'Have I made a mistake?'

'It's not that,' she cut in swiftly. 'It's just I'm used to my own money. I—'

'You don't feel you can take anything from me? That's ridiculous, Sienna. You are my wife. In a few days you will have a bank account in your own name. Meanwhile, I want you to use this card. Treat yourself.'

'And what else do you plan doing for me, Adam?' she enquired sharply. Everything was moving too quickly. How many days ago had it been since she had gone to see him? Eight! Eight short days. And look what had happened in that short space of time.

'What else do you want?'

It was the impossible tone in his voice. The way his blue eyes looked as though they were made of ice. The way he held his body stiff and formidable, looking nothing like the lover who had shared her bed. And whose bed she was going to have to share again!

'I want nothing.' He thought she was being ungrateful. Which in a way she supposed she was. But she did not like the fact that she been uprooted from her comfortable flat into this monster of a house that looked like a show home. A beautiful home admittedly, but a lifeless one. She would make it hers eventually, she would stamp it with her own personality, but at this moment she felt as though she had been lifted up and dropped into a soulless building.

Strangely, she had not felt this way before Adam had left. Which meant, she supposed, that he had such a big physical presence that it filled every room.

It had felt as though something was missing when he had walked out. Her whole life had changed in a matter of hours and she wasn't sure that it was for the better.

CHAPTER NINE

'DADDY.' Ethan heard Adam's voice and came running down the stairs, launching himself into his arms. 'Come and see me on the rocking horse.'

Instantly Adam picked Ethan up, glancing at Sienna over his shoulder as he climbed the stairs. 'Are you joining us?'

It was Ethan's 'Please, Mummy' that persuaded her. She had been relieved by Ethan's interruption and would have preferred some breathing space, but she didn't want Adam acceding to any more of his son's requests. Whatever he asked for he would get, she knew that, and it wouldn't be good for him.

After a few minutes' rocking, encouraged by his father shouting, 'Ride 'em, cowboy,' Ethan grew tired of the horse and took them into his new bedroom. 'Which is your room, Daddy? Is it next to mine?'

'If that's where you'd like me and Mummy to sleep.'

Sienna drew in a shocked breath. It made the whole moving-in process sound so final.

'I do, I do. I want you near me in case I wake up in the night. It's a big house, Daddy. I might be frightened in the dark.'

'You have nothing to fear, Ethan. I shall be here to look after you.'

Sienna still struggled with the fact that she would be sharing Adam's bed. She wanted him and yet she didn't. She wanted to be free of him and yet their lives were inextricably woven together. Could she really spend the rest of her days with a man who did not love her? The fact that he was a spectacular lover was a point in his favour—but would it be enough?

When Ethan had settled down to play with his toys they went back downstairs and Adam declared that he really was going this time. 'Don't miss me while I'm away,' he said, his mocking expression making her grit her teeth.

Miss him? She wanted to lock and bolt the doors. It was hard finding out that her life was no longer her own.

'And when you're ready to go shopping call my driver—he will take you. Here's his number.'

Sienna glared as the door closed behind him. He really did think money was the be all and end all of everything. He had no idea that it was just as easy to be happy without store cards and big houses and posh cars and chauffeurs.

She did not go out. She hung her clothes instead in the built-in wardrobe in the room she was being forced to share with Adam. 'Forced' felt like an appropriate word, even though she had agreed to this arrangement.

Then she and Ethan toured the gardens. The pool was set into raised decking with inset lights and easy chairs for relaxing. There were even lights in the pool. Sienna was glad that she had taught Ethan to swim at a very early age. He was like a water baby, he loved the water, so she had no fear for him living here.

He wanted to jump in right now but she persuaded him against it and instead they explored the rest of the garden with its massive lawns and a shrubbery and a small wooded area where Ethan could hide. It was paradise as far as he was concerned.

It seemed like only minutes before Adam returned, although it was actually about three hours, she realised when she glanced at her watch.

'I don't know about you but I'm starving,' Adam declared. 'Do we eat in or out? The choice is yours.'

'In,' she answered swiftly. She'd given Ethan a sandwich for his lunch but she'd had nothing for herself and she was hungry now too. 'There's enough food in the house to feed an army.'

Ethan became the buffer between her and Adam as she prepared their meal. He never stopped talking to his father and she was able to laugh and even enjoy herself.

'So what did you buy?' Adam asked when they finally sat down to eat.

'Nothing. Ethan and I explored outside instead. The garden's amazing. The pool's amazing. Ethan wanted to swim. I told him that —'

'But I wanted you to get new clothes.'

Sienna's chin set in a mutinous line. She had changed into a clean pair of jeans and a plain pink T-shirt and had thought she looked OK. 'Are you ashamed of me?'

'I'd never be that,' he answered softly, his eyes resting for a few seconds on the soft swell of her breasts.

Annoyingly she felt a faint response, a faint hardening. Her nipples tingled and she glared.

'Every woman likes new clothes. I thought you'd be off like a shot. I thought you'd have a mad spending spree.'

'Then you don't know me very well at all, Adam.' Blue eyes met blue. Sienna was the first to look away. 'I will shop, but in my own good time.'

She remembered now that Adam liked his women feminine. He liked floaty dresses and low-cut tops. He didn't approve of jeans. They had their place, he'd once said, but he preferred to see a woman's legs. He was definitely a legs man. He had once complimented her on her legs, which were long, and when she wore high heels they seemed to go on for ever. Or so he had said. But that had been then and this was now. Jeans were more practical.

After dinner it was Ethan's bedtime and Adam again read him a story. He seemed to enjoy doing this, it had become a ritual now, and Sienna sat quietly and listened and watched. It actually felt good to see him bonding with Ethan in this way.

Ethan's eyes never left his father's face and every now and then Adam looked at him and smiled, such a soft, gentle smile.

And it was not only Ethan he held in thrall. The deep tones of his voice were mesmerising. She had always found his voice sexy, especially when it went very low, and tonight was no exception. She didn't listen to what he was saying, just the cadence. It reverberated through her nerve ends, heightening her tension until in the end she got up and walked out of the room.

How could she sit there and carry on listening when he was doing unmentionable things to her body? How could she hide the very real emotions that were careening through her veins? Fortunately Ethan had his eyes closed by this time, he was probably even asleep, so he had no idea that she'd gone.

What she couldn't understand was why she felt like this when she had been forced into the situation. No— that was wrong. She hadn't been forced. She had brought it all on herself by her ludicrous suggestion. How the hell had she been supposed to know that Adam would agree? She ought to hate the very sight of him. She ought to feel nothing. And yet, conversely, she felt everything. All her old feelings were tumbling back with indecent haste.

Which was good in one way as she'd talked herself into sharing his bed. If she had no feelings for him, if they remained dead, it would be hell. In fact, it would be impossible. There was no way on this earth that she could let any man make love to her who she didn't have strong feelings for.

Adam finished the story, kissed his son, and then went in search of Sienna. The intervening years had done nothing to stem the hunger he had always felt for her. He had buried it somewhere deep down inside him, concentrating on building up his empire, and it hadn't risen again until the day she had come to see him.

When he'd first seen her standing hesitantly outside his apartment, her face on his monitor a picture of unease and impatience, he had felt a swift surge of desire race through his body. There and then he had wanted her.

And now she was his!

Today was only the beginning. Today had actually been easier than he had thought it would be. He had been prepared for her to flatly refuse to leave her home. He had expected a challenge on his hands.

But it hadn't happened, and she was here now, and

with Ethan fast asleep she would have to spend time in his company.

When Adam joined her out on the terrace Sienna's heart began an erratic beat. He had a look in his eyes that worried her. He wanted her and, yes, she wanted him too, very much so, every bone in her body ached for him. And yet it didn't feel right.

Their marriage had been a lie. Even now it was hard to believe that he had never loved her. He had been an attentive lover but that had been all, and she had been drawn into his web with the same unerring skill as a spider catching a fly.

And the question still remaining was why he had married her in the first place. Had it been for her body? Had she simply been a conquest?

It looked like it and she ought to despise him—yet her spark was still there, the hunger, the need. It didn't please her but there was nothing she could do about it. Her body had a mind of its own.

'Ethan's fast asleep,' he said softly.

'He was very tired—he's had an exciting day.'

'And your day? Has that been exciting too? Do you like your new home?'

Adam's eyes never left hers as he waited for her answer. But what could she say without hurting his feelings? She could hardly tell him that it wasn't to her taste. That it was too big, too pretentious. Not when he had made this magnificent gesture for his son's sake. She was not stupid. She knew that everything he did was for Ethan.

'It's a fine house,' she managed at last. 'You've been very generous, too generous. It's going to take some getting used to.'

'Ethan loves it.'

'He can't believe all the space he's got,' she said with a fond smile as she thought of her son's pleasure. 'It's a little boy's dream.'

'But not your dream?'

Her dream was of a man who truly loved her, for herself, not because she happened to be the mother of his child and they came as a pair. Not simply because he wanted a woman in his bed, available to him whenever he felt like it. 'I was happy in my flat.'

'And you think that you won't be happy here?'

Adam's eyes narrowed and Sienna knew that she needed to be careful. It was not only herself she had to think about but Ethan as well. 'I'll get used to it.'

'I want you to do more than get used to it, Sienna, I want you to enjoy it. I want you to feel relaxed and happy. I want us to be a family here.'

How could they ever be a proper family? He was asking the impossible.

'Sienna?'

'It will take time.' She evaded his eyes, turning away instead, walking across the lawn towards a summer-house. As a child she had always wanted her own play-house and she was thinking now that this might be somewhere where Ethan could play. Not that he needed any extra space, but children loved hiding and this would be a perfect den for him.

She heard Adam's phone ring and looked back, expecting it to be something to do with work. His expression changed from anger to concern as he listened. 'Yes. OK. I'll be there immediately. Thank you.'

But it was not his office who had called. He looked

at Sienna. 'My grandfather's been taken ill. He's in hospital. I need to be there. I haven't spoken to him in years but I cannot ignore him now. I'll try not to be long.'

'Of course.' Sienna felt compassion as well as relief. She had never had much to do with his grandfather, she had met him a few times but for some reason he had seemed to disapprove of her. And she actually hadn't known whether he was still alive, but it was important that Adam go to him now.

Adam had mixed feelings as he drove to the hospital. There was no love lost between him and his grandfather and he couldn't help wondering whether his visit would be appreciated.

What would the old man say, for instance, if he told him that Sienna had borne him a son? That he was now a father and he and Sienna were back together? It would probably finish him off altogether. His grandfather disliked Sienna intensely for the simple reason that she was too much like Adam's mother, and in his own warped mind he actually blamed his daughter-in-law for dying and ruining his own son's life.

It didn't make sense that he hated Sienna for this reason, but when Adam saw his grandfather lying pale and lifeless in his bed he knew that he couldn't open up old wounds. So he said nothing about her being back in his life. In fact, neither of them spoke very much at all. The old man kept his eyes closed, although Adam felt sure he wasn't asleep. But he didn't feel that he could just get up and go, he had to stay a decent length of time.

Sienna had been thinking of going to bed when Adam's car pulled on the drive. There were taut, tired lines on his face and she wondered whether she ought to suggest making him a drink of hot chocolate before he retired. Except that Adam probably wasn't a hot-chocolate man. He never had been in the past, whereas it was her favourite bedtime drink.

And she was right. Adam wanted strong coffee. Any sort of coffee. Instant would do.

'How is your grandfather?' she asked tentatively, putting the kettle on to boil and spooning coffee granules into a mug. He did not look as though he welcomed questions and she guessed that even his grandfather's illness had not bridged the gap between them. Which Sienna thought was sad.

'He's had a heart attack. A bad one. He may be in hospital for some considerable time.' His tone was clipped, his words concise, and it was clear that he did not want to talk about him.

'I'm sorry.'

'Even in his illness he did not welcome my presence. We barely spoke.'

Sienna felt even sorrier. 'I didn't actually realise he was still alive. He must be a great age.'

Adam shrugged. 'Late eighties He's made of tough stuff without a doubt. I wouldn't be surprised if he doesn't pull through.'

'Does he live by himself?'

'He has a housekeeper. She keeps him under control—or tries to,' he added with a wintry smile. 'He's a cantankerous old devil. But enough about him. I appreciate you waiting up for me, Sienna.'

'It was the least I could do.'

Without warning, without so much as a change of expression, he slid his arms around her waist and urged her against him.

Sienna had no time to protest, no time to lift her arms in defence. She was effectively his prisoner. The throb of his heart against her breastbone echoed the sudden frantic beat inside her.

It was fairly clear where this was going to lead. Adam needed something, someone, to take his mind off his hospital visit—and losing himself in her body would be the perfect solution. Already she could feel him growing hard and every sane emotion in her body told her to push him away before it was too late.

And yet she was committed. There was no escape. Even if she wasn't a magnet pulled and held her against the steel hardness of him. A magnet stronger than herself.

Adam appeared bigger and darker and extremely dangerous. Already every pulse in her body leapt into life. Her heartbeat was loud and irregular, thudding against her ribcage, echoing in her ears, tightening her throat.

This was what it was going to be like. They would settle into happy family life—on the surface at least. Ethan would believe his parents loved each other and loved him. He would be in his element. Yet there would be no love involved.

For all Adam's money, for all his success, he had denied her the one thing she really wanted.

Nevertheless, Sienna found herself leaning further into him. The scent of his body, his individual male scent that reminded her of when they had first met—when she had fallen in love with this impossibly good-looking man—stung her nostrils, swept a flash-flood of desire through her entire body.

Adam groaned, sensing her acquiescence, and his lips swooped down to claim hers in a mind-blowing kiss that sent every sane thought into outer space. The heat of him, the taste of him, both contrived to spin her senses, to leave her reeling, to want more!

How stupid was that when their marriage was over and the only reason he was being nice to her was because of Ethan? He had let her walk out of his life once before and had not once tried to find her, but now, now that he had a son, he wanted her again.

His coffee forgotten, Adam swung her up into his arms and carried her upstairs, kissing her senseless as he did so, giving her no opportunity to protest. Not that she wanted to. And once in the room they were to share his arms relaxed and she slid slow inch by excruciating slow inch down the length of his body until her feet touched the floor.

There was no disguising the fact that he was ready for her but he seemed in no hurry now. Sienna had thought that he would drop her onto the bed, rip off her clothes, and make love without any preliminaries.

How wrong she was. Instead, he traced the contours of her face with warm fingertips. 'You're incredibly beautiful, do you know that, Sienna?' His eyes were an amazing blue, a deep, dark navy, and Sienna felt herself drowning in them.

They sent dangerous signals through her sensory system. Was it because Adam had looked so tired when he'd come home that she felt sorry for him? Or was it because once he had touched her she couldn't help herself? Whatever, the feelings were crawling all over her body.

Adam's arms tightened around her. And his kisses

became more demanding. Sienna felt an explosion burst from the very centre of her, reaching out to fill her entire body. Sensations that exceeded everything she had ever felt before.

She had been young and immature when she had married Adam. Now older and wiser, she knew the power of his kisses, how they could trigger a potent response.

Arching her body into him, Sienna returned his kisses with fire, fire in her body, fire in her mind. Every sane thought had fled. And as soon as he felt her response Adam groaned, a deep, agonised growl low in his throat, and his kisses deepened, their tongues entwining, their hunger spinning them out of control.

For just a second his mouth left hers while he dragged off her T-shirt and unclipped her bra. His eyes were drawn to her softly moulded breasts with their dark pink nipples standing proud and ready, aching for him to touch them.

She felt no shyness, no distress. Everything was forgotten except the power of the moment. Her breasts swelled and seemed to surge towards him of their own accord, and when he lowered his head to take her nipples into his mouth, when his tongue and teeth nipped and teased, Sienna's head fell back, her eyes closed, her mind taking her into a world where only sensations mattered.

Her fingernails dug into his back as she urged her lower body deeper and harder against him. The heat and power of his erection only added to the hunger sweeping through her. She did not want to wait, she did not want foreplay, she wanted him to take her now, swiftly and fiercely.

Even though she was unaware of it she must have groaned and wriggled even more fervently against him because Adam's response was to rip off his shirt and let the muscular hardness of his chest with its springy dark hairs take the place of his hands and mouth. His body hair was like a whisper over skin, over her breasts, over her nipples, and yet its very softness created an entirely new sensation.

Hips ground against hips now and with trembling fingers he unfastened her jeans and slid them downwards. With a quick hop and a skip Sienna was out of them. He wanted to touch her then, he wanted to feel for himself the urgency pounding inside her, but Sienna wanted to free him of all restrictions as well.

Her fingers were equally as shaky as she undid his trousers and he was out of them so swiftly that it was a miracle he didn't fall over. Underpants were disposed of, thrown across the room, haste was the word. And now their liberated bodies came together.

It was all heat and passion, fingers exploring, mouths tasting, tongues teasing. Sienna felt as if her world was being blown apart. She could feel her heart thudding against her breastbone, feel the strength going out of her legs, and as if aware that any moment she would collapse Adam lifted her up and laid her down on the bed.

'You're beautiful, Sienna. You always were, but you're different now. You're a woman who wants to be made love to. I've never seen you more lovely, more exciting, more...' His words faded as he lowered himself over her.

'I need you, Sienna,' he groaned. 'I need you *now*!'

As she needed him.

Their coming together was powerful and instant, like thunder and lightning. Like a firework exploding. Like a rocket soaring.

A sheen of sweat covered Sienna's body as she lay exhausted by Adam's side afterwards. He was on his stomach, one arm draped over her, and she felt the heat of his body too. It was several minutes before their breathing returned to normal, before she felt able to move.

Then she shivered and Adam was instantly alert. 'You're cold?' He pulled her into his arms, his hands massaging her back.

'You're really something, Sienna, do you know that?' he questioned softly, his mouth against her cheek, caressing her skin with more kisses. 'Why did I ever let you go?'

His touch evoked fresh emotions, renewed hunger, and before Sienna could answer, before she could even think of an answer, he was making love to her again. More slowly this time, more eloquently. Except that the slowness became torture and Sienna gripped his shoulders hard, moving with him, driving them swiftly into a further climax that shattered her body and left her gasping for breath.

For several minutes she was too sensitised to move, she lay there in a haze of pleasure, marvelling at such exquisite feelings. She hated to admit it but it got better every time. There was no going back. Not now that she had tasted heaven.

CHAPTER TEN

SIENNA felt amazingly lonely when she discovered the bed beside her empty. It was almost as though she had dreamt what had happened. And yet how could she have dreamt such magic? It had been real all right. They had woken in the middle of the night and made love again. It was as if the years she and Adam had spent apart had never taken place. Their love life had suddenly blossomed and deepened again—and her body hungered for him.

Except—that all it had really been was sex. What was she thinking? There had been no emotions involved. She and Adam were no closer together. She would be as well to remember that and not let herself get carried away.

The house was quiet, too quiet. Ethan! Where was he? He always woke early and jumped on her bed. She looked at the clock and saw to her dismay that it was almost half past nine. Adam would have left for work so where was Ethan? With a groan she leapt out of bed. The first thing she thought about was his injury. He'd been extraordinarily brave about the whole thing but perhaps the excitement of moving had been too much and he—

She skidded to a halt when she saw his room empty. Her stomach felt hollow. Then she heard voices in the garden. When she looked through the window she could not quite believe her eyes. Adam and Ethan—in the swimming pool.

So Adam had not gone to work!

Wonders would never cease.

She swiftly showered and dressed and ran downstairs. Adam grinned when he saw her. 'Come and join us.'

In the brief second she looked at him Sienna saw Adam as she had never seen him before. A man in his element, relaxed, his normally unruly hair plastered to his well-shaped head. He looked happy, and she hated to use the word, but he looked human. He was not a machine who went to work and came home late every day. He was a family man. A man who cared for his son.

Amazing. Totally amazing. She actually felt the prick of tears in her eyes. This was something she had thought never to see.

'Mummy,' called Ethan. 'Look at me, I can swim on my back. Daddy showed me.'

'Why don't you join us?' suggested Adam. 'Work up an appetite for your breakfast.'

'No, thanks,' she said. She did not want to spoil their time spent together. Ethan looked so very happy swimming with his father. It was easy to see that he idolised Adam. 'I'll get breakfast ready instead while you two continue your swim.'

By the time breakfast was cooked Adam and Ethan had showered and dressed. She had heard Ethan giggling as his father tried to dry him. Ethan was like an eel, especially when his ticklish bits were touched. It did her heart good to hear them laughing together.

She had cooked Ethan a sausage sandwich, which was

his favourite food, and when Adam saw it he said that that was what he wanted too. So the two of them munched on their sandwiches while she ate a bowl of cereal.

Afterwards, when the dishwasher was loaded, Adam opting to do it, he suggested they take a ride out to Hampstead Heath where Ethan could run around to his heart's content. 'Have you ever taken him there before?' he asked Sienna.

'Actually, no. I've never had a car, for one thing.'

'Then that's something I must see to,' he declared. 'There's always my driver at your disposal but sometimes you'll want to be able to drive yourself.'

He was being too understanding for Sienna's peace of mind. But she quickly forgot it as she packed a picnic and it turned out to be a day that she would never forget. Adam was like a boy let out of school. He and Ethan kicked a ball, they all played hide and seek; they even caught a butterfly. And Ethan spent the whole day giggling.

She felt totally relaxed. She had never seen Adam play like this before. He had always been such a serious man that she had thought he must have been born that way. But with Ethan he let his hair down and did everything on his son's level, as though he was trying to make up for all his missed years.

A streak of guilt ran through her. When she had discovered that she was pregnant she should have gone back to him. Or at least let him know so that he could have been a part of his son's early life.

'Look,' said Adam suddenly and quietly. They were standing by one of the ponds, looking for fish, when a kingfisher landed on the far side.

Even Ethan held his breath. 'Daddy, he's beautiful,' he whispered.

'And you're very lucky to see him.'

'And I'm lucky, Daddy, that you brought me here.'

It was a special moment between them. Sienna felt a lump in her throat as father and son hugged, and she felt certain that Adam too was welling up inside. He kept his face turned carefully away from her.

Afterwards they ate their picnic. They had sausage rolls and egg sandwiches, crisps and pork pie, even tiny individual trifles that Sienna had found in the freezer and were by now perfect to eat.

'My parents used to bring me here when I was a child,' she told Adam. 'That was before they separated. I had such an idyllic childhood, it's a shame it all—' And then she stopped, suddenly realising what she was saying.

'It's not too late,' Adam said softly. 'Ethan has his best years in front of him. I bet you can't remember what you did before you were four?'

'I can't remember much,' she agreed. 'I do remember a tricycle I had and I got lost. My mother panicked. My father was at work. But I hadn't gone far, I was soon found.'

Adam smiled and stroked the back of her hand. It was the lightest touch yet it sent tremors down her spine. 'I did a similar thing. I loved my little trike. It became whatever I wanted it to be. A racing car. A train. A tractor even.'

Sienna conjured up an image of Adam as a little boy. He would look just like Ethan did now, with dark springy hair and a wicked grin. She'd like to bet that he had lived life dangerously and always worried his parents.

'Does Ethan have a bike?'

'No.' She shook her head, her eyes vaguely sad. 'There was never anywhere for him to ride safely. He can ride a bike, of course, they have them at nursery, but Ethan's never actually had one.'

'So we'll have to see about getting him one, won't we?'

It was the way he said 'we' that got to her. She had expected him to state that *he* would buy Ethan a bike. That he would do it without consulting her. This was turning into a day that she would always remember. A surprisingly happy day.

After another energetic game of football Ethan grew tired and Sienna suggested they go home. He was asleep almost before they set off and she sat quietly too.

Inside her, hope began to grow that their relationship could be turned around. She was forced to admit that she was still very much in love with Adam, that she had actually never truly fallen out of love, despite everything. And Adam—well, he needed to learn that just because his father had gone to pieces after his mother's death, it didn't mean that every man was the same. Besides, she didn't intend leaving this mortal earth for many years yet. She wanted to live into blissful old age with Adam at her side.

That night their love-making was better than ever, as though the day they had spent together had somehow intensified their feelings. And in the days that followed she let him see in every way possible that she loved him.

And yet no words of love ever passed his lips. He wanted her, he enjoyed her, and he adored his son. He played with Ethan endlessly. He never worked late, he honoured her wishes, but she was forced to the sad re-alisation that everything he did was for Ethan's sake.

His grandfather remained in hospital but Adam rarely visited him, which Sienna found sad. 'Perhaps I should go to see him?' she suggested. They were sitting outside after dinner. The air was still, it was one of those warm, balmy summer evenings when the scent of roses filled the air and the birds sang their evensong. 'It can't be any fun lying in a hospital bed with no visitors to relieve the monotony.' Although Sienna had never had anything to do with Adam's grandparent, she did feel sorry for him.

But Adam shook his head. 'He wouldn't appreciate it.'

'Why not?' Her fine brows drew together in a frown. 'How do you know?'

Adam sucked in a lungful of air and seemed to be having difficulty in finding the right words. Eventually, though, he spoke. 'Because—because he's never liked you, Sienna. He never approved of you. It's the reason why he and I fell out.'

Sienna felt her heart stop and then race. 'He doesn't like me? What have I ever done to him?' It didn't make sense. All these years he and Adam hadn't spoken and she was the reason! She racked her brains, trying to recall whether she had ever said anything to cause offence. And came up with nothing.

Adam did not answer her question. 'It's all water under the bridge, Sienna,' he said instead. 'Grandfather and I will never see eye to eye. We're too much alike.'

Too pig-headed. Too proud. Too busy making money. His grandfather was a rich man. He'd made his money in advertising. Sienna had often wondered why Adam had not followed him into the business, the same as his father had done, why he had started up for himself in developing properties.

'Nevertheless, I don't like being the reason you and he fell out,' she declared strongly. 'I think I should go to see him after all and try to put matters right.'

'The hell you will, Sienna. It's too late, I tell you.' Adam's eyes grew starkly cold, filled with a sudden anger that she didn't understand.

That night they did not make love. Adam lay with his back to her, still and silent, and although Sienna wanted to put her arms around him and tell him that she understood and was sorry for him, sorry for his grandfather, too, she did not dare.

He had erected a barrier around himself and she knew that only he could take it down. It was a pity because they had been getting on so well. Adam had shown a warmth towards her that had been absent even in the early years of their marriage. It was as though being a father had made a world of difference to him.

Now all that had gone again. Simply because she had suggested going to see his grandfather. Why on earth hadn't he told her all those years ago that the old man didn't like her? Surely they could have sorted it out.

Adam slept little, knowing that he ought to try to make amends with his grandfather. When Ethan grew up and hopefully had children of his own he would be heartbroken if they hated him as much as he had hated his grandfather all these years. Admittedly the old man had brought it all on himself. But Adam felt differently now that he was a father and he actually did not want his grandfather going to his grave believing that no one loved him.

A few weeks ago he would never have dreamed that his feelings would change so dramatically. And he had Sienna and Ethan to thank. Sienna was teaching him that relationships had to be worked at. Nothing came easily. Not love or hate. They were each born of communication and honesty. And when that was lacking...

For all these years he had worked towards one goal, he had let no one stand in his way. A selfish attitude and it had cost him his wife and the first years of his son's life, but changing was hard, especially since his visit to his grandfather had dragged up old memories, old hatreds.

It really was not that simple to let go. Only in bed with Sienna could he lose himself. Then the world was a perfect place. He was never happier. Everything was forgotten except that moment in time.

Last night had felt like hell.

CHAPTER ELEVEN

I'D LIKE to come with you,' said Sienna, her fine eyebrows lifted in hopeful anticipation. She didn't care that Adam's grandfather didn't like her. She simply felt that he ought to have more visitors.

'I don't want you leaving Ethan,' he told her firmly.

'Marie will look after him.' Marie was a woman who came in daily to do the jobs Sienna could easily have done for herself. It had been Adam's idea but she hadn't dared argue. And Marie had told Sienna that any evening she and Adam wanted to go out she would be more than willing to babysit.

'You really think my grandfather would be pleased to see you?' Adam's eyes were much darker than normal, even his body language told her that it was a definite no-no. He stood rigidly in front of her, almost challenging her to argue with him.

'Are you saying that he still hates me?' Sienna began to find the whole conversation bizarre. 'How can you be sure?'

'He doesn't know that we're back together.'

It was a plain, matter-of-fact statement, but it shocked

the hell out of her, made her heart pound. 'You haven't told him? He doesn't even know about Ethan?'

She saw a flicker in Adam's eyes, gone almost immediately, a blank expression taking its place. 'I saw no need to. He's very ill, Sienna, you seem to be forgetting that. I wouldn't like to distress him further.'

'Distress him?' It was impossible not to raise her voice. 'Why would telling him that he has a great-grandson distress him?' Surely it would give him the will to live? Or did he still hate her that much that it would kill him off altogether? Was that what Adam thought?

'You do not know my grandfather,' he replied bitterly. 'But if it will make you feel any happier, I will tell him tonight. Be prepared, though, to hear that he doesn't want to see either of you.'

'You are unbelievable,' she said. 'Your grandfather's unbelievable. What kind of a family have I married into?' She let her breath out on a long hiss of confusion and incredulity. In fact, she walked out of the house and into the garden, kicking at a blade of grass that had dared to grow on the immaculately mowed lawn.

They, of course, had a gardener, and a man to look after the pool. All of these things seethed in Sienna's mind now. Adam could afford to do anything he wanted, buy anything he wanted, and yet he was afraid to tell his grandfather that his wife was back and they had a child.

It made no sense. None of it made sense. Was the whole world going mad or was she the crazy one? She ought never to have walked back into Adam's life. She and Ethan had been happy as they were.

Actually, Ethan was still happy. Even happier. He loved his dad. He didn't see his faults, he was too young to understand. All he knew was that he had a father to play with him, to read to him, to buy him wonderful gifts. His world was rosy.

Adam knew that he owed it to Sienna to tell his grandfather but it was not that simple. Sienna did not know the whole truth. Neither did he ever want her to.

Not now that their marriage was beginning to mean something to him! He wanted nothing to ruin it. And the truth, if it came out, would spell the beginning of the end. He would lose her altogether. And possibly Ethan too, even though he would fight for him. But Sienna was a fighter too and she would not relinquish her son to anyone, not even to his father.

It would be a blood battle, and did he want that?

'So you've finally come to see me again?' Adam's grandfather was propped up with pillows, his face still pale and drawn but a surprisingly fierce light in his eyes. 'About time, too.'

Adam groaned inwardly. He was glad to see the old man looking a little better, but he didn't want a confrontation, not after he'd just walked away from one. 'I'm glad you're feeling better, Grandfather.'

'No thanks to you,' he growled. James Farley had wispy white hair and a pale complexion, with grey eyes not dissimilar in shape to his grandson's. 'What have you been doing instead of coming to see me?'

'I didn't think you were well enough for visitors.' Which was only half a lie.

'Poppycock! You'll do whatever you want and to hell with everyone else.'

'In that case, I take after you.' It was always the same

when they met. He had been prepared to talk quietly, to have the sort of comfortable conversation that grandfathers and grandsons should have, he'd been going to tell him that he had a great-grandson, but somehow in the space of a few seconds they had each managed to stir each other's blood.

'It's a pity your father didn't have the same backbone.'

Adam agreed with him. If his father hadn't gone to pieces after his mother had died, he would never have fallen out with his grandfather over Sienna. It was a vicious circle and he could see no way out of it.

Neither did he dare now to tell the old man that he was back with her or all hell would break loose. It might possibly kill him off altogether. And he didn't want that on his conscience.

Instead, he talked about the success of his business. 'I'm doing better than I ever expected. I'm in Europe and America. I'm expanding all the time.'

Instead of being impressed, the old man snorted. 'You wouldn't have done that if you hadn't got rid of Sienna. She would have held you back, your vision would have been clouded. It would be history repeating itself. Your father loved my daughter too much. He was no good without her. It's a case in point, Adam. You're better off without a woman in your life. You'd best remember that.'

Long after he had left the hospital his grandfather's words swam round and round in his mind. He had always believed that he had been better off without Sienna. He had got on with his life without her to hold him back, he had become the success that he was. But success hadn't bought him the happiness he expected. It had brought him loneliness instead.

Which he hadn't truly discovered until Sienna and Ethan had erupted into his life. He had thought he was happy but now he knew that it had all been a pretence. Nothing had prepared him for the joy he felt knowing he had a wonderful son like Ethan.

It gave life a whole new meaning. He loved lying on the floor with him, racing cars around a track, he loved swimming in the pool with him—he was a brave little swimmer already—and he truly loved hearing Ethan call him Daddy. It gave him a warm, comfortable feeling.

But even more than this he loved having Sienna back in his life.

He had never fully realised what he had been missing. She had brought a whole new meaning to the word marriage. She was sensational in bed but even better than that she kept his feet firmly grounded. She taught him that family life meant a whole lot more than making pots of money.

On that point alone he did not agree with his grandfather.

Sienna was waiting for Adam. She had spent her time imagining the conversation he would have with his grandfather. James Farley would be surprised to hear that they had got back together, maybe shocked even, but he would surely be pleased. She couldn't imagine that he would still hold his grievance against her—whatever it was. And he would be astonished to hear that he had a great-grandson. And once he'd got used to the idea, he would want to see Ethan.

Ethan, too, would be tremendously excited to find out that he had a great-grandfather. It would be a one-up on

all of his friends who had grandfathers. A great-grandfather would be so much more important than a mere
grandfather.

Her own father had gone to live in New Zealand after
his divorce and she never heard from him. Her mother
was remarried and had moved to Ireland but much to
Sienna's disappointment they saw little of each other.
She had never been able to afford to go over there, and
her mother hadn't visited. They kept in touch by phone
but that was all. It wasn't the same.

Adam looked tired, she thought, when he walked in.
He had lines of strain on his face and didn't quite meet
her gaze. She knew instantly what had happened.

'You haven't told him, have you?' she demanded
fiercely and loudly, not even waiting for him to speak.
'After everything I've said, and after promising, you
still haven't told him.'

Her anger triggered anger. Adam scowled, his eyes
navy and savage, his thick brows jutting ever more
fiercely over them. 'My grandfather's a very ill man.'

'And what's that supposed to mean?' She was fired
up and ready to go. 'That it would be too a big a shock?
I would have thought that hearing he had a four-year-
old great-grandson would cheer him up. Not the other
way round.'

Adam towered over her like an avenging angel.
His body was taut, looking ready to snap. Even his
nostrils flared.

Sienna sensed danger and knew that she ought not to
press the issue but something drove her on. Ethan
deserved to know his great-grandfather. And the old man
deserved to know Ethan as well. It was as simple as that.

Why couldn't Adam see it? Why was he being so stubbornly obstinate? Why couldn't he see the wider picture?

'You can't go on ignoring the bond between you.' It was criminal that he was denying his grandfather the pleasure of young blood. 'Ethan will light up his life. You're being extremely unfair and negative about the whole thing.'

'You do not know what you are talking about, Sienna.' Adam rubbed the back of his neck and looked suddenly tired.

'Then tell me.'

The look he gave her suggested that she was being irrational but Sienna did not think so. As far as she was concerned, she had made a perfectly normal request— and he had failed to carry it out. When he turned away she accepted that there was nothing more she could do tonight. Continuing to protest most certainly wouldn't help matters.

In bed that night, when she had expected Adam to ignore her, he did nothing of the sort. He groaned and pulled her into his arms instead. 'It's been a hell of a day, Sienna. I need you like I've never needed you before.'

What she ought to have done was declare that she wouldn't allow him to make love to her again until he had told his grandfather. Except that his nearness drove her crazy. Her body melted against him and the instant his knowing fingers touched and tortured, everything else was forgotten, she wanted nothing but Adam's body beside her and inside her. She wanted everything he had to offer. And more importantly she wanted him to feel that way too. She wanted to help him forget his torment.

He made love without the usual preliminaries,

driving himself into her like a man who was having his last wish granted. And it was all the more exciting because of it. Sienna felt as though she had died and gone to heaven.

And later, when they had both regained their breath, he touched and stroked more gently, seeking out all her erogenous places. He knew precisely how to suck her nipples into his mouth and stroke them with his teeth until she bucked and wriggled and wanted him inside her again. He knew that to nibble behind her ears created a similar response. He knew that even her belly button was responsive to his touch.

So many places, so much mind-blowing pleasure.

When he wanted to enter her again she bucked away from him. 'Oh, no, Adam, it's your turn this time.' And she teased his nipples in exactly the same way, enjoying his reaction, the deep groans, the way his face screwed up as if he was in agony. Then she kissed her way down to his navel, exploring it with her tongue, then lower and lower.

Before she could reach her goal he hauled her on top of him. 'Take me inside you, Sienna. Do it now, do it quickly.'

With their positions reversed, Sienna guided him into her. It was the first time they had ever made love this way and it gave her a feeling of power. Until his groan rent the air and he quickly turned her over. Within the space of a heartbeat he lost control.

Sienna stretched languorously when she awoke the next morning. She felt good, she felt warm and happy and wanted Adam to make love to her again. But the bed beside her was empty, and a note on his pillow said that he had gone to work. She smiled at the thought of him writing the note, it was something he had never done before. Perhaps a turning point?

As she showered her thoughts turned to his grandfather. Maybe James Farley didn't like her, but was that any ground to hide Ethan from him? Adam was being pathetically cautious. There and then she made the decision to go and see him as soon as she had taken Ethan to nursery. She would deal with Adam's fury when the time came.

Her heart pounded as she entered the hospital, a private one naturally—would the old man go anywhere else? And when she announced who she had come to see she was taken to a pleasant room where she found him sitting in a chair near the window. A fountain played in the centre of a lawn and a dovecote was alive with white doves. It was a satisfyingly peaceful scene.

He looked at her long and hard, and Sienna began to wonder whether he recognised her, before he said gruffly, 'What are you doing here?'

Not a very auspicious beginning, thought Sienna, not the welcome she would have liked, but she ignored his beady stare and smiled instead. 'I thought you might be in need of some company.'

A snort followed her words. 'It depends who the company is.'

Meaning that she was not on his list of favourite people!

'Adam's at work. I thought—'

Another loud exclamation of disgust, a flash of pale eyes. 'So you've wheedled your way back into his life? How the hell did you manage that? He's a very busy man, he can do without distractions like you.'

Sienna was beginning to see why Adam had found it difficult to tell his grandfather about Ethan. James Farley had become more obstreperous with old age. He'd always been difficult but…

What did she do now? Did she blurt out the fact that she had borne Adam a son and that's why they were back together? Or did she try to get him onside first?

'I guess we never really stopped loving each other.' What a lie that was, but perhaps he didn't know about his grandson's incapacity to love.

'And it took you five years to discover that?'

James Farley might be old but his mind was still sharp. It hadn't taken him long to work out how long they'd been apart.

Sienna shrugged. 'We were both busy.'

'He's a fool.'

'I'm sorry if that's your opinion,' she said quietly. 'May I sit down?'

'Are you staying?'

'I'd like to.'

'Why?'

'Because we've never really got to know each other. I thought that—'

'You thought that you'd wheedle your way into my good books so that I'd leave you something in my will, is that it?'

Sienna shot her eyes wide. 'Of course not.'

'Good, because you're not getting anything.'

Such bitterness. Didn't old people usually mellow? Why was he like this? And would she be doing more harm than good if she told him about Ethan now? But this was her mission and he deserved to know. It might turn him around, give him something nice to think about, give him an incentive for living. It couldn't be easy, sitting here day after day with no company. Perhaps it was loneliness that was making him bad-tempered.

'If you really don't want my company, I'll go,' she said, thinking carefully as she spoke, already turning back towards the door. 'I was going to tell you something I really feel you ought to know, but—'

'Wait!' His voice wasn't strong but it was a command nevertheless. 'If you've come here for a specific purpose—apparently not simply to see me—then for pity's sake have the decency to tell me. Don't walk away like a coward.'

Sienna turned and fixed her blue eyes on James Farley's rheumy grey ones. Swallowing hard, she said, 'It's something Adam should have told you, but felt he couldn't. We have a son, Mr Farley. His name is Ethan and he's four years old.'

Silence followed. A long silence. And Sienna was afraid that she had gone too far, that he wasn't ready for such information. But amazingly his lips quivered, a smile followed. A weak one, a ghostly one, but a smile nevertheless.

'I have a great-grandson?'

Sienna nodded. And waited.

'Is he why you came back?'

'Yes,' she whispered.

'What took you so long?'

'Adam always put his work first. He's a driven man. I thought he would be angry and send me away again. At the very least he would have accused me of holding up his chances of success.'

'Which you would have done,' he announced bluntly.

'I'm aware of your feelings,' answered Sienna, keeping her chin high. 'It's why you've never liked me.'

'Adam told you that?' he asked, a frown now adding to the other creases on his brow.

She nodded.

'But it didn't stop you coming here today? You have guts, girl. In the end you thought Adam deserved to know. The same as you felt that I should know. I've underestimated you, Sienna. It must have taken a great deal of courage to come here. Does Adam know?'

'No,' she said softly.

'Why didn't he tell me himself?'

'Do you have to ask?' she questioned with a wry smile.

'I guess I wasn't very well disposed towards him. I'm in shock, Sienna. How about I ring for a pot of tea?'

Sienna was amazed at how well he had taken her news. She had expected to be shooed out. She had thought he would show no interest in his great-grandson, just as he'd had no interest in her. Instead, it appeared that finding out about Ethan had performed a miracle.

She stayed another hour, telling him about Ethan and the life they'd had together, and she promised that she would bring him on a visit one day.

When she got back to the house Sienna felt pleased with herself. She had actually achieved something today. But her happiness was short-lived when Adam came home and she told him where she had been.

'You did what?'

'I went to see your grandfather,' she repeated.

Adam groaned and closed his eyes and she knew exactly what he was thinking. 'Did he throw you out?'

'He wanted to at first when he found out that we were back together, but once I'd told him about Ethan we got on like a house on fire.' She almost laughed at the expression on Adam's face. 'Don't you believe me?'

'He wasn't angry?'

'Why should he be? When he learned that he had a great-grandson he went all soft.'

Adam's eyed widened. 'My grandfather soft? I don't believe you.'

'Well, perhaps not quite soft and mushy,' she agreed with a laugh, 'but he warmed towards me and he's looking forward to meeting Ethan. I thought perhaps we'd go at the weekend. What do you think?'

Adam did not know what to think. He had been horrified when Sienna had told him where she'd been, he had imagined all sorts of repercussions. And when she'd confessed to telling him about Ethan he'd gone cold all over. Much as he wasn't overly fond of his grandfather he had no wish to see him further displeased.

And yet here she was, saying that James Farley actually wanted to meet Ethan. The very thought sent his mind spinning out of control. Ethan had brought him and Sienna back together, now it looked as if he was going to do the same with his grandfather.

Did the boy have magic powers? Or were children naturally good ambassadors?

He shook his head. 'I cannot believe all that I am hearing.'

'Believe me, it's true,' Sienna told him with one of her incredible smiles. She slid her arms about his waist and turned her face up to his. 'This is one happy day.'

But her happiness did not last.

She said nothing to Ethan about his great-grandfather, she wanted it to be a surprise. She could imagine his pleasure, his whoop of joy, and if she told him too soon he'd be so excited that he would not sleep, and he'd keep pestering her as to when they were going to see him.

In the end Ethan never got to see his grandfather. Adam had a phone call on Friday evening to say that his grandfather had died. He'd suffered another heart attack.

CHAPTER TWELVE

TEARS slid down Sienna's cheeks. She had been looking forward to getting to know Adam's grandfather, seeing more of him, introducing Ethan, watching the two of them interact and bond.

Now it was too late, it would never be. It was so sad and she couldn't help wondering whether her visit had had anything to do with it. Her heart felt heavy at the thought.

Adam turned away and Sienna wondered whether he was blaming her, as well. Or if he was wishing that he had tried long before now to make amends. The old man hadn't treated him fairly but even so he was Adam's only blood relative. She saw the way his shoulders sagged and she wanted to comfort him but didn't know how, whether it would even be welcome.

At least it had been quick, that was one consolation. James wouldn't suffer any more. But the sadness remained with them, and Adam had the job in the days that followed of arranging the funeral.

It was a quiet affair. His grandfather had outlived all of his cronies so there was no one except Adam and Sienna to stand by his graveside and wish him a last farewell. More tears rolled down Sienna's cheeks. What a sad ending to his life. She held Adam's hand tightly as they walked away. He didn't know it but she had seen a tear in his eye too.

Later that evening, after Ethan was in bed, unaware of the traumatic day they had had—Sienna hadn't thought it fitting to tell him about the death of someone he had never known—Sienna asked Adam why his grandfather had never liked her. 'It came across in waves when I went to see him, it was only after I told him about Ethan that he melted. It wasn't a comfortable feeling to be hated so much.'

Adam drew in a deep sigh and shook his head. 'It's not a story that you'd want to hear, not today anyway.' His lips thinned, his thoughts clearly flying back over the years.

But Sienna insisted. 'It can't make any difference now. I thought he was a lonely old man. I actually felt sorry for him.' And she knew that she wouldn't rest until Adam told her the whole story.

'You wouldn't feel sorry if you'd known him properly,' asserted Adam, jumping to his feet and striding across the room. He looked out across the gardens and Sienna knew he was fighting his demons.

The air was very still outside, the sky even at this hour an intense blue. It felt as though the world was holding its breath, waiting to hear about his grandfather.

'And since I didn't get to know him, I'm looking to you to tell me about him,' she added softly.

He turned then and looked at her with eyes that were filled with immense sorrow. Which Sienna found odd considering he had never liked the old man. Clearly a lot had gone on between them that she knew nothing about.

Finally he spoke. 'He said that you reminded him of my mother.' Adam's voice was so quiet that she had to strain to hear. 'And he wanted no reminders. He actually blamed her for dying, for the way my father went to pieces afterwards.'

Sienna saw raw emotion on his face, his eyes once again moist with unshed tears. Was she asking too much of him too soon? He had never spoken much about his mother but she knew that he had loved her dearly and had never got over her death. And his grandfather's attitude must have made it far worse.

Several long seconds passed. So many unhappy memories were flooding his mind that it was painful to watch and yet she knew that she had to ask the crucial question. 'So you went the opposite way and married me *because* I reminded you of your mother? You did it to spite your grandfather.'

His denial was instant and emphatic. 'That was not my reason.'

Of course he would say that. He wouldn't admit to such derisory grounds for asking her to marry him. There wasn't a cat in hell's chance of him admitting the truth. Sienna curled her fingers into her palms. This was not a day when they should be arguing and yet she could not help herself. He couldn't make such a profound statement and then expect her not to react.

'No?' she asked, her eyes wide. 'And yet you fell out with your grandfather because of me. It doesn't make sense, Adam.' None of it made sense. The whole thing was growing more bizarre by the second.

Adam drew in a deep breath, compressing his lips until they were almost non-existent, his whole being as still as the calm before a storm, and what he said next blew Sienna away.

'I fell out with him because he said that if I married you he would disinherit me.'

She stopped breathing.

'I couldn't believe he had said that.' Adam shook his head as if reliving the scene. 'Did he think I couldn't stand on my own two feet? That I couldn't make a go of my life without *his* money? And you can bet your life that I wasn't going to let him tell me who I could or could not marry.'

His words were suddenly harsh, his face flooded with anger.

Silence filled the air between them. A loud silence.

Sienna felt her head spin and thought she might faint.

Adam had married her simply to prove to his grand-father that he could do whatever he wanted! That he would not be dictated to.

Unbelievable!

It meant that there was no truth in his statement that he was unable to love because of what had happened to his father. The fact was he simply didn't love her!

The only reason he had married her was to prove himself to his grandfather. It had been a war between the two men.

She had been stuck in the middle!

And now she had marched right back into his life!

Adam closed his eyes, needing to block from his view Sienna's shocked face. It had been wrong to have this discussion today of all days. Today should have been a day of mourning, not disclosures.

He felt truly sorry now for having told her. He should

have waited, he should have left it. He shouldn't have mentioned it at all.

He hadn't realised all those years ago that his grand-father had been trying to protect him when he had declared that Sienna was wrong for him. That his grand-father simply hadn't wanted history repeating itself. He hadn't wanted Adam to love Sienna so much that if anything happened to her he would fall into the same trap as his father.

In that moment Adam realised that the incredible had happened. He was truly and deeply in love with Sienna. He was in that trap. He wouldn't be able to function without her.

But Sienna looked at him with eyes of stone. 'I cannot believe that I am hearing this. I rue the day I ever met you, Adam. I thought that we had married for love. I know I accused you of loving your work more than me but deep down in my heart I didn't mean it. I truly thought that you loved me. What a fool I was. I loved you more deeply than you'll ever know. But it's gone now. We're over, Adam. I wish that I'd never come to see you.'

'You cannot walk out, I will not let you.'

His voice was immediately strong and a fierce light shone from his eyes, a light that warned her, told her, that if she dared to attempt it he would be there to stop her. Well, let him try. He would soon discover how serious she was.

'Sienna...' Adam closed the space between them, ignoring the signs in her eyes, knowing only that some-how he had to make amends.

But Sienna was quicker, sidestepping away from him, darting to the other side of the room. Near the doorway. 'It's over, Adam. You have no idea how much I'm hurting. In fact, I don't think the hurt will ever go away. Not that you're worthy of such pain. I hate you, Adam, with the whole of my breaking heart.'

She ran out of the door and up the stairs, intent only on escaping him. She needed to be alone with her thoughts. Her heart was indeed breaking in two. Her whole world was crumbling around her. Hot, plump tears slid down her cheeks as she threw herself down on the bed.

It was amazing how one short declaration could change everything. She found it hard to believe that Adam had married her simply to spite his grandfather. What sort of a man did that? And what woman in her right mind would carry on living with someone who had made such an admission?

He hadn't been backwards in using her body. It had been the best part of their relationship. It was ironic that he had made her feel so very special when all the time it had been part of his devious plot to get one over on James.

Sienna clamped her lips tightly together, her mind going over and over the events of the last weeks. It had actually seemed as though everything was coming together, the future had looked rosy. And yet in an instant it had been shattered. It lay around her feet like shards of glass, like petals dashed from a rosebush by heavy rain. Never in her life had she felt so worthless.

The realisation dawned that Adam never actually kissed or cuddled her except when they were making love. Why hadn't she put two and two together and rec- ognised that all he needed was a bed partner? It saddened her to accept that this was all he had ever wanted her for.

There was no doubt in her mind now that it was imperative she get out of here. Where she would go she had no idea. But escape was her goal. She had Ethan to think about too. He would be devastated if he thought he was losing the father he had only just found. All of this needed to be taken into consideration.

She expected Adam to come after her, was surprised when he didn't. But at least it gave her thinking time, planning time. How long she lay on the bed Sienna had no idea. At some stage she must have fallen asleep because she awoke shivering. She pulled the covers over her, still fully dressed, but did not go back to sleep.

The green glow from the clock told her that it was almost midnight—and the bed beside her was empty. Not that she cared. Adam could go to hell. She would never forgive him for the way he had treated her. Never!

The night was long and cruel, her mind tormented, but when morning came she had made her plans. Thankfully Adam had left for work by the time she got up, and after taking Ethan to school she began making phone calls.

For a few days they barely spoke. She slept in one of the other rooms, getting up early so that Ethan would not know there was anything wrong. Even Adam acted normally in front of Ethan, swimming with him, promising to take him out on his boat again, reading him bedtime stories, including Sienna in everything he did.

Sienna was suspicious. If he thought that by pretending nothing had happened it would all go away, he could think again. She kept cheerful for Ethan's sake but as soon as he was in bed and asleep she ignored Adam totally, usually shutting herself in her room, watching TV or reading a book.

Until the night Adam came to see her. He pushed the door open without even knocking. 'Things have gone on for long enough, Sienna. We need to talk.'

'About what?' she asked, her blue eyes coldly hostile. 'About the fact that you don't love me, never have and never will? That our marriage is a sham and Ethan is stuck in the middle? Is that what you want to talk about? Do you have a magic recipe to put everything right? I don't think so. You and I are finished, Adam. I'll soon be out of your hair.'

His nostrils flared as he stared at her for several long condemning seconds. 'And Ethan?'

'You'll have rights.' She noticed that he didn't say anything about her leaving, it was only Ethan who concerned him. Just as she had thought.

'Rights be damned! Ethan is not leaving this house. I've lost enough years already.' His eyes were cold and condemning, his chin tilted arrogantly, the cleft beneath his lips clearly defined. He was firmly of the belief that he could make this happen.

Sienna thought otherwise. 'If you really expect me to stay here, locked into a loveless marriage, Adam, you're crazy.'

Jutting black brows gathered fiercely together. 'We can work at it, for Ethan's sake.'

'Let's leave Ethan out of this.' Sienna kept her back ramrod straight, her eyes declaring war. Her chestnut hair was tousled where she had raked her fingers through it, but she did not care what she looked like. There was no way that she was going to give in. Her mind was made up.

She was leaving him.

And Ethan was going with her.

'How can we leave him out of it when he is a part of both of us?' Adam's voice had never been stronger. It was like steel and Sienna shivered as a chill ran down her spine. 'I will not stand by and let you take him from me.'

She would need to be careful. It had been wrong to tell him that she was planning to leave because he would now watch her like a hawk. She heaved a sigh. 'I guess I wasn't thinking straight.'

'Indeed you weren't.' Gruffness filled Adam's voice. 'We don't have to sleep together, Sienna, if you cannot face that, but Ethan has to be our main consideration.'

'Of course,' she said quietly, looking down at her feet, not wanting him to see that she was lying through her teeth.

'Then I will say no more.'

She had half hoped that Adam would go back to his apartment after their argument. It could actually work if they lived that way. She and Ethan in this house, Adam in his apartment. Then Ethan could see his father frequently and she would be happy with him out of her hair.

But dared she even suggest it? Or would the fact that she would still be forced to see him periodically make matters worse?

She guessed plan number one was the best. She had already warned her mother to expect her.

Happily Adam did not know in which part of Ireland her mother lived. And if he tried to find her it would be like looking for a needle in a haystack. She would be perfectly safe.

On the day they left she waited until Adam had gone to work before she packed their clothes and a few of

Ethan's toys, telling him that they were going to Ireland to visit his grandmother.

'How about Daddy?' he asked.

Not wanting to tell him an outright lie, Sienna said, 'Daddy has his work, he can't come with us.'

'But I will see him again soon?'

'Of course you will,' she assured him. Though she did not know how long it would be before she allowed that to happen. The way she was feeling at this moment it would be a very long time.

It wasn't being fair on Ethan, she knew that, and she didn't want him to forget about Adam altogether. They had had such a short time together it wasn't really fair on him, or Adam either. But how could she stay under the circumstances? It still made her hackles rise every time she recalled that he had married her simply to get one up on his grandfather. What sort of a man would do a thing like that? Had he ever meant to tell her, or had he planned to go through his whole life keeping it a secret?

There would come a time when they would need to see each other again, perhaps when she wasn't so angry, but meanwhile Ethan would be happy living in a new place with his grandmother. He'd have all sorts of new things to do, places to explore.

She had told them at the nursery school, though she hadn't said exactly where they were going as she did not want anyone passing the information on to Adam. And she had hired a taxi to take them to the airport, rather than using his driver. They were taking a flight to Dublin and she had paid cash for everything so that Adam could not track her movements. The account he had opened for her was the one thing she could thank him for. For once she did not have to worry about money.

Although Ethan had been fretful when they were leaving the house, excitement soon took over when he found out that he was going on a plane. 'Wow, Mummy!' he exclaimed when they reached the airport. 'Are we going on Daddy's plane? Is he coming with us?'

Sienna frowned. 'Daddy's plane?'

'Yes, he told me about it, he promised to take me on a ride one day if I was very good.'

This was the first Sienna had heard about it but she was not surprised. Whatever money could buy, Adam seemed to have. In her opinion it hadn't made him into a better person, though. He had ridden roughshod over her, buying the house, insisting they move in, spoiling Ethan terribly with all the presents he bought. Every night there was something different. It wasn't good for her son.

And Adam wasn't good for her!

'Well, we're not going on Daddy's plane today.'

Sienna suddenly realised how sharply she had spoken and softened her voice. 'We're going on a much bigger one. This is the biggest adventure of your life, Ethan.'

His little face split into a wide smile. 'Thank you, Mummy. And when Daddy comes, I'll be able to tell him all about it.'

'You certainly will,' she answered, grimacing inside, wishing that his hopes were not so high. Deep down she hated what she was doing to him. But for her own sanity she had to get away. She could not carry on living with a man who didn't love her, who had never loved her.

During their wait at the airport Sienna constantly

looked over her shoulder and it was not until they were
on the plane that she was able to relax.

When they reached Dublin her mother was waiting.
Sienna had tears in her eyes as they hugged. It wasn't
until she had had Ethan that she had realised the power
of a mother and child relationship. It was a bond too
strong to break, and they hadn't seen enough of each
over the years.

'And look at you, Ethan,' said his grandmother,
folding him into her arms. 'How you have grown.'

'I'm four and a half,' said Ethan importantly.

'And do you go to school?'

'Yes.'

'Then you must tell me all about it when we get home.'

Home was a cottage on the coast. It was an hour and
a half's drive away from Dublin and Sienna had never
seen anywhere look more welcoming or peaceful. This
was exactly what she needed. Somewhere remote,
somewhere where Adam would never find them. What
little bit of guilt she felt for taking Ethan away from him
she quickly forgot once they settled in.

Her mother was a good-looking woman in her forties
with blonde hair and grey eyes, still as slender as she had
been in her teens, and was clearly happy with her life here.

Her husband, Niall, was an artist and had a studio at
the bottom of the garden. He specialised in seascapes
and Sienna could not think of a better place for an artist
to live and work.

Ethan was fascinated with all the brushes and paints
and poor Niall was soon being bombarded with questions, leaving Sienna time alone with her mother.

'Is there something wrong?' asked Anne. 'I didn't

want to question you before but as soon as you said you'd like to come and stay with us I couldn't help wondering.'

Sienna sighed, a heavy sigh that lifted her chest before relaxing again. 'I went to see Ethan's father.'

Anne's pale eyebrows rose. 'And?'

'We moved in together.'

'I see. I take it it's not working out?'

'Not at all,' declared Sienna, shaking her head. 'I thought he deserved to know about Ethan, but it was a mistake. Marrying him was a mistake. The biggest one I've ever made. Bigger than agreeing to move in with him again.'

Anne took her daughter's hands in hers. 'We all make mistakes, darling. It's how we deal with them that counts. Is running away the best solution, do you think? I met mine head on. I divorced your father. Why have you never wanted a divorce from Adam? Do you still love him?'

It took Sienna a long time to answer, and then all she said was, 'I don't know.' There were times when she did and times when she didn't. It was like riding a roller-coaster. There were so many ups and downs that she couldn't keep count.

'Which means you do still love him,' said her mother sagely. 'Otherwise it would have been a definite no.'

Adam was anxious to get home. As each day had passed and Sienna had still been there, he had counted his blessings. When she had announced that she and Ethan were going to walk out on him he had felt raw, as though he had been cut wide open. It had felt like salt being rubbed into a wound. And it had hurt like hell.

Thank goodness he had persuaded her to stay. He wanted her at his side for the rest of his life. He needed to be patient, though. He shouldn't have told her about his grandfather. It had been an insane thing to do. And now he had to find some way of making amends.

Simply telling her that he loved her wouldn't do. She wouldn't believe him, she would think that he was saying it to try and get her back into his bed. Which wasn't his main reason at all, even though it was one he would certainly enjoy. The nights had been hellish without her.

The house was quiet. Too quiet! It was too early for Ethan to be in bed, so where were they? Suspicion built in him and he raced up the stairs, taking them two at a time, calling out their names at the same time.

Her room was neat and tidy—and empty! The same with Ethan's. He snatched open wardrobe doors and saw nothing but more emptiness!

His heart slammed down into his feet.

She had gone! Despite her promise, she had left him. She had taken Ethan, his precious son, and they had gone God knew where.

In that split second Adam wanted to sit down and cry. He wanted to drop his head in his hands and sob. Nothing had ever made him feel like this before.

CHAPTER THIRTEEN

ADAM had had no idea that Sienna was still planning to leave. He should have been more alert. He thought that he had persuaded her to stay. How wrong could he be?

'*I will not stand by and let you take him from me.*' His own words came back to haunt him.

'*I wasn't thinking straight.*'

'*Indeed you weren't. We don't have to sleep together, Sienna, but Ethan has to be our main consideration.*'

'*Of course.*'

'*Then I will say no more.*'

She had looked truly contrite and he had been satisfied. He thought that she was of the same opinion as him, that Ethan needed both his parents.

And now she had gone!

Without leaving a single clue!

The first thing he did was try her mobile phone, but it was switched off. Every time he tried it, it was off. Then he phoned Maria, but he drew a blank there as well. It was her day off, he should have known. Sienna had cleverly waited until she knew that no one would see her leave.

He went to see Jo. Sienna's old neighbour was as

shocked as he to hear that Sienna had run away. 'I've not heard from her. I thought she was happy with you.'

'So did I,' he growled. 'Have you any idea where she might have gone?'

Jo shrugged. 'Not really. Anywhere, I suppose.'

Which was no answer at all! 'Does she have other friends?'

'I don't think so. She's never mentioned anyone special.'

Adam felt that he was getting nowhere fast and his blood pressure was rising. How could Sienna do this to him? And, more importantly, to Ethan? It was unfair on both of them.

Did she really hate him that much that she couldn't bear living with him any more? He shouldn't, of course, have told her the real reason he had married her. It had been a fatal mistake, a damning admission, and had damaged their relationship further.

But hadn't he shown her recently that he loved her? Surely she must have picked up on it? Did it matter what had happened in the past? Wasn't the present more important?

He realised how little he knew about Sienna. He had, by his own insensitive behaviour, sent her running. He felt terribly guilty. Everything was his fault. Every damn thing! And now he hadn't a clue where to start looking.

He checked her bank account and discovered that she had drawn out a huge amount of cash but paid nothing by cheque or on her card. He even checked Ethan's school in case Sienna had told them the reason she had pulled him out, perhaps left a forwarding address. But to no avail. So what did he do now? The driver he had

put at her disposal said he hadn't been asked to take her
anywhere—which meant she must have called a taxi.

She was clever. She had left no clues whatsoever.

By this time Adam was pulling his hair out. Sleep
became impossible. How could he sleep without
knowing where Sienna and Ethan were? And where did
he begin his search? Because if he had to search every
inch of the country, he would do so. Unless she had gone
abroad, gone as far away from him as she could. Hadn't
she once said something about a distant relative in
Australia? He groaned.

The thought that she had put as much space between
them as she could cut deep. It stopped him breathing. It
was like a knife turning in a wound. If that was the case,
it would be impossible to find her.

Except that nothing was impossible! He would check
all the airports. See if she had been booked on any flight.

Didn't her mother live in Ireland? He was sure that
she'd once mentioned it, many years ago when they
had first met. Maybe they had gone there? He felt a brief
glimmer of hope. As far as he knew, they never saw each
other but where else would she go? Would it be a wild-
goose chase? He had no address, nothing. He racked his
brains to try and recall whether Sienna had ever dropped
a clue. But he drew a blank.

Sienna was constantly on her guard, afraid that Adam
would discover her whereabouts and come after her like
a raging bull. She had done all she could to cover her tracks
but was aware that Adam would leave no stone unturned.

Ethan, on the other hand, was in his element, learning
to paint. Sienna was actually quite proud of him. He

seemed to have a natural talent, which Niall said should be nurtured. He naturally kept asking where his father was, and Sienna's answer was always the same. 'Any day soon, my darling, you'll see him. Don't forget Daddy's a very busy man.'

She tried to ignore her own aching heart. Despite everything, despite vowing to hate Adam for the rest of her life, there was no hiding the fact that she was still crazily in love with him. Her wise mother had been right. There were times when she even wondered whether they ought to go back, whether putting space between them was worth all the heartache.

It was then that she had to remind herself that Adam wanted only his son—not her, never her. She was someone to be used in bed! Making love was magical, she was able to forget everything in those moments, but was it enough? Enough to survive on for the rest of her life, or at least until Ethan was grown up and left home?

Her heart simply couldn't take the pain.

'Adam!'

'Peter! What are you doing here?' The last person Adam had expected to see was Peter Wainwright. He had been in Ireland for two days but so far hadn't been able to pick up Sienna's trail. She had definitely flown to Dublin, that was as much as he knew. But no one remembered seeing a beautiful chestnut-haired Englishwoman with a young, dark-haired son.

Peter was a long-time business acquaintance who he sometimes met socially. He had even been at their wedding.

'Business, old boy. And I guessed you must be some-where around because I saw Sienna yesterday.'

Adam went very still. He even stopped breathing. But he gave nothing away. 'She never mentioned seeing you. Where was that?'

Peter smiled. 'She didn't notice me, she was too en-grossed in your son. You're a dark horse, Adam, you never told me you had a boy. I assume he is yours? He's fine looking without a doubt.'

'Of course he's mine.' Adam was swift to confirm it. Not many people outside his own immediate circle even knew that he'd been separated from his wife. But why hadn't Peter answered his question? He did not want to give away the fact that he was here looking for them, but he was anxious to find out where they were.

'They were going into that grocery shop down the road. Are you living here now?'

'Goodness, no,' answered Adam. 'We're visiting Sienna's mother.'

As soon as they had parted company Adam went into the shop in question and when he came out he was smiling.

'It's Daddy!'

'Don't be silly, Ethan, it can't be your daddy. He would tell us if he was coming.' Nevertheless, Sienna felt her heart miss a beat before starting to hammer alarmingly.

'But it *is*, Mummy.' Before she could stop him Ethan had run out of the house and down the path. 'Daddy, Daddy!' he cried, and threw himself into Adam's arms.

Through the window Sienna saw Adam swing Ethan up and hold him close. She saw their happiness.

Complete happiness. And in that instant realised how selfish she had been in keeping Ethan away from the father he had only just got to know. The father he loved with all of his dear little heart.

She had thought only of herself, and her hurt. She had ignored what she was doing to their son.

How Adam had found them was a mystery. He wore a black cotton shirt and jeans and looked relaxed, as though he was on holiday. And yet she knew that he would be far from relaxed. He had obviously been hell bent on finding them and with his determination had left no stone unturned. Though goodness knows what had brought him to this tiny corner of Ireland so quickly. Somehow, some way, she must have left a clue.

The smell of scones fresh from the oven filled the air. Ethan had helped her make them and they had been looking forward to a tasting session. Her mother had already taken a couple to her stepfather in his studio.

She saw Ethan chattering away to his father, saw his animated face, his arms linked around Adam's neck. And she closed her eyes. It was a scene that would remain etched in her mind for ever—no matter what the future held.

She moved to the doorway and her eyes met Adam's. She watched as he slowly walked towards her, Ethan still clinging happily to him. Her heartbeat accelerated and she felt a prickly heat all over her body.

This was a defining moment.

It was make-or-break time.

What the outcome would be she did not know. There would need to be a lot of changes before she went back to Adam. Even knowing that Ethan was the hub of their relationship, she could not see herself living happily as a family unless there was also love on Adam's side.

She needed to know whether he had come to take Ethan away from her, or whether he wanted her as well.

Her eyes remained on his face as he walked slowly up the narrow path. His expression was unreadable. He gave her no clue whatsoever as to what was going through his mind.

'Mummy, Daddy says he's come to take me home.'

Sienna's heart grew heavy. So he had come for Ethan alone! Her chin immediately lifted, her eyes hardening as they met Adam's. And she waited for him to qualify Ethan's statement. But not a word was spoken. His eyes locked with hers but they told her nothing.

He came to a halt in front of her and finally spoke. 'Aren't you going to ask me in?'

'How did you find us?' she asked, uncaring that her voice was sharp.

Adam shrugged. 'That's not important now. What is important is that we need to talk.'

Sienna reluctantly stepped back and allowed him entry. Then she walked through to the sitting room with its view down the garden to the sea beyond. It was normally peaceful sitting here but right at this moment everything inside her churned sickeningly.

She could see Niall's studio and her mother standing talking to him. What would her mother say, she wondered, if she knew that Adam was right here in her house?

'Ethan,' she said gently, 'why don't you go down and see Grandma and Grandad?'

'But—'

'Daddy and I need to talk.'

'I want to talk too. I've missed my daddy.'

'Ethan!' she warned, and he took one look at her face and fled.

Sienna knew that her mother would keep Ethan with them, giving her time to sort things out with Adam.

'You've been baking.'

Sienna nodded.

'It smells good.'

Such banal talk when she knew he must be dying to lash out at her, give her hell for running away, taking his son away from him.

'And you're looking good too, Sienna.'

That was a lie, she looked anything but. Her face was pale and drawn without a scrap of make-up and she looked nothing like the vibrant woman with whom he had once enjoyed mind-blowing sex.

Sex! It's all it had been. All it had ever been. She was a mad fool to still be in love with him. Simply looking at him drained the energy from her and she sat down.

Adam, on the other hand, remained standing, his eyes fiercely dark, almost black, thick brows beetling over them. 'Why did you run away?'

'Isn't it obvious?'

'You promised you would stay.'

Her eyes met his defiantly. 'What woman would want to live with a man who had married her for all the wrong reasons?' Only a woman who still loved him despite what he had done!

She watched the conflicting emotions cross his face. She saw grimness and doubt, she saw sadness, but she did not see what she wanted to see. There was no love, no tenderness.

What she would have liked was for him to say that he could not live without her. That he wanted to give their marriage another go. Actually, what she would have *really* liked was for him to say that he loved her.

'Were you being fair on Ethan?' Adam dropped down on the settee opposite, his knees apart, his elbows resting on them as he leaned towards her. His hands loosely linked.

He looked relaxed now and yet she knew that he wasn't. He was wired for an argument. He was damned angry with her and he was here to take Ethan home.

Over her dead body!

'Ethan hadn't seen my mother for a long time.' She tried to keep her voice reasonable. 'He's enjoying himself. He's not cried himself to sleep at night because he's missing his father, if that's what you're thinking.' She didn't tell him that Ethan constantly asked when he was going to see him again. No way was she going to put herself back in the firing line.

'And how about you? Have you cried yourself to sleep?'

His eyes locked with hers and Sienna felt a tingle run through her as though she had touched an electric wire. Damn! How could she still feel like this? Here was a man who did not love her. A man who enjoyed her body but nothing else. The fact that he was the father of her child was incidental.

'That will be the day,' she declared, hiding her feelings behind a strong contemptuous voice. 'I really don't know why we ever married. It was a disaster waiting to happen. You conned me, Adam. It's not something I can easily forgive you for. In fact, I might never forgive you.'

'You don't think that for Ethan's sake we—'

'Let's leave Ethan out of this.' Fire lit her eyes now, filled her belly. 'He is the innocent party. And I wish with all of my heart that he wasn't stuck in the middle.'

'We could make our marriage work.'

Sienna stared at him for several long seconds. 'You're kidding!'

'We'd both need to work at it, of course, but—'

'But what, Adam? We both know that you do not love me. You took *my* love and threw it back in my face. How are we supposed to ignore that? How are we supposed to live happily in front of Ethan if we hate the sight of each other?' She watched the play of shadows on Adam's face, could almost hear his brain ticking away.

'I do not hate you, Sienna.'

His voice was nothing more than a low growl now, coming from somewhere deep inside him. He was filled with an emotion that she did not understand.

'Whatever,' she snapped. 'It's not enough for me to move back in with you.'

'I love you.'

The whole world came to a standstill. Had Adam actually said that he loved her? And if he had, did he mean it? Or was it simply a ruse to get her back on side? He wanted Ethan and he knew that she would never be parted from him so he had to say something drastic.

Like he loved her!

'Yes, and the world's going to end tomorrow.' Her eyes flared magnificently. 'I'm not a fool, Adam, I know what your game is.' Love wasn't even a part of his vocabulary.

'I mean it, Sienna.'

His eyes met and held hers and a faint shudder ran
down her spine. If only!

'I've not always loved you, I freely admit it. Though
I was damned attracted to you.'

Yes, he had certainly proved that. He had invited her
into his bed with the swiftness of a sparrowhawk
catching its prey. And she had enjoyed every minute!
But marriage wasn't totally about sex, it was about love
and trust and honesty. They had been dismally absent.

'Asking you to marry me was an irresponsible thing
to do. I wanted to get back at my grandfather and I've
regretted it ever since. I've lived with that guilt. Every
day of my life I've lived with it. Inevitably I pushed
myself hard to become a success. I needed to prove to
the old bastard that I could do it. And you took the
brunt, I'm afraid. I'm sorry, Sienna. From the bottom
of my heart I'm sorry.'

To give him his due he did look repentant, but Sienna
wasn't fooled. 'It's not enough, Adam. Anyone can say
they're sorry. I was in love with you. Really in love.
Have you any idea how it makes me feel, knowing that
I've been used?'

'Rock bottom, I guess.'

'To put it mildly.' Her eyes flashed into his. 'And
when I found out that I was having your child, I wanted
to kill myself.'

Adam groaned and she saw pain in his eyes but she
did not care. He deserved it.

'Thank God you didn't,' he said hoarsely.

'I would never have gone through with it, I didn't
have the courage,' she confessed, 'but it was how I felt
at the time. Now Ethan is the biggest joy in my life. I

love him to bits and when he was so poorly I nearly went out of my mind.'

'You shouldn't have had to suffer alone.'

'But I did, didn't I, Adam?' Her blue eyes blazed into his much darker ones. 'I've had years alone. And God knows why I ever thought I was doing the right thing in introducing you to your son. Because it's him you want now, isn't it? It's not me. You're saying you love me but—'

'*Sienna!*'

He spoke with such force that her words dried up in her mouth.

'Sienna, I do love you.'

Her eyes flashed strong disbelief. 'So what's happened to this afraid-to-love thing that you told me about?'

'I *was* afraid, because of my father, the way he reacted to my mother's death.' His voice was fierce and urgent, wanting her to believe in what he had to say. 'But I realise now that if you love someone, you love them no matter what.'

'You didn't love me when you married me.'

'No, that's true.' He winced as he said it. 'But I do now. I can't face the future without you, Sienna.'

Sienna saw the plea in his eyes, but still something held her back. How could she be sure? He could be saying all this just to get Ethan. His son had made such a difference to him. It had turned him into a different man. And that man she loved. But was he the true Adam? How would she ever know?

'I know I'll have to change. I know I need to regulate my working hours in order to spend time with my family. Actually,' he admitted with a wry grimace, 'my business can run perfectly well without me. I'm just a figurehead these days. My directors even tell me I put too much time in. But I enjoyed doing what I did. I had nothing else to do. But now I do have something, Sienna. I have a whole beautiful new life in front of me, with a son I adore and a wife I'm deeply in love with.'

There was such pain and honesty in his eyes that she finally accepted that he was speaking the truth. New life breathed into her body, she felt it creep up from her toes and fill every bone, every sinew, every vein, every artery. It heated her blood and threatened to engulf her.

'You really mean that?' Even her voice had grown stronger and she could not take her eyes away from his.

'More than you'll ever know.'

She heard sincerity, she saw clear truth in his eyes, and her heart felt like bursting.

Adam loved her!

He truly loved her!

A miracle had happened today, here in this beautiful corner of Ireland where the air was soft and the desolate beauty blew your mind away.

'I know that you don't love me any more, but—'

'Adam, I *do* love you.' She leaned forward and pressed the tips of her fingers to his lips. 'I've never stopped loving you.' Maybe she had told herself that she had but in truth her love for Adam had never gone away. There had always been a part of him in Ethan. And she loved her boy. 'You've made me laugh and you've made me cry, but I love you still.'

The look in his eyes, the incredulous look, made her smile.

'I don't deserve you,' he groaned.

His arms slid around her, pulling her gently against him where she could feel the frantic beat of his heart echoing the thud inside her own body.

'Tell me I'm not dreaming this.'

'You're not dreaming it.' Neither was she. There was fierce honesty in Adam's eyes, humility too, which was something she had never expected to see. Adam had been brought to his knees by love. She too was bowled over. It was as if a fairy godmother had waved her magic wand over them. The past was swiftly forgotten, all the pain and heartache. Their future was rosy.

Together, the three of them—and the new little life that was already forming inside her...

millsandboon.co.uk Community

Join Us!

The Community is the perfect place to meet and chat to kindred spirits who love books and reading as much as you do, but it's also the place to:

- **Get the inside scoop from authors about their latest books**
- **Learn how to write a romance book with advice from our editors**
- **Help us to continue publishing the best in women's fiction**
- **Share your thoughts on the books we publish**
- **Befriend other users**

Forums: Interact with each other as well as authors, editors and a whole host of other users worldwide.

Blogs: Every registered community member has their own blog to tell the world what they're up to and what's on their mind.

Book Challenge: We're aiming to read 5,000 books and have joined forces with The Reading Agency in our inaugural Book Challenge.

Profile Page: Showcase yourself and keep a record of your recent community activity.

Social Networking: We've added buttons at the end of every post to share via digg, Facebook, Google, Yahoo, technorati and de.licio.us.

www.millsandboon.co.uk

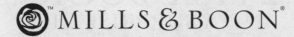

2 FREE BOOKS
AND A SURPRISE GIFT

We would like to take this opportunity to thank you for reading this Mills & Boon® book by offering you the chance to take TWO more specially selected books from the Modern™ series absolutely FREE! We're also making this offer to introduce you to the benefits of the Mills & Boon® Book Club™—

- **FREE home delivery**
- **FREE gifts and competitions**
- **FREE monthly Newsletter**
- **Exclusive Mills & Boon Book Club offers**
- **Books available before they're in the shops**

Accepting these FREE books and gift places you under no obligation to buy, you may cancel at any time, even after receiving your free books. Simply complete your details below and return the entire page to the address below. You don't even need a stamp!

YES Please send me 2 free Modern books and a surprise gift. I understand that unless you hear from me, I will receive 4 superb new books every month for just £3.19 each, postage and packing free. I am under no obligation to purchase any books and may cancel my subscription at any time. The free books and gift will be mine to keep in any case.

Ms/Mrs/Miss/Mr_____ Initials _____

Surname _____
Address _____

_____ Postcode _____

Send this whole page to: Mills & Boon Book Club, Free Book Offer, FREEPOST NAT 10298, Richmond, TW9 1BR